STP 1314

Water Leakage Through Building Facades

Robert J. Kudder and Jeffrey L. Erdly, editors

ASTM Stock #: STP1314

ASTM
100 Barr Harbor Drive
West Conshohocken, PA 19428-2959

Printed in the U.S.A.

Library of Congress Cataloging-in-Publication Data

Water leakage through building facades / Robert J. Kudder and
  Jeffrey L. Erdly, editors.
      p. cm.—(STP : 1314)
    The symposium on Water Leakage Through Building Facades
  was held 17 March 1996 in Orlando, Florida"—Frwd.
    "ASTM stock #: STP1314."
    ISBN 0-8031-2042-7
    1. Dampness in buildings—Congresses. 2. Facades—
  Congresses. I. Kudder, Robert J., 1945–   . II. Erdly,
  Jeffrey L., 1951–   . III. Symposium on Water Leakage Through
  Building Facades (1966 : Orlando, Fla.) IV. Series: ASTM special
  technical publication : 1314.
    TH9031.W374 1998
    693.8′9—dc21   97-52152
                                                          CIP

Photocopy Rights

Peer Review Policy

Each paper published in this volume was evaluated by two peer reviewers and at least one
editor. The authors addressed all of the reviewers' comments to the satisfaction of both the
technical editor(s) and the ASTM Committee on Publications.

To make technical information available as quickly as possible, the peer-reviewed papers in
this publication were prepared "camera-ready" as submitted by the authors.

The quality of the papers in this publication reflects not only the obvious efforts of the
authors and the technical editor(s), but also the work of these peer reviewers. The ASTM
Committee on Publications acknowledges with appreciation their dedication and contribution
of time and effort on behalf of ASTM.

Printed in Ann Arbor, MI
February 1998

Foreword

The Symposium on Water Leakage Through Building Facades was held 17 March 1996 in Orlando, Florida. ASTM Committee E6 on Performance of Buildings sponsored the symposium. Robert J. Kudder, Raths, Raths & Johnson, Inc., and Jeffrey L. Erdly, Masonry Preservation Services, Inc., presided as symposium cochairmen and are editors of this publication.

Contents

Overview

The sponsoring Subcommittee for this Symposium is ASTM E06.55 on Exterior Wall Systems. The Subcommittee was started in 1985 by Alan Yorkdale to establish a "systems" approach to wall performance, and to depart from the prescriptive, material specific, and procedural approaches to wall performance evaluation and testing.

In October 1990, the first Symposium on wall leakage was held in Dearborn, Michigan, chaired by Thomas Schwartz. Tom retold the advice from an architect in the 1930s about common errors, omissions, and wrong thinking which would guarantee a leaky building.The irony was that if so many buildings leaked, that must be what people wanted. The remarks were as timely in 1990 as they were in the 1930s, and it appeared that little progress has been made in the intervening sixty years.

We believe that progress is being made to reduce the frequency of wall leakage problems, at least in buldings involving informed design and construction professionals working with owners who commit sufficient resources to construct workable designs. The papers in the 1990 Symposium presented examples of the mistakes which caused walls to leak, and diagnostic and testing methods to determine the causes of leakage. In contrast, many of the papers in today's Symposium discuss design and quality assurance topics intended to prevent leakage, refined techniques for diagnostic and quality assurance procedures, and a broadened perspective to include durability issues. We like to think that this shift in Symposium topics reflects an evolution in how we think about and deal with wall leakage. With better dissemination of information which these ASTM Symposia represent, better attention to details and quality control, and a clearer understanding of performance requirements, we should expect a progressive reduction in wall leakage problems.

While a reduction in building leakage is acknowledged, portions of our industry continue to build structures with walls that leak. As the pressure to build lower cost structures continues, the resulting design requires the utilization of thinner, lighter building envelopes, less capable of withstanding the damage caused by even minimal water leakage. When reviewing the papers contained in this publication, we encourage the user to be aware of how everyone from the architect to the technician who installs the final linear foot of joint sealant, has a critical role in the success or failure of these building walls.

Evaluating and repairing wall leaks remains an art. Many of the papers, particularly the case studies, present authors' varying approaches to diagnosing and repairing leaks. As an art, there is much room for the creative application of proven techniques, but there is usually no one "right" way to address a leakage problem. It is hoped that this Symposium will illustrate how many skilled technical professionals have attempted to prevent, diagnose, and correct wall leakage.

Robert J. Kudder,
Raths, Raths & Johnson, Inc.,
  835 Midway Drive, Willow Brook, IL 60521;
  symposium cochairman and editor.

Jeffrey L. Erdly
Masonry Preservation Services, Inc.,
  PO Box 324, Berwick, PA 18603;
  symposium cochairman and editor.

Design

Edmund C. C. Choi[1]

CRITERIA FOR WATER PENETRATION TESTING

REFERENCE: Choi, E. C. C., "**Criteria for Water Penetration Testing,**" Water Leakage Through Building Facades, ASTM STP 1314, R. J. Kudder and J. L. Erdly, Eds., American Society for Testing and Materials, 1998.

Abstract: A major function of the envelope of a building is to protect the interior from weather and to provide a comfortable environment inside the building. Recently, there have been significant advancements in construction techniques and material science relating to building envelope construction. The information (the amount of wind and rain) required for the weathertightness design and testing of a building envelope is not as developed. There is no rational approach to obtain such criteria and the values used in the current practices involve significant uncertainties.

This paper proposes the use of a computational fluid dynamics (CFD) approach to obtain the intensity of wind-driven rain which impinges a building's faces. This wind-driven rain intensity and the associated wind pressure are estimated systematically using CFD method and extreme-statistics analysis. Results of the analysis, which give the criteria for water penetration testing for a building envelope, are obtained as a function of the return period. This method is applied to a sample rectangular building situated in Sydney, Australia, and finds that the testing pressure is significantly higher than the value currently specified in ASTM E331-86.

Keywords : Wind-driven rain, Weathertightness, water leakage, water penetration, testing criteria.

The primary function of a building envelope is to keep the wind and rain outside of the building. It is important to ensure that building envelopes are weathertight. Unfortunately, water leakage is still a very common problem. The reasons for this are principally due to poor design and bad workmanship. However, the uncertainties in the

[1]   Assoc. Professor, School of Civil and Structural Engg., Nanyang Technological University, Nanyang Ave., SINGAPORE

3

criteria for weathertightness design and testing and the lack of a rational approach to the matter also contribute to the problem.

Water leakage of the building envelope during a rain storm is influenced by several factors, mainly, the air pressure difference across the cladding and the amount of rain water impinging onto the building envelope. Other factors, such as the velocity and direction of raindrops, also contribute. This paper proposes to establish the watertightness testing criteria for building envelopes by the following steps.

(a) Calculating wind-driven rain (w.d.r.) intensity on a building face as a function of the upstream wind speed and rainfall intensity using computational fluid dynamics technique.

(b) Applying the result obtained from (a) to a building using the on-site wind and rain records to calculate the actual w.d.r. intensity on the building face.

(c) Carrying out statistical analysis on the w.d.r. intensity and wind pressure on the building face, taking into account their co-occurrence characteristics and the results expressed as functions of the return period.

METHOD FOR WIND-DRIVEN RAIN CALCULATION

In the early years, wind-driven rain was studied with field measurements of wind and rain on an open site. It is not until recently that w.d.r. intensities on building faces were measured. Lacy [1],[2] obtained field measurements of w.d.r. on the faces of a building. However, such site investigations are costly and difficult to parameterize. A semi-analytical approach was later proposed by Rodgers[3]. More recently, a full numerical method for the systematic analysis and calculation of w.d.r. on building faces by using a computational fluid dynamics technique was proposed by Choi[4]. The method involves the calculation of flow pattern around a building, raindrop trajectories and w.d.r. intensity. A brief outline of Choi's method follows.

(a) Wind Flow Around A Building

With the advancements in computational fluid dynamics methods, the wind flow pattern around a building situated in a boundary layer can numerically be calculated. The velocities over a 3-dimensional domain around the building are obtained by solving equations of the k-ε turbulent flow (high Reynolds number) model. The finite volume numerical scheme was used in the present study. Velocities obtained over the domain are used for the calculation of raindrop trajectories in the next phase of the study. Figures 1a and 1b show typical flow patterns around a building.

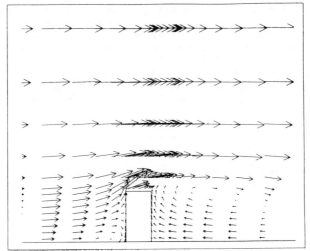

FIG 1a--Typical longitudinal flow profile around a building

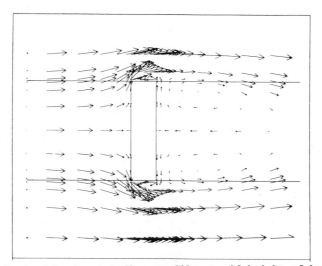

FIG 1b--Typical horizontal flow profile at mid-height of building

(b) Raindrop Trajectory

Raindrops falling in the atmosphere where the wind is blowing are acted
upon by two forces: self weight and drag force of the wind. The drag
force is a function of the Reynolds number and the relative velocity
between the wind and the raindrop[4]. With the wind velocities at every
point in the flow field known from (a), the motion of the raindrops can
be computed by solving iteratively the equations of motion. The
equations and the solution method are given in the paper previously

referenced[4] and will not be duplicated here. It is important to note
that, since the drag coefficient is a function of the drop size,
trajectories for raindrops of different sizes will be different. They
are also different for different wind speeds. Figures 2a and 2b show
trajectories around a building for raindrops of 0.25mm and 5.0mm radius,
respectively, under a 10m/s boundary layer flow field. It can be
observed that the trajectories of the smaller raindrops are more
inclined and, therefore, more affected by the local flow close to the
building.

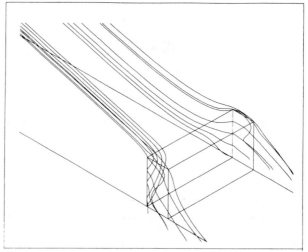

FIG 2a--Wind-driven rain trajectories of 0.25mm raindrops
around a wide building

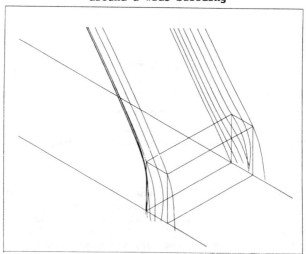

FIG 2b--Wind-driven rain trajectories of 5.0mm raindrops
around a wide building

(c) Wind-driven Rain Intensity On Building Faces

The next step of the study calculates the intensity of w.d.r. on the building face. Since w.d.r. intensities on different locations of the building are expected to be different, the front face of the building is divided into three, equal, vertical strips and four, equal, horizontal rows as shown in Figure 3. For each zone, the raindrop trajectories (of drop size r) terminating at the four corners of the zone are computed. These trajectories are traced upstream to a point far away from the building where the wind flow is not affected by the local effect of the building. An imaginary tube formed by these four trajectories bounds all raindrops (of size r) falling onto the zone. At the far upstream end (the four trajectories are more or less parallel to one another) the sectional area of the tube cut by a horizontal plane is h(r).

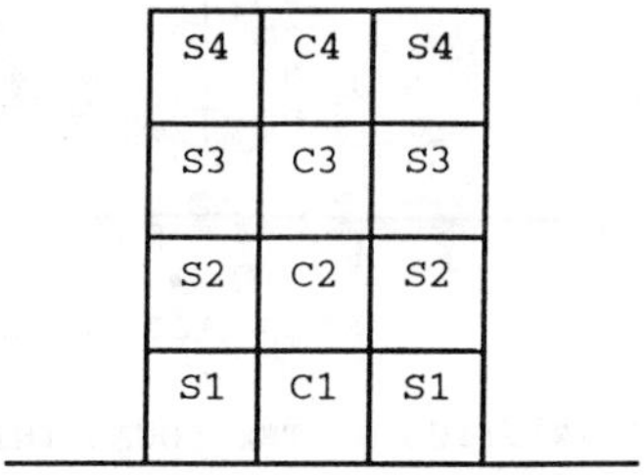

S4	C4	S4
S3	C3	S3
S2	C2	S2
S1	C1	S1

FIG 3--Zones on the front face of a building

The rain falling onto the zone comes from those which fall onto h(r). The w.d.r. intensity on the zone is thus equal to the unobstructed rainfall intensity (u.r.i.) of drop size r times h(r) and divides by the area of the zone. The area ratio is termed local effect factor, LEF(r), which represents the local effect of the building on the wind and rain. LEF(r) varies with the raindrop size. The overall w.d.r. intensity on the zone is obtained by summing up all the contributions from every raindrop size, which can also be expressed as the product of u.r.i. and a local intensity factor (LIF). LIF is the sum of all LEF(r) for all radii weighted by f(r)dr, the probability of the drop size distribution of the rain.

$$LIF_{zone} = \frac{\text{w.d.r. intensity on zone}}{\text{u.r.i.}} = \int LEF(r)\,f(r)\,dr \qquad 1$$

In the calculation of LIF using equation 1, the rainfall drop size distribution is required. There are many models for drop size distribution, such as models proposed by Best[5], Mualem & Assouline[6] and Laws & Parsons[7]. These models were developed from rain data gathered from different parts of the world and were usually expressed as functions of the rainfall intensity. Different drop size distribution models can be used for the calculation of LIF. However, studies by Choi[8] indicated that the LIF values are not sensitive to drop size distribution models. In the present study, the Best[5] model was used. LIF values for the different zones on a narrow, rectangular building (height:width:depth=40m:10m:10m) are plotted in Figure 4. It is observed that the top row experiences much higher w.d.r. intensity than the lower portions. The highest intensity is at S4, the top zone of the side strip. The center portion receives the least w.d.r.

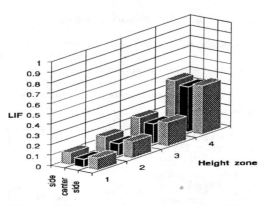

FIG 4--LIF values for a narrow building

CHARACTERISTICS OF THE LOCAL INTENSITY FACTOR

Wind-driven rain around a building is a complex phenomenon. It involves the interaction between the building and wind flow, and the interaction between raindrop movements and air movements. Thus, the value of LIF, besides being a function of the drop size distribution, is also affected by a number of other parameters, e.g., the geometry of the building. The parameters and their effects on LIF have been investigated and reported by Choi[8]. The more important of these parameters are:

(a) Effect of building geometry

When a building is placed in a wind field, it presents a blockage effect to the wind flow. The local flow pattern around the building indicates a slow down of the wind upstream of the building. Wind is forced to sweep sideways around the corners of the front face and upwards around the top of the building. The wider the building, the stronger this local effect is, and the more the raindrops are diverted away from the building face. LIF values for buildings of different height to width ratios are computed. Figure 5 shows the variation of LIF with the width to height ratio of the building for zones S4, S2, C4 and C2. It can be seen that LIF values are higher for narrower buildings.

(b) Effect of wind speed

Wind-driven rain moves in an oblique direction. The horizontal component of the motion is a direct result of the wind drag on the rain drop. Therefore, the higher the wind speed, the more inclined the w.d.r. and the higher the w.d.r. intensity is on a vertical plane. LIF values are expected to increase with the wind speed. Figure 6 shows the variations of LIF values for zones S4, S2, C4 and C2 of a narrow building with the wind speed being that at a height of 250m (the building is situated inside the boundary layer where the unobstructed wind speed is assumed to vary with altitude as that of a suburban area). From the figure, it can be observed that the LIF values increase very fast with the wind speed. For the top quarter of the front face (S4 & C4), LIF increases from less than 0.5 at 10m/s to more than 2.0 at 30m/s. That is, at 30m/s, the w.d.r. intensity on that portion of the

building face is twice that of the unobstructed normal rainfall
intensity. A curve fitted to the S4 values is:

$$\text{LIF}_{S4} = 0.025 V^{1.3} \qquad\qquad 2$$

where LIF of the S4 is the largest value over the building face, and V
is the 250m height wind speed in m/s. The value 250m was selected as a
height far above the building where the wind is not affected by the
presence of the building. This relationship between LIF and wind speed
is used in the next phase of the study.

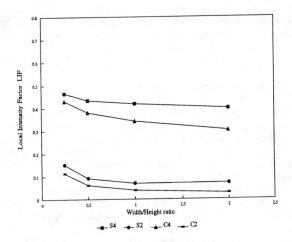

FIG 5--Variation of LIF with width to height ratio of building

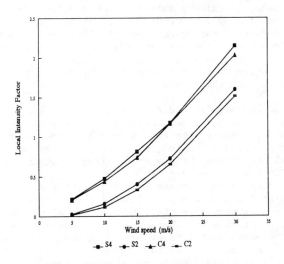

FIG 6--Variation of LIF with wind speed

Summary Of Wind-driven Rain Calculation

To summarise, it is shown that the intensity of w.d.r. on the
front face (other faces receive less w.d.r.) of a building, expressed as
a ratio of the u.r.i., can numerically be calculated. The value of this
local intensity factor is affected by many parameters, e.g., the
raindrop size distribution, the rainfall intensity, the wind profile and
its turbulent intensity. However, the parameters with a major impact on
the value of LIF are the building geometry, the location of the point of
interest on the building face and the wind speed. In the next section,
the top zone (S4) of the front face of a narrow building with
height:width:depth equal to 40m:10m:10m is selected for investigation.
For this given zone, the LIF value is only dependent on the wind speed
as in equation 2. From the wind data, the LIF value is calculated and
the w.d.r. on the building face can be obtained as the product of the
LIF and the unobstructed rainfall intensity.

WIND-DRIVEN RAIN ON A BUILDING IN SYDNEY

In order to calculate the actual amount of w.d.r. on a building,
the actual values of wind and rain measured on-site have to be used. In
the present study, a building situated in Sydney, Australia, is used as
an example. There are several meteorology stations in Sydney. The one
with the best exposure is the Mascot Station, located in a large
airfield. The surrounding country is flat and level with the ocean
immediately to the east. A database consisting of hourly mean wind
speed, gust speed, wind direction and hourly rainfall is constructed.
Twenty five years of data are used in the present study.

Using the hourly wind speed, the LIF value of S4 for every hour
can be calculated using Equation 2. In the calculation, the velocity at
a height of 250m is required; this is converted from the speed at the
anemometer height using a procedure as recommended by the Australian
Wind Loading Code[9]. Having obtained the LIF value, the hourly w.d.r.
intensity on zone S4 of the building can be calculated by multiplying
the LIF value by the simultaneous rainfall intensity of the hour. The
procedure is repeated for every hour, producing an hourly w.d.r.
intensity record over the 25 year period.

Values of the highest w.d.r. intensity for every year are
selected, and extreme distribution analysis is carried out. Figure 7
shows the w.d.r. intensity plotted against the reduced variate(also
shown as return period on top of the graph). It can be observed that
the points fall on a reasonably straight line. A Type-I distribution
was used to fit the points, also shown in the figure. The w.d.r.
intensity is observed to increase from 22mm/hr for a return period of 2
years to 43mm/hr for a return period of 10 years. The extreme
distribution of the normal rainfall (u.r.i.) is also shown in Figure 7.
The points do not form a straight line. It seems that, within this 25
years, there were two high intensities which may not belong to the same
family as the other points. It is interesting to note that these two
very high rainfall intensities do not produce exceedingly high w.d.r.

values. For convenience, a Type-I distribution is also fitted to the normal rainfall. Comparing the w.d.r. intensity with that of the normal rainfall, the w.d.r. is calculated to be about 70 to 80 percent of the u.r.i. value.

Extreme distributions of the hourly mean wind speed and the gust speed for the 25 years are shown in Figure 8. It can be seen that they fall into straight lines. The Type-I fitting for the two lines are also shown in the figure.

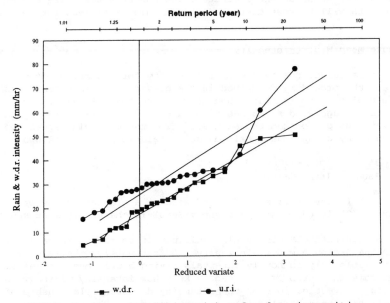

FIG 7--Normal rainfall (u.r.i.) and w.d.r. intensities

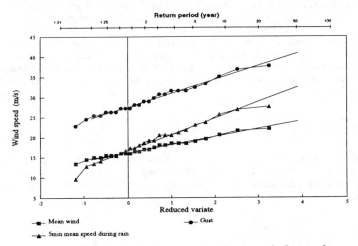

FIG 8--Hourly, 5-minute mean and gust wind speeds

TESTING CRITERIA FOR WATER PENETRATION

In the previous section, we have obtained the mean hourly w.d.r. intensity on the upper portion of a building. We also have the corresponding mean wind speed for any given return period. But are these the testing criteria? Consider the practical problem of water leakage of building facades. Under a practical situation (not testing), how long must a leak persist before we consider the cladding to be faulty? Is it 1 minute, 5 minutes or 10 minutes? For this illustration, we adopt the 5 minute value. Under a real life situation, the tenants will be most disturbed should rain water leak for more than 5 minutes.

5-minute Mean W.d.r. Intensity

To calculate the mean w.d.r. intensity for a duration of 5 minutes, the procedure described in the previous sections can be used. The only difference is that, when calculating the LIF value, the 5-minute average wind speed has to be used. The average wind speed for any averaging period can be calculated from the mean wind speed and the gust speed by using logarithmic duration relationship as follows.

$$\frac{v(t)-v(3600)}{v(3)-v(3600)} = \frac{\ln(t/3600)}{\ln(3/3600)} \qquad 3$$

where v(t) is the average wind speed with an averaging period of t seconds, v(3) is the gust speed and v(3600) is the hourly mean speed.

After obtaining the 5-minute LIF, multiply it to the 5-minute u.r.i. to obtain the 5-minute w.d.r. intensity. Unfortunately, the rain records are available only in hourly intervals giving hourly mean intensities. To overcome this problem, we need to know how intensity varies with duration. Investigations on the intensity-duration relationship of rainfall have been carried out for many decades. Charts and equations on the intensity-duration-frequency relationship of rainfall are well established(IEA[10], Linsley et. al.[11]). Their absolute values are different from country to country and from location to location. However, the forms of the equations and the shapes of the curves are very similar. In fact, the 5-minute rainfall intensity is more or less three times the hourly intensity given for a diversity of climatic conditions. Using an expression proposed by Linsley[11], the following value is obtained.

$$\frac{u.r.i.(5min)}{u.r.i.(60min)} = \left[\frac{60}{5}\right]^{0.42} = 2.84 \qquad 4$$

The 5-minute w.d.r. intensity is obtained as the product of 2.84, the hourly u.r.i., and the 5-minute LIF. Their values plotted against the reduced variate are shown in Figure 9. The hourly w.d.r. is also shown for comparison.

5-minute Mean Wind Speed During Rain

To obtain the criteria for the testing pressure, we need to know the 5-minute mean wind speed during rain. That is, we need to consider only those occasions when the cladding was wet. All those wind speeds occurring while the cladding was dry were not considered. A threshold of hourly w.d.r. intensity of 5mm/hr on S4 was used in the present study. The maximum yearly values were selected and the extreme distribution of this 5-minute mean wind speed during rain is plotted in Figure 8. This is the wind speed for the testing pressure criteria.

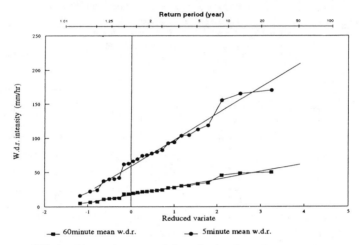

FIG 9--Five-minute and hourly w.d.r. intensities

Testing Criteria

The 5-minute w.d.r. intensity and the 5-minute mean wind speed during rain obtained in the previous section are used to give the water penetration testing criteria. Knowing the wind speed, the pressure on the cladding can be calculated.

$$\text{pressure} = C_p \frac{1}{2} \rho V^2_{5\text{-minute during rain}} \qquad\qquad 5$$

where ρ is the air density and C_p is the pressure coefficient which is a function of the shape and the location on the building.

For water leakage consideration, the critical pressure is the largest positive pressure normally occuring somewhere above the mid-height along the center line on the front face of a building with a value close to unity. A pressure coefficient of 1.0 is used. This pressure and the 5-minute w.d.r. intensity are the testing criteria which are given for different return periods in Table 1. Furthermore, in order to see the meaning and significance of the test pressure, it is appropriate to relate it to the design wind pressure of the building. Normally, the

50-year return, 3-second gust dynamic wind pressure is taken as the
design wind pressure for a building. This is adopted in the present
calculation. The test pressure, expressed as a percentage of the design
wind pressure, is also given in Table 1.

Water penetration is a serviceability criteria; it should not be as
stringent as the wind loading criteria. A 10-year return period
probably will be adequate. Accepting this 10-year return period, the
testing criteria are: a rate of water spray of 2.43 litre per minute per
meter square (3.6 US gal/hr per square foot), and a test pressure of
410Pa or 40 percent of the design pressure. The current testing
criteria specified by ASTM E331-86 for the water penetration test are:
rate of water spray of 3.4 $1/min/m^2$ and a test pressure of 137 Pa.
Compared with the calculated values, it seems the amount of water as
specified is adequate. However, the specified test pressure is
significantly below the calculated value (for a location with similar
wind and rain conditions as in Sydney).

Return period (year)	Amount of water		Test pressure	
	Intensity (mm/hr)	Rate $(1/min/m^2)$	Pressure (Pa)	% of Design Pressure
5	117	1.95	320	31
10	146	2.43	410	40
20	174	2.9	510	49
50	210	3.5	650	63

Table 1 Testing criteria for water penetration

The values as presented are calculated for a rectangular building
with height:width:depth equal 40m:10m:10m. For other geometry ratios,
the w.d.r. intensity will be different. However, the major contribution
towards the amount of w.d.r. on the building face comes from zone S4.
W.d.r. for other geometry ratios can be obtained by proportion as
follows.

$$\frac{\text{w.d.r. for building (H:W:D)}}{\text{w.d.r. for building}(40:10:10)} = \frac{\text{LIF of S4 for building(H:W:D)}}{\text{LIF of S4 for building}(40:10:10)}$$

where the ratio of LIF of S4 for buildings of different geometry ratios
can be obtained from figure 5.

DISCUSSION AND CONCLUSION

This paper presents a method whereby the wind-driven rain
impinging a building face can be numerically determined. The method,
together with extreme statistics analysis, were utilized to determine
the testing criteria for water penetration tests. The testing criteria
is a function of the wind and rain condition at the site of the
building. In the present study, the wind and rain records in Sydney

were used to demonstrate the method. The values obtained are: amount of water spray of 2.43 $l/min/m^2$ and a test pressure of 410Pa.

For buildings situated in places other than Sydney, use the wind and rain records of that particular location. Depending on the wind, the rain and their co-occurrence characteristics, the result will differ. The absolute values may significantly differ from the 2.43 $l/min/m^2$ and 410Pa obtained for Sydney. However, as a rough guide, a test pressure of 40 percent of the design pressure of the building can be used. For the amount of wind-driven rain, since w.d.r. is dependent on the combined action of wind and rain, it is found to be roughly proportional to the driving-rain index (annual rainfall times the annual mean hourly wind speed). The driving-rain index for Sydney (Mascot Airfield) is 3.87 m^2/s. For places with a similar value of driving-rain index, the amount of water spray can be taken to be 2.43 $l/min/m^2$.

In deriving the testing criteria, certain assumptions were adopted. The major ones are (a) the critical duration of w.d.r. is taken to be 5 minutes, (b) the threshold for wet wind is taken to be a w.d.r. intensity of 5mm/hr and (c) a 10-year return period serviceability criteria was selected. These values are used because they reasonably represent the practical problem. Nevertheless, the method as presented can take on any other values, if required.

Finally, this paper presents a systematic method for the numerical determination of the testing criteria for water penetration tests. The method was analytically derived based on engineering principles, and takes away the uncertainties of previous practices which were mainly educated guesses based on engineering experience. Using this method, with wind and rain records of the building sites, more realistic testing criteria can be specified for the construction of the building facade.

REFERENCE

(1) Lacy, R. E. (1965), "Driving rain maps and the onslaught of rain on buildings," Current paper No 54, Building Research Station, UK.

(2) Lacy, R. E. (1971), "An index of exposure to driving-rain," BRE Digest 127, Building Research Station, Garston, UK.

(3) Rodgers, G., Poots, G., Page, J. K., Pickering, W. M., (1973) "Theoretical predictions of raindrop impaction on a slab type building," Report No. BS12, Dept. of Building Science, University of Sheffield, U.K.

(4) Choi, E. C. C., (1994), "Determination of wind-driven rain intensity on building faces," Journal of Wind Engg. & Industrial Aerodynamics, 51 (1994), 55-69.

(5) Best, A. C., (1950), "The size distribution of raindrops," Quarterly Journal of Royal Meteorology Society, 76, 16-36.

(6) Mualem, Y. and Assouline, S., (1986), "Mathematical model for rain
     drop distribution and rainfall kinetic energy," Transaction of
     American Society of Agricultural Engineering, vol. 29(2) March
     1986, pp494-500.

(7) Laws, J. O. and Parsons, D. A., (1943), "The relation of rain
     drop-size to intensity," Transaction American Geophysical Union,
     Vol24, pp452-460.

(8) Choi, E. C. C., (1994), "Parameters affecting the intensity of
     wind-driven rain on the front face of a building," Journal of Wind
     Engg. & Industrial Aerodynamics, 53 (1994), 1-17.

(9) "AS 1170.2-1989, SAA Loading Code Part 2: wind loads," Standards
     Association of Australia.

(10) IEA (1977) "Australian Rainfall and Runoff : Flood analysis and
     design," 159pp.

(11) Linsley, R. K., Kohler, M. A., Paulhus, J. L. H., (1975), "Applied
     Hydrology," McGraw-Hill.

Christopher L. Galitz[1] and A. Rhett Whitlock[1]

THE APPLICATION OF LOCAL WEATHER DATA TO THE SIMULATION OF WIND-DRIVEN RAIN

REFERENCE: Galitz, C. L. and Whitlock, A. R., **"The Application of Local Weather Data to the Simulation of Wind-Driven Rain,"** Water Leakage Through Building Facades, ASTM STP 1314, R. J. Kudder and J. L. Erdly, Eds., American Society for Testing and Materials, 1998.

ABSTRACT: Due to the mismanagement of penetrating water, many masonry walls deteriorate long before the end of their intended life-span. The amount of penetrating water is dependent upon the permeability characteristics of the facade and the severity of wind-driven rain. Therefore, it would be useful to designers to know more precisely the environment in which their structures will be subjected, and also for investigators to have accurate means for assessing the performance of structures through the use of non-destructive water testing.

Current standards include methods for water test chamber, spray rack, and calibrated nozzle testing. Typically, these methods differ in water flow rates, impact velocity of water, air pressure differential and duration. These tests historically have not allowed the variation of testing parameters to compensate for realistic site conditions. The use of appropriate weather data can greatly improve the relevance of such testing.

This paper explores the conversion of published weather data to testing parameters which can be used to simulate weather conditions. Included is an analysis of the dynamics of rainfall and its impact on surfaces of various orientation. The analysis is based on the effects of wind speed, direction, surface orientation, and rainfall intensity. Also discussed are the appropriateness of water chamber, spray rack, and spray nozzle testing, with regards to accurate rainfall simulation.

KEYWORDS: concrete, interior leakage, masonry, spray rack, water penetration, water testing

---

ɔject Engineer and President, respectively, Whitlock Dalrymple Poston & Associates, Inc., 8832 Rixlew Lane. ∎assas, Virginia 22110.

The mismanagement of penetrating water in building walls can lead to failures long before the end of their intended life spans. Penetrating water and water-born salts can be devastating to steel-reinforced concrete and masonry structures. Improper handling of rainfall incident upon building surfaces causes innumerable problems, both aesthetic and structural, e.g., efflorescence, mildew, corrosion, and freeze/thaw damage. To avoid this, it is helpful if researchers, investigators, and designers understand the behavior of incident rainfall.

Attempts have been made by various organizations to simulate wind-driven rainfall through the use of test chamber, spray nozzle, and spray rack testing. The standards governing each of these test methods have historically specified constant parameters used with a standardized apparatus. These methods do not allow the flexibility for realistic site conditions necessary for field use. Likewise, the severity of these tests, as compared to actual storms, is not known. Therefore, it is essential for the tester to make modifications to the test methods that are deemed to be appropriate to accurately assess the quality of construction and repairs, and to assure a lack of leakage under realistic weather conditions. To this end, one must examine the conditions that are to be simulated.

Choi [1] has presented a detailed analysis of wind-driven rainfall and how it is affected by building geometry. His paper concentrates on the effects of building geometry upon the intensity of wind-driven rain, where the drop sizes are modeled using a probabilistic distribution. His numerical analysis of the paths of rain drops is similar to that presented herein, and show that higher factors for intensity of incident rainfall may be applied at building corners and parapets than at the main portions of the wall. However, for purposes of this paper, the local effects of building geometry were ignored.

MECHANICS OF WIND-DRIVEN RAINFALL

Water vapor exists in the upper atmosphere as clouds. During conditions of temperature and/or barometric changes, this vapor can condense to form tiny droplets. As condensation increases, the droplets grow and their weight overcomes the upward forces keeping the drops in the cloud formations. At that point, the condensed water vapor becomes a drop of rain.

As the drops begin their descent, they are subjected to forces brought about by the air flowing around them. This air flow creates a boundary layer along the bottom and sides of the drop up to the point of separation. The top of the drop is within an area of turbulent air which is accompanied by a localized low pressure. This causes the top of the drop to stretch upward, which in turn causes the bottom of the drop to flatten in order to equalize internal pressures. The approximate shape of a falling drop is shown in Figure 1.

The amount of deformation of the drop is largely dependent upon the drop's size [2]. The smaller the drop, the less it will deform, due to the high surface tension to mass ratio. For purposes of this evaluation, it will be assumed that raindrops are spherical.

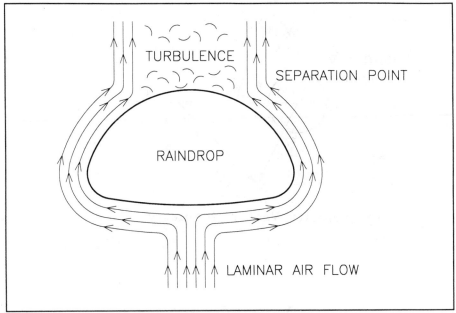

Figure 1 - Approximate Shape of a Falling Rain Drop

As any object falls through the atmosphere, it is subjected to the forces of self-weight, buoyancy, and drag. Weight is the mass of the object under the influence of gravitational acceleration. Buoyancy is the weight of the air the object displaces. Drag is caused by the air's resistance to being displaced and is a function of the object's shape and velocity. For the case of a raindrop, weight is equal to the drop's volume multiplied by its density. Buoyancy is assumed to be negligible, and drag is equal to the drag coefficient multiplied by the drop's cross-sectional area multiplied by the air's density times the magnitude of the drop's velocity squared, divided by two. These forces are shown in Figure 2 and are summarized by equation (1).

$$\sum \underline{F} = (-\frac{4}{3}\pi r^3 \rho_w g)\,\underline{j} + (\frac{1}{2}\pi r^2 C_D \rho_A V^2_{R/W})\,\frac{V_{R/W}}{V_{R/W}} \tag{1}$$

where

$\underline{F}$ = forces on the drop, N,

r = radius of the raindrop, m,

ρ_w = density of rain water, kg/m^3,

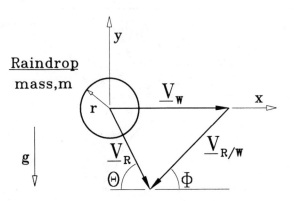

(a) Velocity Vector Geometry

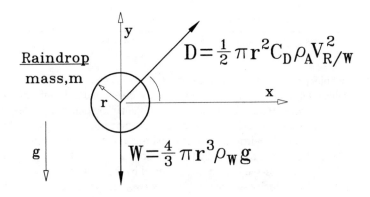

(b) Free-Body Diagram

Figure 2 - Forces Acting on a Falling Raindrop

g = gravitational acceleration, m/s^2,
j = unit vector in upward direction,
C_D = coefficient of drag of the drop,
ρ_A = density of atmospheric air, kg/m^3,
$\underline{V}_{R/W}$= relative velocity of the raindrop relative to the wind, m/s,
$V_{R/W}$= magnitude of relative velocity vector, m/s.

From Newton's second law, $\sum \underline{F}$ must equal the drop's mass multiplied by its acceleration. Thus, eq. (1) can be re-written as follows:

$$\sum \underline{F} = (-\frac{4}{3}\pi r^3 \rho_w g)\,\underline{j} + (\frac{1}{2}\pi r^2 C_D \rho_A V^2_{R/W})\,\underline{e}_v = \frac{4}{3}\pi r^3 \rho_w \frac{dV}{dt} \qquad (2)$$

where
   $\underline{e}_v$ = unit vector in the direction of the drop's velocity.

The x- (horizontal) component of the resulting differential equation can be reduced to the following:

$$\frac{8}{3} r \int \frac{1}{V^2} dV_x = \rho_A \int C_D \cos\phi\, dt \qquad (3)$$

where
   Φ = incident angle of the raindrop.

Note that the drag coefficient, C_D, is a quantity determined solely through experimentation, and is not easily definable in terms of velocity. Therefore, the solution to eq. (3) is most easily obtained numerically.

The numeric approach used to solve eq. (2) for velocity, and thus determine the angle of incidence at any point during the drop's descent, started with a newly-formed drop and tracked its fall over small time periods. During each small interval of time, $\Delta \underline{V} \equiv \underline{a}\,\Delta t$. The acceleration is equal to the sum of drag and weight forces divided by the mass of the drop. These quantities can be determined given the drop size, its velocity at the beginning of the time interval, and the wind velocity during that interval. The quantity Δt was chosen sufficiently small to ensure sufficient accuracy of the solution for most engineering applications.

The computer program used for the model was designed to allow a full range of realistic wind speeds and drop radii, as determined from weather data [3]. As test cases, selected drop radii were subjected to wind speeds varying from 0 to 25.4 m/s (0 to 50 ~ts). It was found that, given a constant wind speed, a drop reaches its terminal vc.ɔcity and resulting angle of incidence within 7 to 10 meters of formation. The results of these test cases are presented graphically in Figure 3. It can be seen that, for a given drop size, the angle of incidence decreases as the wind speed increases. Similarly, for a given wind speed, the angle of incidence increases as the drop size increases. These results agree qualitatively to what would be expected. Small drops have a greater tendency to ride the wind than do large drops.

WEATHER DATA

The National Weather Service monitors weather stations throughout the world which record climatological information, including wind speed and rainfall. These conditions are usually reported every hour, with some gaps possible, depending on the station. Reports for any of the weather stations are readily available through the National Climatic Data Center in Asheville, North Carolina. These reports can be used to generate a profile of hourly rainfall and mean wind speeds for any time span such as is illustrated in Figure 4. This chart shows rainfall intensities and wind speeds for an 18-hour storm in Charleston, South Carolina, on October 10 and 11, 1989 [4].

In the numerical analysis of the behavior of wind-driven raindrops, the drop size and wind speed were determined from measured observations. From the Weather Service, one can find the necessary wind speed data, but the only information related to the rain is its intensity. According to Humphreys [5], there is a direct correlation between rainfall intensity and raindrop size. This relationship, as presented by Humphreys for six discrete rainfall intensities, is given in Table 1. Using curve-fitting and interpolation techniques, the average raindrop size for any other rainfall intensity can be determined. Therefore, available weather data will supply values necessary to numerically simulate the behavior of wind-driven raindrops.

WATER TESTING

Typically, the purpose of water testing in the field has been to determine if and why leakage has occurred into a building. The tests were designed to simulate, to some extent, rainfall incident upon a building surface, as illustrated in Figure 5. According to the numerical analysis presented earlier, there are five components (not fully independent) of accurate simulation of wind-driven rainfall: rainfall intensity, rain drop size, raindrop velocity at the time of impact with the surface, wind speed, and the incident angle of the rainfall. From supplied weather data, all five of these values can be computed. In an ideal rainfall simulation, there should be methods to allow all five components to be adjusted. In current water testing methods, this is not the case.

For purposes of this paper, five common types of water tests, which are commonly used for masonry and curtain wall construction, were considered: water chamber, calibrated nozzle, spray rack, garden hose, and rilem tube.

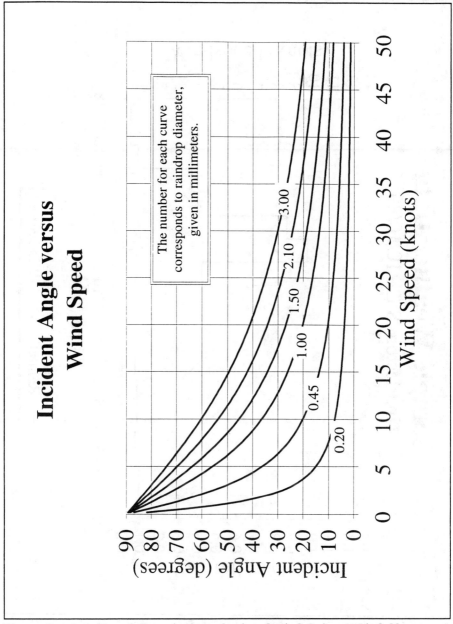

Figure 3 - Results of Numerical Analysis of Wind-Driven Rainfall

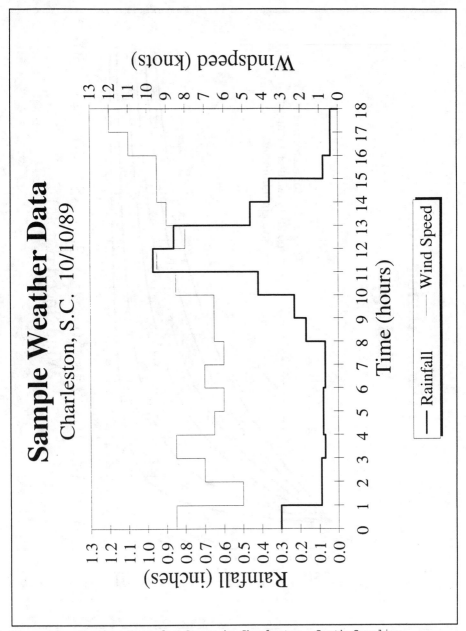

Figure 4 - Weather Data for Storm in Charleston, South Carolina

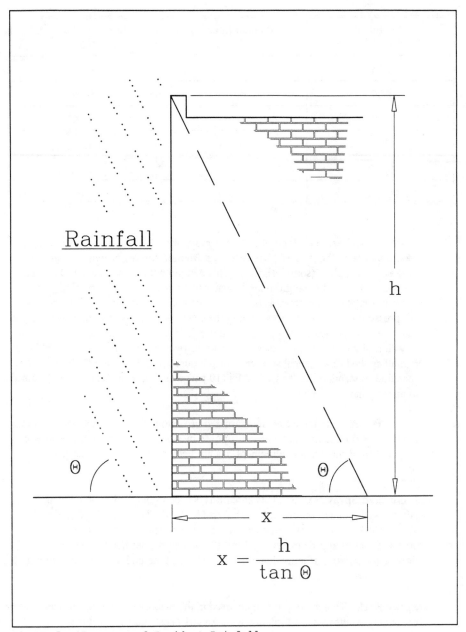

Figure 5 - Geometry of Incident Rainfall

Table 1 Raindrop Size Versus Rainfall Intensity

Rainfall Intensity (mm/hr)	Rainfall Intensity (in/hr)	Raindrop Diameter (mm)
0.25	0.010	0.20
1.00	0.039	0.45
4.00	0.157	1.00
15.00	0.591	1.50
40.00	1.575	2.10
100.00	3.937	3.00

Water Chamber: This type of testing is most often used in the laboratory in accordance with the ASTM "Standard Test Method for Water Penetration and Leakage Through Masonry" (E514). This method uses a test chamber 0.9 m (3 ft.) wide x 1.2 m (4 ft.) high to apply water to a vertical masonry surface. The water is applied as fine streams through a spray bar across the top of the chamber. Air pressure is applied by pressurizing the chamber mounted on the tested surface. The rate at which water is applied is standardized at 138 L/hour per square meter of wall (3.4 gal/hr. per sq.ft. of wall). This corresponds to approximately 5"/hr. of rainfall applied to a vertical surface. Air pressure applied to the wall, if not specified, is standardized to be 500 Pa (10 psf) which corresponds to a wind speed of approximately 55 knots.

Presently, there are no standardized provisions for using ASTM E 514 in the field. Modifications have been proposed by others [6], but, as of the time of preparation of this article, agreement has not been reached on this test for field use.

Calibrated Spray Nozzle: This apparatus is used in the field on window and curtain wall joints in accordance with AAMA "Methods of Test for Metal Curtain Walls" (501.2). The test uses a calibrated spray nozzle to apply water to the test area at a rate of approximately 91 L/m^2 (2.2 gal/sq.ft.) per hour, depending on flow characteristics of individual nozzles. This test method does not incorporate a forced air pressure differential.

Spray Rack: This method is usually used in the field over building surfaces containing windows in accordance with ASTM "Test Method for Field Determination of Water Penetration of Installed Exterior Windows, Curtain Walls and Doors by Uniform Cyclic Static Air Pressure Differential" (E1105). The test uses a series of small nozzles attached to a water rack to apply water to the test area at the minimum rate of 204 L/hour per square meter of wall (5.0 gal/hr. per sq.ft.). When testing areas of windows, the specification allows for differential air pressure, as specified by the engineer running the test.

Garden Hose: This non-standardized test method has been used by many as a qualitative measure of acceptable or unacceptable behavior of a building surface subjected to wind-driven rainfall or as a method to determine leakage sources. Typically, it consists of inundating masonry surfaces, joints, windows, and interfaces with water at variable unknown rates using a garden hose with or without a nozzle.

Rilem Tube: This method can be used in the field or in the lab to test the relative absorption of a small surface area of a masonry unit[7]. The test uses a small L-shaped tube to apply water to a small area using a head of water as a driving force.

During a rain storm, there are five mechanisms which are the driving forces behind moisture penetration: capillary forces, kinetic forces, pressure differential, gravity, and surface tension [7]. Of these, only kinetic forces and differential pressure are a function of water application; the remaining are a function of material properties. Therefore, a successful rain simulation should allow for the variation of kinetic energy of the incident water as well as differential pressure to simulate wind. These values should be varied within the test to accurately model the time characteristics of a given historical rain and wind pattern as found in the weather data.

The five testing methods presented earlier all have limited abilities to accurately simulate wind-driven rainfall. Kinetic energy is governed by the size and velocity of water drops or streams impacting a building surface. This impact is partially simulated within three of the five tests. Differential pressure is used within three of the tests. Dynamic variability with time is used by none of the tests. Table 2 contains a summary of each test method's advantages and disadvantages with respect to the accurate simulation of wind-driven rainfall.

None of the above-listed testing methods are perfect for storm simulation. Therefore, an ideal simulation must be defined using the results of numerical analysis and practical experience to formulate a viable apparatus for testing. This ideal simulator would first and foremost be variable in all important testing parameters to allow for dynamic variability with time. Theoretical testing parameters are defined in the numerical analysis: differential pressure due to wind, rate of water application, drop size, drop velocity, and incident angle of applied water. However, using practical styles of testing, there are three important variables: kinetic forces, differential pressure, and the rate of water application. The pressure differential and rate of water application are identical for both the theoretical and practical test methods. The kinetic energy in the practical model can be determined using the drop size, velocity, and angle from the theoretical model. Therefore, using published weather data and numerical analysis, accurate testing parameters can be derived for use by the appropriate testing apparatus.

IDEAL RAINFALL SIMULATION

No current test method ideally simulates actual rainstorms. Therefore, a new method should be derived that allows weather histories of a particular geographic location to be used to determine testing parameters. Using the weather data presented in Figure 4 and the results of numerical analysis summarized in Figure 3, one can determine the differential air pressure, water intensity, drop size, and angle of incidence for the water for an ideal simulation. For the sample storm, these results, based on actual weather data, are given in Table 3.

The parameters given in Table 3 are based on the actual weather data of a storm, as taken from the local weather station. The ideal simulation of a particular storm pattern would utilize these parameters as they appear. However, for some applications, it may be desirable to scale the magnitude up or down, leaving the storm profile intact. Further, because conditions of wind and rain concentrations vary, depending on building geometry, surrounding terrain, etc., these factors, where used, should be applied to the profile as a whole to maintain the variability in typical stormy conditions. Finally, it is anticipated that a long storm simulation is not practical for some applications. Steps should be made to preserve the parameters while shortening the test duration through the use of the principles of similitude.

RESEARCH NEEDS

The principles of storm simulation should be applied to data from specific local weather stations throughout the United States. This research could help refine or re-define the Driving Rain Index and lead to a more rational standard for rain resistant construction. Also, a test method which can simulate the most important aspects of wind-driven rain, i.e., water droplet impact, flow rate, and air pressure difference, should be developed. Furthermore, future efforts should be made towards including such spatial factors as global building geometry and location of tests on a specific building.

Table 2 Comparison of Commonly Used Water Testing Methods

Type of Test	Test Simulates			Test Could Simulate			Other Relative Advantages	Other Relative Disadvantages
	Drop Impact	Wind Pressure	Time Variable	Drop Impact	Wind Pressure	Time Variable		
Water Chamber	No	Yes	No	No	Yes	Yes	Most quantitative Most controllable Long history of use	Fairly small area Requires expertise Expensive
Calibrated Nozzle	Yes	No	No	Yes	No	Yes	Easy to use Inexpensive	Small test area Qualitative only
Spray Rack	Yes	No	No	Yes	Yes	Yes	Large test area Controllable	Requires expertise Qualitative only Expensive
Garden Hose	Yes	No	No	Yes	No	Yes	Easy to use Inexpensive	Small test area Qualitative only
Rilem Tube	No	Yes	No	No	Yes	Yes	None	Tiny test area Subject to bias

Table 3 Conversion of Weather Data to Testing Parameters

Time Interval (1 hour each)	Rainfall Intensity (in/hr)	Drop Size (diam) (mm)	Wind Speed (knots)	Pressure from Wind (Pa)	Incident Angle (degrees)	Water Test Intensity (L/m²/hr)
1	0.30	1.29	8.5	11.73	47.0	7.11
2	0.09	0.76	5.0	4.07	50.5	1.88
3	0.09	0.76	7.0	7.95	40.9	2.64
4	0.07	0.66	8.5	11.73	32.5	2.79
5	0.08	0.71	6.5	6.85	41.6	2.29
6	0.08	0.71	6.0	5.84	43.9	2.11
7	0.07	0.66	7.0	7.95	37.7	2.30
8	0.07	0.66	6.0	5.84	42.0	1.97
9	0.17	1.34	6.5	6.85	49.4	3.70
10	0.23	1.17	6.5	6.85	52.3	3.34
11	0.42	1.41	8.5	11.73	49.0	9.27
12	0.97	1.70	9.5	14.65	50.0	20.67
13	0.86	1.64	8.0	10.39	53.8	15.99
14	0.46	1.44	9.0	13.12	47.8	10.59
15	0.36	1.36	9.5	14.65	45.0	9.14
16	0.08	0.71	9.5	14.65	31.3	3.34
17	0.04	0.45	11.0	19.63	18.7	3.00
18	0.04	0.45	12.0	23.37	17.3	3.26

CONCLUSIONS

In order to assess the performance of structures subjected to wind-driven rainfall, investigators have traditionally used a variety of water testing methods which are standardized by various organizations including ASTM. However, the commonly used testing methods do not allow the flexibility to be modified for field use on a site-by-site basis. To accurately predict a particular structure's response to its weather patterns, it is necessary to accurately simulate wind-driven rainfall using appropriate water testing methods and historical weather data which is readily available through the National Weather Service.

Given weather data for a particular geographic location, it is possible, through the use of numerical analysis, to predict the behavior of rainfall incident upon a building surface. This behavior is dependent primarily on the characteristics of individual raindrops as affected by descent through wind. At the instance of impact on a building surface, the drops have kinetic energy which is transferred to the wall at a given rate and angle. The amount of energy as well as the rate and angle can be predicted using theoretical analysis and subsequently converted into testing parameters.

Commonly used testing methods, such as water chamber, spray rack, and calibrated nozzle, do not accurately model rainfall incident upon a building surface. A combination of methods, or an entirely new procedure, is necessary for accurate rainfall simulation. This method would have to allow the variability of testing parameters to coincide with the values obtained from actual weather data analyzed theoretically. Therefore, given weather data for a particular location, one could accurately simulate wind-driven rainfall to determine building performance.

REFERENCES

[1]   Choi, Edmund C. C., "Parameters Affecting the Intensity of Wind-Driven Rain on the Front Face of a Building," Wind, Rain, and the Building Envelope, Invitational Seminar, University of Western Ontario, Canada, May 1994.

[2]   McDonald, James E., "The Shape of Raindrops," Scientific American, 190, February 1954, pp. 64068.

[3]   Galitz, Christopher L., "Simulation of Wind-Driven Rainfall," Undergraduate Thesis for B.S. Degree in Engineering Science and Mechanics, Virginia Polytechnic Institute and State University, Blacksburg, Virginia, 1992.

[4]   National Weather Service, National Climatological Center, Asheville, NC, Hourly Rainfall and Wind Speed Data, 1990.

[5]   Humphreys, W.J., Physics of the Air, J.B. Lippincott Company, Philadelphia, PA, 1920, pp. 257-270.

[6]   Monk, C.B., Jr., "Adaptations and Additions to ASTM Test Method E514 (Water Permeance of Masonry) for Field Conditions," Masonry: Materials, Properties, and Performance, ASTM STP 778, J.G. Borchelt, Ed., American Society for Testing and Materials, Philadelphia, PA, 1982, pp. 237-244.

[7]   Driscoll, M.E. and Gates, R.E., "A Comparative Review of Various Test Methods for Evaluating the Water Penetration Resistance of Concrete Masonry Wall Units," Masonry: Design and Construction, Problems and Repair, ASTM STP 1180, John M. Melander and Lynn R. Lauersdorf, Eds., American Society for Testing and Materials, Philadelphia, PA, 1993.

Kenneth M. Lies and Brian A. Faith[1]

WINDOW DETAILING CONSIDERATIONS FOR LEAKAGE PREVENTION

REFERENCE: Lies, K. M. and Faith, B. A., **"Window Detailing Considerations for Leakage Prevention,"** Water Leakage Through Building Facades, ASTM STP 1314, R. J. Kudder and J. L. Erdly, Eds., American Society for Testing and Materials, 1998.

ABSTRACT: The focus of this paper is on the design development considerations for window detailing to prevent water leakage. Architectural design and detailing considerations discussed include: performance criteria; secondary flashing systems; integration with facade waterproofing; air seals; sealant selection and joint geometry; mullion and stack joint options; fastener locations and selection; and effects of product non-performance. Each of the design considerations are discussed with their effects and role on the waterproof integrity of the building facade. Examples of conceptual details to address waterproofing issues are provided.

KEY WORDS: window, design, water leakage

Since the beginning of building construction, penetrations were made through exterior walls of buildings for providing light and ventilation to the interior. The earliest form of windows were developed to accomplish these basic functions and provide a means of protecting the interior space from the elements. Today, windows satisfy numerous functions and are designed and tested by manufacturers to meet a broad array of industry performance standards. The window industry offers a wide selection of window types, materials, finishes, performance levels and options. Technological advances in performance and durability have been made in nearly every facet of window design including materials and components such as gaskets, sealants, glass, weatherstripping, hardware, coatings and finishes. Industry organizations such as American Society for Test and Materials (ASTM), Architectural Aluminum Manufacturing Association (ABMA), American National Standards Institute (ANSI), National Wood, Window & Door Association (NWWDA), and others provide designers with product criteria, performance testing and standards that are essential to making informed decisions regarding specifying windows.

[1] Mr. Lies is a Principal and Mr. Faith is a Project Architect II, with Raths, Raths & Johnson, Inc., 835 Midway Drive, Willowbrook, Illinois 60521

Despite industry advances in product technology, certifications and laboratory testing, buildings continue to have water leakage problems at window openings. The writers have learned that most damaging water leakage at window openings can be avoided by selecting window products that comply with industry standards, appropriate product selection and thoughtful detailing of the window installation. This paper focuses on detailing considerations for leakage prevention from the perspective of architectural designers. The content is based on the writers' experience in performing field evaluations and testing on numerous window installations throughout the country, as well as experience gained from specifying new and remedial window applications on design projects.

CONSIDERATIONS FOR WINDOW SELECTION

Industry organizations such as AAMA, ANSI and NWWDA provide design guidelines and voluntary specifications which are relied upon by designers for window selection and establishing performance criteria. The failure of the product to perform to these standards can result in water intrusion to the interior or within the exterior wall system. The individual responsible for selection of the window, whether it be a design professional, general contractor or builder, must be able to rely upon the window manufacturers to insure that the products provided for a project comply with industry standards and the referenced certified performance reports and labeling.

A common cause of non-performance is selection of a window based solely on the design wind load criteria. An important aspect which has been often misunderstood or overlooked is the need to establish an appropriate water penetration performance level for a given project. Water penetration test pressures defined for primary performance in industry guide specifications for aluminum and vinyl windows are established as 15 percent of the structural design pressure for the building, but never less than 2.86 psf. For example, an aluminum window with a structural design pressure of 20 psf would be required to pass a laboratory water penetration test, ASTM E 547[1] , at a minimum test pressure of 3.00 psf. The water penetration performance on wood windows is determined by Grade designation which is related to the structural design load. For example, a Grade 20 (20 psf structural design pressure) has a laboratory water penetration test, ASTM E 547, at a minimum pressure of 2.86 psf. Because the water penetration performance levels are less than wind load design pressures, the guide specifications assume that it is generally accepted that water leakage can be tolerated during rare events which combine high winds and rains. This basic assumption is not always applicable to a given site such as one with a coastal exposure. The individual responsible for product selection must consider what the appropriate water penetration performance level should be for a given application and make the selection based upon site specific performance criteria.

The designer should consider many factors in determining if the primary performance levels given in the guide specifications are adequate for a given project. To establish a reasonable water penetration performance level for the windows, one should consider at least the following:

1.1   Geographic location of the building and its annual climatic conditions.

1.2   Occupancy and building use. Determine what degree of water leakage is acceptable for the functionality of the interior space and tolerance level of the owner or user.

1.3   Building height and geometry. Design loads and exposure conditions will generally increase with building height and can be dramatically impacted by the form and geometry of the building.

1.4   Building exposure within the surrounding terrain. Determine how the building is sited and what effect the landscape, terrain and adjacent structures may have on exposure to wind driven rain conditions.

1.5   Impact of building construction and materials. Consider the effects the exterior wall assembly and its construction tolerances will have on the level of water leakage which may result from the selected window performance level.

1.6   Facade features such as roof over hangs, balconies, slab extensions and other feature which may influence the exposure to rain.

A meaningful analysis and understanding of these and other factors will allow a designer to make an informed decision in establishing an appropriate water penetration performance level for the windows for a project.

CONSIDERATIONS FOR WINDOW INTEGRATION

Despite following industry guidelines for window selection and industry recommendations for installation, a designer can elect to provide a higher degree of assurance that water penetration at windows will be prevented or controlled. One effective means to consider is to include detailing that introduces the concept of a second line of defense or control against water leakage. This added level of assurance may be appropriate depending on project requirements and criteria for the following reasons:

2.1   Many window types are manufactured with internal seals that are installed manually. The effectiveness of the seal will rely on the mechanic in the shop performing the work and the manufacturer's level of quality assurance.

2.2   It has been determined that some internal window seals and components can degrade over time. These seals are essential to product performance given any wall design. An example of a latent defect in some aluminum window products is dry shrinkage of the poured and debridged urethane thermal break material, as shown in Figure 1.

Figure 1:   Dry shrinkage of thermal break material.

2.3   Wall claddings and installations rely on perimeter sealants to achieve water tightness. The effectiveness of these seals relies on proper field installation, material selection and maintenance to assure water tight performance.

2.4   Window assemblies and features such as horizontal and vertical stack joints, subsills, receptor systems and other accessories are not normally considered in product grading and certification. Unless required for a specific project, laboratory certifications of window products may address the performance of the window only, not an assembly with accessory features. The designer should insist that the actual performance certification for a given application include the accessories.

2.5   Imperfections in installation and variations in technique can occur depending on the skill level and training of the mechanic.

The designer does not have direct control over aspects of window product manufacturing and installation into the building. However, the writers have found that there are detailing considerations that are effective in reducing the amount and risk of unacceptable water leakage related to window installations.

Flashings With Weather Barriers

In drainage wall type claddings, the integration of flashings and weather barriers with the window installation is critical **to** the prevention of water leakage. Water can infiltrate through claddings such as lap siding and brick masonry. Improper integration detailing or installation techniques will permit water which infiltrates through the cladding to penetrate into the wall system or interior at the rough window opening.

Building codes typically require that flashing be installed above windows with the intent that water penetration from above will be collected and controlled. However, to be effective, the flashing needs to be adequately integrated with the wall assembly. It is all too common an occurance to find that a source of water leakage in a building is the direct result of improper integration or absence of the flashings, or weather barrier at window openings, as depicted in Figure 2.

Although recommended by industry practice, if the exterior cladding material is considered by code to be a weather covering, no protective weather barrier is required. Claddings such as wood, aluminum and vinyl siding, brick masonry, and even plywood, can be considered by some codes as suitable weather coverings even though most professionals would agree that they allow varying degrees of water penetration either as a material or by design.

Figure 2:   Improper integration and absence of flashings at window openings.

In secondary weather barrier designs, the most direct approach to effectively detail flashing integration at window heads is by incorporating a weather barrier such as building felts in the wall design.   For wood framed residential construction, integration detailing which includes incorporation of building paper has recently been published in CAWM 400-95, *Standard Practice For Installation of Windows With Integral Mounting Flange in Wood Frame Construction.*[2] An example of proper integration of flashing and weather barrier is depicted in Figure 3.

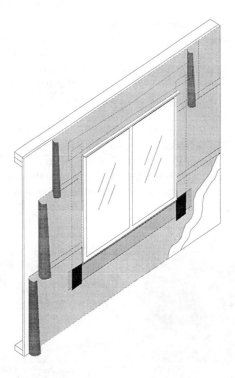

Figure 3:   Standard practice for installation of windows with integral mounting flange in wood frame construction.

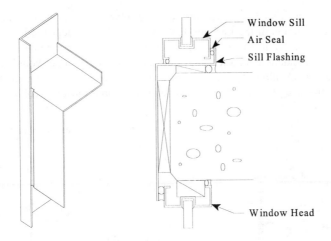

Figure 4:   Sill pan flashing isometric and section detail.

Secondary Sill Flashings

Metal flashings, similar to Figure 4, can be an effective means of providing a secondary line of defense at sills. The detailing concept is that the metal flashing will provide a means to prevent leakage into the building or wall framing in the event that deficiencies exist with the window or its installation. For this secondary sill flashing to be effective, a number of design considerations must be understood or the flashing may have little effectiveness or actually create a leakage problem.

The first determination to make is whether or not the flashing should be weeped. The general philosophy behind the concept of flashing is that it collects and controls water. After it collects water, control is usually accomplished through weeping the water to the exterior. Wind driven water can enter through open weep holes or tubes depending on how they are designed and detailed. Secondary sill flashing is typically low in profile, due to the height of the window sill section. If an effective continuous interior air seal is not achieved between the window and the flashing, water can actually be drawn through the weeps and into the interior by differential pressure. A continuous interior air seal is therefore required to effectively pressure equalize the cavity created by the secondary flashing.

Another design philosophy, which the writers have found effective, is based on the premise that the secondary sill flashing is provided to collect only small amounts of incidental water leakage. The secondary flashing can either have a restricted means of weepage by use of rope wicks or not be weeped at all. Any incidental water that is collected can be contained until it evaporates to the interior or is discharged by the rope wicks to the exterior. The use of rope wicks provides assurance that any build up of water in the secondary flashing can be weeped to the exterior.

Another potential problem with a secondary sill pan flashing is attachments at the sill that can create a penetration of the flashing that is inaccessible, as depicted in Figure 5. Consideration should be given to determining if the window can span from jamb to jamb, thus avoiding any penetrations at the sill. If sill attachment is required, one should consider a clip anchor detail which allows for a means of easily and effectively sealing around any penetration in the flashing. Blind sealing of fastener penetrations must be avoided.

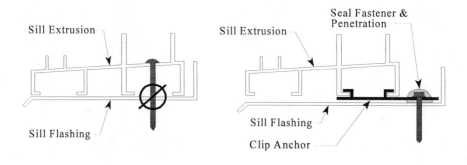

Figure 5:   Sill anchorage considerations to avoid blind penetrations in sill flashings.

Perimeter Sealant

Regardless of the cladding system on the building, nearly all window systems rely on sealants around the window perimeter to seal to the cladding system and to preclude direct water penetration. To provide long term serviceability, the industry and sealant manufacturers provide recommendations for proper installation including substrate preparation and priming, use of bond breakers and backer rod, and appropriate sealant profiles. Despite the abundance and availability of the information on good sealant design and installation practice, deficiencies occur.

It is common for sill, jamb and head sections on some aluminum and vinyl windows to provide no more than the wall thickness of the extrusions to bond sealant to and nothing to support a backer rod, as illustrated in Figure 6. When a contractor tries to install sealant to the window edge, the sealant backing falls into the extrusion prohibiting consolidation of the sealant during tooling. The combination of insufficient sealant adhesion surface and lack of consolidation can result in an adhesive failure at the window section. To compensate for these deficiencies, contractors typically install a fillet profile sealant joint to the face of the window frame which, without a bond breaker, is subject to cohesion failure in the event of movement between the window and the cladding.

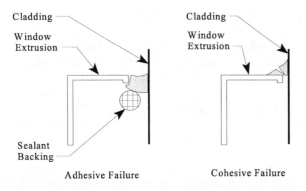

Figure 6:   Sealant failure modes due to improper joint configuration.

Some window manufacturers offer alternate extrusions or will work with designers to resolve such problems so that conventional proven sealant geometries can be executed. On large commercial projects it is not uncommon for the window manufacturer to produce custom extrusions to accommodate not only sealant geometries, but also specific cladding integration requirements.

An alternate means of sealing, using the basic geometry of the fillet bead profile, involves utilizing a foam bond breaker tape as shown in Figure 7. Laboratory testing and in-place applications have demonstrated that these two methods are viable alternates that can be utilized with standard window profiles. [3,4,& 5]

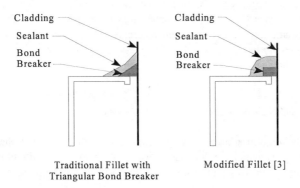

Figure 7:   Fillet sealant profiles.

Facade Design Features

In the design of the building facade there are practices that can be considered that have a proven history of deterring leakage at windows. These basic design practices are often overlooked or their effectiveness under estimated.

3.1   Roof Overhangs and Slab Extensions -- These features can reduce direct exposure to rain. Effectiveness relates to, among others, the degree of overhang protection and site exposure.

3.2   Drips -- Incorporated into slab extensions, roof copings, and flashings that can shed water away from window joints, glazing and seals.

3.3   Recess the Window -- Even a small degree of recess into the wall plane affords some protection from exposure of water running down the face of the building.

3.4   Slope Sills -- Slope sills away from windows. Avoid creating horizontal or back sloping surfaces which will allow water and snow to collect at sills.
                                                                    & headers

3.5   Select Durable and Compatible Materials -- These materials provide long term serviceability. The small added initial costs of selecting high performance sealants and durable materials is justified when considering the potential costs associated with non-performance and component replacement.

3.6   Textured Surfaces -- These surfaces on surrounding cladding such as exposed aggregates should be eliminated at window perimeters. Pin holes at the sealant adhesion surface will be created by an irregular substrate surfaces since the sealant cannot be effectively tooled and consolidated to eliminate pin holes.

CONSIDERATIONS FOR WINDOW ACCESSORIES

The most common source of water leakage at windows, other than ineffective integration detailing, is associated with accessories. Accessories are often installed by the mechanic in the field, and frequently rely on sealants for water tightness. As previously discussed, window accessories, including receptors, subsills, vertical mullions, extensions, moldings and panning, are often not included in window certification and grading. This is not to imply that window manufacturers do not perform tests to verify performance; however, it is the writers' experience that, frequently, test reports will not be available that are applicable if accessories are included in the detailing. Both laboratory and field testing should be considered for all projects, especially window installations involving field applied accessories. Based upon experience, field testing of initial installations proves meaningful in assuring that the installer is aware of installation and sealing requirements, and the consequences of variations or omissions from the approved shop drawings and contract documents.

Subsills

Subsills or sill starters should always be considered with window arrangements involving multiple windows side-by-side. Serving as a water collection device, subsills often function as a second line of defense for potential leakage of mullions, jamb receptors and internal window system seal failures. Weeped subsills are designed to provide varying levels of water penetration performance; therefore, a designer must select the appropriate subsill based upon the project requirements.

The traditional means of attaching a subsill is by direct fastening through the subsill, thus creating a penetration that must maintain water tightness. To reduce the risk of leakage at such penetrations, a designer should consider eliminating this method of attachment altogether. Clip anchor devices which mechanically engage with the extrusion eliminate fastener penetrations, and the risks associated with installation error or sealant degradation over time.

Stack Joints

Stacking mullion accessories are used to join windows that are side-by-side or one on top of another. They are often the source of water leakage due to inherent problems with some stack joint designs. The stack joint details on economy windows frequently will rely solely on field applied bed sealants, or in some cases no sealant at all, as depicted in Figure 8. Such details should not be considered reliable. It is recommended that such designs be either avoided altogether, or the designer should incorporate a method to control any anticipated water leakage.

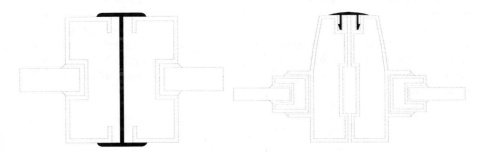

Figure 8:   Typical window mullions lacking gasketing and permanent seals.

Stacking mullions that incorporate gaskets can reduce the risk of leakage. Additionally, a back bed of sealant can usually be added to provide protection. Tee mullions with pressure plates are often selected on commercial type projects for additional structural support at the jambs and the compression gaskets provide a much higher level of reliability against water leakage. A tee mull section is shown in Figure 9.

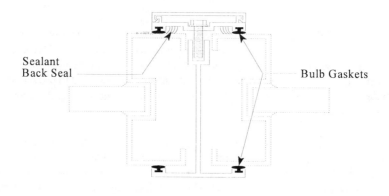

Figure 9:   Tee Mullion with Pressure Plate.

Receptors

Head and jamb receptors are used to accommodate movement of the structure or variations in the geometry of a rough opening. The exterior seal on receptors is typically achieved using a bulb type gasket that is compressed to the window frame.

Leakage problems at receptors relate to how it is integrated at its ends. Head receptors should incorporate a sealed end cap to allow sufficient adhesion surface for the perimeter sealant. Standard practice is that end caps will not be provided by the window manufacturer unless specified and then demanded. Although the compressed bulb gasket seal is often reliable in preventing water from entering across the interface between the window frame and receptor, the extruded spline on the receptor which receives the gasket can be a channel for water to enter. Therefore, the ends of the gasket splines need to be reliably sealed.

CONCLUDING REMARKS

Leakage prevention through and around windows requires that designers properly address a number of important factors. Selection of a window should be based upon many aspects including its intended function, geographic location, building use and construction type, building height and geometry, and project performance and weather proofing requirements. The use of facade features such as overhangs, drips, etc., are some of the design options that a designer should take in consideration in selecting and designing a window installation for prevention of water infiltration.

Proper integration of the window with the surrounding wall system and materials must be achieved. In barrier type claddings, the details must integrate the window in a manner that precludes water penetration. In drainage type claddings, flashings and weather barriers must be integrated to allow for the collection and control of any water which will infiltrate through the cladding. Proper detailing and consideration of critical elements, such as perimeter sealants, flashings, secondary sill flashings, and anchorage locations, can assist in preventing uncontrolled leakage through the building facade. In addition, proper consideration should be given to accessories such as subsills, stacking joints, and receptors, that are to be utilized in the window assembly. When appropriate for a project, the full window assembly with the specified accessories should be tested to demonstrate its performance characteristics.

A common sense approach to detailing which includes meaningful performance criteria analysis and consideration of the various design options, and considerations on a project by project basis, is the most effective means to assure that installed performance meets reasonable design expectations.

REFERENCES

[1]   ASTM E-547, Standard Test Method for Water Penetration of Exterior Windows, Curtain Walls, and Doors by Cyclic Static Air Pressure Differential.

[2]   CAWM 400-95, Standard Practice for Installation of Windows with Intregral Mounting Flange in Wood Frame Construction, 1995.

[3]   Hoigard, K.R. and Kudder, R.J., "Performance of a Modified Sealant Fillet Detail", Science and Technology of Building Seals, Sealants, Glazing and Waterproofing: Second Volume, ASTM STP 1142, J.M. Klosowski, Editor, American Society for Testing and Materials, Philadelphia, 1992.

[4]   Meyers, J.C., "Behavior of Fillet Sealant Joints, "Building Sealants: Material, Properties and Performance, ASTM STP 1069, Thomas F. O'Connor, Ed., American Society for Testing and Materials, Philadelphia, 1990.

[5]   O'Connor, T. F., "Recent Developments in the Design of Sealant Joints for Movement and Other Effects," <u>Science and Technology of Building Seals, Sealants, Glazing, and Waterproofing: Fifth Volume, ASTM STP 1271</u>, Michael A. Lacasse, Ed., American Society for Testing and Materials, 1996.

Richard L. Quirouette[1] and Jacques Rousseau[2]

A REVIEW OF PRESSURE EQUALIZATION AND COMPARTMENTALIZATION STUDIES OF EXTERIOR WALLS FOR RAIN PENETRATION CONTROL

REFERENCE: Quirouette, R. L. and Rousseau, J., **"A Review of Pressure Equalization and Compartmentalization Studies of Exterior Walls for Rain Penetration Control,"** Water Leakage Through Building Facades, ASTM STP 1314, R. J. Kudder and J. L. Erdly, Eds., American Society for Testing and Materials, 1998.

ABSTRACT: Recent studies have demonstrated that the amount of water penetrating through cladding systems can be significantly reduced by integrating the rainscreen concept into their design. Research has also shown that the mean pressure difference across the cladding governs the significant amount of rain penetration. A study on compartmenting the cavity has indicated that the location of compartment seals and the placement of the vents are important considerations in the control of wind driven rain.

KEYWORDS: Rainscreen, pressure equalization, air barrier, air sealing, compartmentalization, vents.

The control of rain penetration through the exterior cladding and walls of most new buildings in Canada is based on the application of the rainscreen principle and is referred to as the rainscreen wall. To function satisfactorily, the rainscreen wall must baffle or deflect rain water from direct entry; it must limit the penetration of water by capillary action; it must drain and vent the cavity behind the cladding and the cladding elements must equalize pressure with wind pressures during a wind driven rain storm. While each function is important to the performance of the rainscreen wall, this report examines the

---

[1]Principal, Quirouette Building Specialists Ltd., 18 Crispin Private, Ottawa, Ontario, K1K 2T8, Canada.

[2]Manager, Highrise Innovation, Technical Policy & Research, Canada Mortgage and Housing Corporation, 700 Montreal Road, Ottawa, Ontario, K1A 0P7, Canada.

pressure equalization performance and the compartmentalization requirements of rainscreen walls. The pressure equalization attributes of a rainscreen wall design exhibit the following features: a cladding, a drained and vented cavity, an air barrier system and compartment seals.

Canada Mortgage and Housing Corporation has recently completed several research projects to better understand the design and engineering characteristics of the pressure equalization phenomenon and its application to exterior wall design. These include a study of the water penetration through a rainscreen brick veneer wall, the effects of dynamic pressures from wind gusting during a simulated wind driven storm, and the pressure equalization performance of a rainscreen wall in a wind tunnel simulation.

Rain Penetration Control Through a Rainscreen Brick Veneer Wall

Typically, most claddings of metal, glass, plastic siding and exterior insulation finish systems (EIFS) rely on the impervious qualities of the surface finish to limit rain penetration. The control of rain penetration through a brick veneer is unlike these claddings because of the absorptive nature of the masonry. Masonry limits rain penetration by deflecting part of the rain, absorbing a part and transmitting the remainder to the backside of a cavity. Rain also penetrates through the mortar joints in the veneer. The amount of water that is absorbed or that penetrates to the inside is dependent on the amount of rain hitting the wall and the air pressure difference acting on the veneer at the time of the storm.

As part of a broader research project on the Rainscreen principle, Canada Mortgage and Housing Corporation undertook a study of the wetting and rain penetration through a typical brick veneer cladding under the effects of pressure equalization and with an air pressure difference. The project was undertaken by Morrison Hershfield Ltd. in their Ottawa Laboratory[1]. The study examined the effects of steady state wind pressure on the absorption of water and the penetration of rain through a brick veneer wood framed wall with an air tight barrier and with an air barrier that leaked air.

The experiment involved the construction of an 8' x 8' wood framed wall with a brick veneer. The wall assembly included: a brick veneer (cladding), a 1" (25 mm) air space, building paper, a 7/16" fiberboard sheathing, 2 x 4 studs and a gypsum board (air barrier) finish. The sample wall was installed in a pressure chamber with the brick veneer facing the interior of the chamber (see Figure 1 below). The pressure chamber, also constructed in wood, comprised a sheet metal liner on the interior surface, an internal rain rack, a floor drain, a water pump and storage tank, and an air pump to pressurize or depressurize the chamber as required. The water tank's weight changes were measured by its load cell.

To determine the quantity of soaking and rain penetration through the brick veneer the chamber was calibrated for water leaks at the intended operating pressure, by masking the sample wall with polyethylene film and applying a specified water spray rate of 5 gal/ft^2.hr and an air pressure difference of 5 lbs/ft^2 (250 Pa). The loss of water from the chamber was noted for calibration purposes.

The rain wetting and penetration test consisted of removing the polyethylene mask and noting the water absorption/penetration of the brick veneer. The pressurization and wetting continued for over 1.5 hours. At the brick saturation mark, approximately 60 minutes later, the wall air barrier was intentionally opened to simulate a leaky wall. The water penetration rate recording continued uninterrupted.

The data from this experiment was plotted as water penetration in litres during 98 minutes of chamber pressurization (see Figure 1). The results indicated that the brick veneer had a large capacity for absorption even though the veneer was fully pressure equalized. It absorbed 32 liters of water after 58 minutes. When the air barrier of the wall was intentionally opened to allow air to leak across the wall, the brick veneer experienced an increase in air pressure difference and a corresponding increase in water penetration. After another 40 minutes or so of wetting, the water penetration appeared to stabilize at about 40 liters for an increase of 8 liters. These results indicated that a pressure difference of 100 Pa. to 130 Pa. across the brick veneer caused an increase in water penetration of 25%. It is also noted that at the time of transition from pressure equalized to non pressure equalized, the rate of water penetration increased rapidly for about 5 minutes (note circled area, Fig. 1). A comparison of the slopes of the water penetration in this region indicates a rate increase of about 10 times.

This study illustrates the importance of an airtight inner barrier (air barrier) to cladding pressure equalization and is one of the key factors affecting the control of rain penetration. The complete experiment and detailed results will be found in the CMHC publication, "A Study of the Rainscreen Concept Applied to Cladding Systems on Wood Frame Walls."[1]

Steady State vs. Dynamic Pressure Equalization and Rain Penetration

One of the issues of the rainscreen principle not fully understood concerns the relation of steady state wind pressure and dynamic pressure variations on rain penetration control. This project examined the amount of rain penetration through a direct opening (defect) in an architectural precast wall exposed to simulated rain and the effects of a steady wind pressure in comparison to a gusting (sinusoidal load at 0.5 Hz) wind load.

Wall Sample

Test Chamber

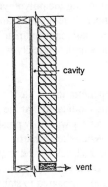

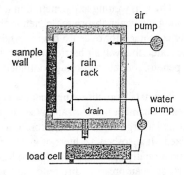

Rainscreen Test

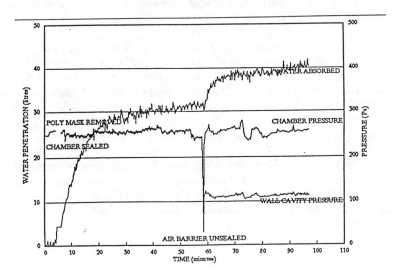

Figure 1--Wall Sample, Test Chamber and Rainscreen Test #3.

In this experiment, an architectural precast sandwich wall comprising an outer leaf (cladding), a cavity, insulation, and an inner leaf (air barrier) was designed and constructed for this research project. The cladding was vented through five 1/2" (13 mm) diameter holes in a sheet metal cover and the inner concrete leaf (air barrier) provided with three 1/4" (6 mm) diameter, leakage holes. In addition, the outer leaf was provided with a horizontal slot (saw cut) direct opening to simulate a defect. The slot measured 4 1/2" (114 mm) by 1/4" (5 mm) high (see Figure 2).

The sample wall was mounted in the dynamic wall testing facility of the Institute for Research in Construction (IRC) of the National Research Council of Canada (NRCC). The cladding part of the precast panel faced the inside of the chamber. The chamber was equipped with a 5'- 4" (1.625 m) diameter piston to create dynamic pressure variations within the chamber. The piston movement was programmed to produce sinusoidal pressure variations up to 10 Hz at a pressure amplitude of 208 lbs/ft^2 (10 kPa). A secondary blower generated the mean or steady state component of the air pressure levels in the chamber. The chamber was also equipped with a rain rack capable of delivering water at 5 gal/ft^2.hr (3.42 L/s.m^2) in a spray pattern. The rate of water entering the cavity of the specimen was measured gravimetrically using a water collection system installed at the bottom of the cavity. The rate of water entry through the defect in the outer leaf of the precast panel was measured under various mean and gusting air pressure load conditions for various combinations of panel sealing and venting.

The penetration of rain through a cladding system may enter directly (through an opening), by gravity, by capillary action, and by an air pressure difference. The latter may be subdivided into mean (steady state) pressure difference and dynamic (gusting) pressure difference.

From the various test results found in this research project, it is possible to determine the amount of direct entry water penetration (direct + gravity + capillary), the amount of water penetration by a mean air pressure difference and by a dynamic (gusting) pressure variation. In the bar chart of Figure 2, there are 6 configurations. The first configuration illustrates a water penetration rate of 0.18 liters/min., through the sample panel by direct entry (direct + gravity + capillary) and without any air pressure applied to the face of the panel. The second configuration illustrates a water penetration rate of 0.6 liters/min. with a 100 Pa air pressure difference across the panel. If the direct entry amount from configuration 1 is subtracted, there remains 0.42 liters/min. due to a mean (steady state) air pressure difference. In this project, the rate of water penetration due to mean pressure was measured for several air pressure differences. In configurations 3, 4, 5, and 6 of Figure 2, the panel was subjected to various combinations of the factors that cause water penetration. These factors included direct entry, a mean air pressure difference and a dynamic pressure difference.

Test Assembly

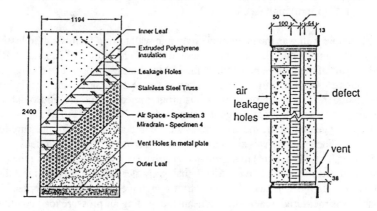

Rain Penetration

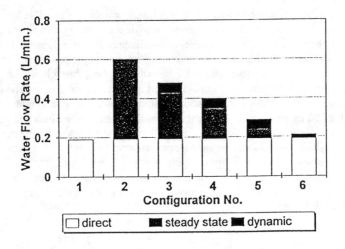

Figure 2--Sample Precast Wall and Water Penetration Chart for 6 Configurations

Assuming that the water penetration into the precast cavity from direct entry remained the same for all configurations of pressures and that the water penetration due to a mean pressure difference is proportional to the mean pressure difference applied, the remainder of the water penetration can be attributed to the dynamic effects.

The results of this study indicate that dynamic pressure variations (gusting) do not contribute significantly to rain penetration. The most significant water penetration occurred from the mean air pressure difference acting across the cladding at 100 Pa. Also, there is a notable contribution of rain penetration from the direct, gravity, capillary effects (no air pressure difference). The complete experiment and the detailed results will be found in the CMHC publication " NRC Testing of Canadian Prestressed Concrete Institute Samples."[2]

Modeling Pressure Equalization in a Wind Tunnel Experiment

The compartmentalization of the cavity behind a rainscreen wall is known to be important to its performance, but the frequency and location of compartment seals is more art than science. Canada Mortgage and Housing Corporation in cooperation with the University of Western Ontario undertook an experiment in the Boundary Layer Wind Tunnel[3] to determine the pressure equalization characteristics of cladding elements and rainscreen cavities of various size placed at various locations on a model building facade.

A building model was constructed to a 1:64 scale. Its full-scale dimensions were 266 ft (81 m) by 59 ft (18 m) by 197 ft (60 m) high. The model consisted of a plywood box enclosed with 2" (51.2 mm) of rigid foam insulation. A pressure module (containing multiple rainscreen cells) was placed at different locations on the facade of the model by cutting out a block of foam insulation and installing the pressure module.

The pressure module contained 16 individual compartments or cells. Each cell was vented to the outside through a single hole, 0.5% of the module surface. The module was designed such that each individual cell could act on its own or be connected to its neighbor. The cells were also provided with pressure taps for external pressure measurement as well as internal cavity pressures. The module was placed at six different locations (see Figure 3).

The experiment was conducted in the low-speed test section of the wind tunnel. The tunnel has a cross section of 5 m wide by 4 m high and a length of 52 m. The building model was then placed in the tunnel and exposed to various configurations of module locations and wind direction. The study revealed that the dynamic effects of wind are critical near the top and edge corners of the building and that strategic placement of compartment seals is significant to the performance of the rainscreen system. For the most part, the cavity pressures were found to be close to the average external pressures in all regions, including the corners. However, the dynamic fluctuation of the cavity pressures in the corners were found to be wider than expected. Further, it would appear that the placement of the vents of the corner cavities would benefit from placement towards the center of the facade rather than centered on the cavity. For example, in an architectural

Pressure Distribution
Across Rainscreen

tap line located 0.5H from top edge

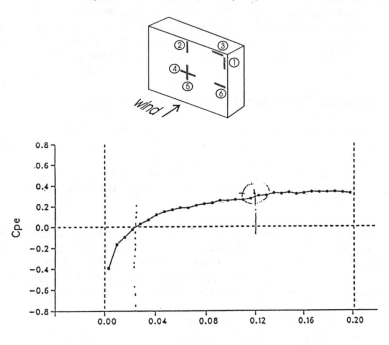

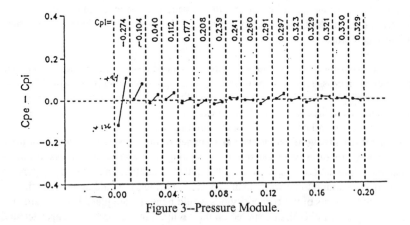

Figure 3--Pressure Module.

precast system, it would be better to locate the vent opening at the bottom of the cavity and away from the building edge. For vertical compartment seals, it would appear from the study that minimum loading variations can be obtained by compartmentalizing at 1%, 3%, 10%, 25% and center of the building width. Similar recommendations are applicable for horizontal compartmentalization starting from the top of the building. The complete experiment and the detailed results will be found in a CMHC publication "A Study of Mean Pressure Gradients, Mean Cavity Pressures, and Resulting Residual Mean Pressures Across a Rainscreen for a Representative Building."[3]

SUMMARY

It has been shown that a pressure equalized brick veneer reduces the amount of rain that may be absorbed or transmitted through the veneer. The pressure equalization depends on the quality of the air barrier and the air sealing it provides to the whole wall assembly. A pressure equalized brick veneer may reduce the penetration of water by as much as 25% or more over a non-equalized cladding system.

In the precast study, it was found that the mean pressure differences between the exterior and the cavity govern the significant amount of rain penetration, although gravity and fluctuating pressures may contribute a slight amount. This is an important finding, particularly with respect to mean wind pressures during a wind driven rainstorm.

Lastly, the compartmentalization study indicated that the location of compartment seals and the placement of vents are important considerations in the control of wind driven rain. Although the corners may experience wide fluctuation in equalization pressures, the mean cavity pressures of a sealed cavity will reflect the mean surface pressures. The strategic placement of vents in edge cavities may significantly reduce the risk of rain penetration.

The research projects described above were undertaken by Canada Mortgage and Housing Corporation to advance the general knowledge of building envelope science and technology and to promote better design, construction and performance of new residential buildings.

References

[1]   Quirouette, R.L., A Study of the Rainscreen Concept Applied to Cladding Systems on Wood Frame Walls, Morrison Hershfield Limited, Canada Mortgage and Housing Corporation, Ottawa, 1990.

[2]   Brown, William C., Ullett, James M., Dalgliesh, Allan W., NRC Testing of Canadian Prestressed Concrete Institute Samples, Institute for Research in Construction - National Research Council of Canada, Canada Mortgage and Housing Corporation, Ottawa, 1995.

[3]   Skerlj, P.F., Surry, D. A Study of Mean Pressure Gradients, Mean Cavity Pressures, and Resulting Residual Mean Pressures Across a Rainscreen for a Representative Building, Boundary Layer Wind Tunnel Laboratory - The University of Western Ontario, Canada Mortgage and Housing Corporation, Ottawa, 1996.

Jacques Rousseau[1] and Richard L. Quirouette[2]

RAINSCREEN COMPUTER PROGRAM

REFERENCE: Rousseau, J. and Quirouette, R. L., **''Rainscreen Computer Program,''** Water Leakage Through Building Facades, ASTM STP 1314, R. J. Kudder and J. L. Erdly, Eds., American Society for Testing and Materials, 1998.

ABSTRACT: Pressure equalized rainscreen walls control rain penetration by eliminating the forces which drive or draw water into a wall. A rainscreen wall incorporates two layers or wythes separated by an air space; the outer layer is vented to the outside. The performance of a pressure equalized rainscreen wall will be dependant on the leakage area of the air barrier system, the area of vent openings, the volume of the cavity, the stiffness of the air barrier and of the cladding and the leakage area of the compartment seals. The design of rainscreen is not intuitive, the RAIN computer program is a tool developed to assist practitioners in their design.

KEYWORDS: Rainscreen, pressure equalization, air barrier

RAIN PENETRATION

Rain penetration is one of the oldest problems building owners have had to deal with, yet it still occurs all too frequently. The penetration of rain can not only damage interior finishes and materials, but it can also damage the structure of the walls themselves.

A notable reference on the topic of rain penetration is Canadian Building Digest CBD 40' "Rain Penetration and its Control", by Kirby Garden. This document was published in 1963 and is one of the earliest references on the rainscreen principles. In fact, the term "Open rainscreen" was coined in this paper. The following discussion on rain penetration is based on the information contained in CBD 40'.

---

[1] Manager, HighRise Innovation, Technical Policy and Research, Canada Mortgage and Housing Corporation, 700 Montreal Road, Ottawa ON K1A 0P7
[2] Principal, Quirouette Building Specialist Limited, 18 Crispin Private, Vanier ON K1K 2T8

Rain penetration results when a combination exists of water at the surface of the wall, openings through which it can pass, and a force to move the water through these openings. The elimination of any one of these three conditions could prevent the occurrence of rain penetration. While wide roof overhangs may help to shelter the walls of a low-rise building, it is not likely that rain will never reach the walls. Therefore one of the remaining two conditions must be eliminated to prevent rain penetration.

The face seal approach attempts to eliminate all the openings in the wall through which water can pass. However, the materials used to seal all these openings are exposed to extremes of weather and to movements of the building. Even if the problems of job site inaccuracies and poor workmanship can be overcome and a perfect seal can be achieved, the in-service weather conditions will eventually cause the deterioration and failure of these seals, creating openings in the wall through which water can pass. Unfortunately, these openings can be extremely tiny and difficult to identify, so that even an extensive maintenance program may not keep the building free of openings.

The alternate approach to controlling rain penetration is to eliminate the forces which drive or draw water into the wall. There are typically considered to be four such forces: kinetic energy, capillarity, gravity and wind pressure differences. Each of these forces is explained below.

Kinetic Energy

For a wind driven rain storm, rain droplets can be blown directly into large openings in the wall. However, if there is no direct path to the interior, the rain droplets will not pass deeply into the wall. Where large openings, such as joints, are unavoidable, the use of battens, splines, baffles or overlaps has been successful in minimizing rain penetration caused by the kinetic energy of the rain drops.

Capillarity

Due to the surface tension of water, voids in a material will tend to draw in a certain amount of moisture until the material approaches saturation. If capillaries pass from the exterior to the interior, water can move through the wall due to the action of capillary suction. While partial water penetration of a wall by capillarity is characteristic of porous cladding material, the introduction of a discontinuity or air gap can prevent through-wall movement of water.

Gravity

The force of gravity will cause water to move down the face of the wall and into any downward sloped passages into the wall. To prevent gravity induced movement through joints, they are typically designed to slope upwards from the exterior. Unintentional cracks or openings are more difficult to control. If there is a cavity directly behind the exterior face of the wall, any water that does flow through the wall will then be directed downward, by gravity, on the inboard face of the exterior wall. At the bottom of the cavity, the water can then be drained back to the outside through the use of sloped flashings.

Air Pressure Difference

An air pressure difference across the wall of a building is created by stack effect, wind and/or mechanical ventilation. If the pressure on the exterior face of the wall is higher than on the interior of the wall, water can be forced through tiny openings in the wall. Research has shown that the amount of rain moved through the cladding by this mechanism is the most significant. This force can be eliminated or reduced by the use of the pressure-equalized cavity. This concept is discussed in detail in the following section.

PRINCIPLES OF PRESSURE EQUALIZATION

The theory of the pressure equalized cladding is that it neutralizes the air pressure difference across the cladding (caused by wind) which causes water penetration (the wind). It is impossible to prevent wind from blowing on a house but it is possible to counteract the pressure of the wind so that the pressure difference across the exterior cladding of the wall is close to zero. If the pressure difference across the cladding is zero, one of the main forces of rain penetration is eliminated.

A rainscreen wall incorporates two layers or wythes separated by an air space or cavity. The outer layer or cladding is vented to the outside. When wind blows on the building facade, a pressure difference would be created across the cladding; however, if the cavity behind the cladding is vented to the outside, some of the wind blowing on the wall enters the cavity, causing the pressure in the cavity to increase until it equals the exterior pressure. This concept of pressure equalization presupposes that the inner wythe of the wall is airtight. This inner wythe, which includes an air barrier, must be capable of sustaining the wind loads in order for pressure equalization to occur. If there are openings in the air barrier, the

pressure in the cavity will not equalize and rain penetration may occur.

A further advantage to consider is that the wind load
will not be imposed on the exterior cladding. Potentially,
it is possible to design the exterior cladding of a rainscreen wall to be much lighter than it has been traditionally and thus economies in construction could be realized.

The concept of pressure equalization is readily understood when steady-state conditions are considered. However, the wind is dynamic and the exterior wind pressures
impinging on a building facade are in a constant state of
flux[2]. Previous research has shown that there is typically
a time lag between the application of the exterior load and
pressure equalization in the cavity. As a result of this
time lag, a pressure difference does occur across the exterior cladding. For the rainscreen concept to be effective,
this time lag should be as short as possible. Therefore,
when we examine the performance of a rainscreen wall, one
of the primary factors considered is the time to equalization. Another is the load distribution on the exterior
cladding. The higher the load, the higher the driving
force moving rain to the interior, and the longer the time
to equalization, more rain is likely to penetrate.
Some rain penetration through the exterior cladding
can be tolerated because the cavity should be designed to
drain. However, it is still desirable to the overall function of the wall to minimize any penetration of rain.
Therefore, the "ideal" rainscreen wall would equalize in-
stantly and the exterior cladding would never experience
any wind load. In reality, this is almost impossible to
achieve. We therefore expect rainscreen walls to have a
short equalization time and small proportion of the peak
wind load on the cladding.

At first consideration, the time to equalization seems
a reasonable intuitive question. The most simplest definition would be the length of time required after application
of an exterior load for the cavity to attain the same pressure. However, from our research, it was found that while
the pressure across the cladding may approach zero, the
equalization follows exponential decay and therefore never
occurs. It may be more appropriate therefore to define the
time to equalization as the time it takes for the cavity to
reach a certain percentage of the applied load or the difference between the applied load pulse and the response
load.

FACTORS AFFECTING PRESSURE EQUALIZATION

There are a number of wall parameters that affect the
rate at which pressure equalization will occur, including:

+ leakage area of the air barrier system
+ area of vent openings
+ cavity volume
+ stiffness of the air barrier system
+ stiffness of the cladding
+ sealing of cavity perimeter (compartmentalization)

The rate of the applied load and the magnitude of the applied load will also affect the time to equalization. Each of these factors is discussed below.

THE AIR BARRIER SYSTEM

If the air barrier is perfectly tight, when a pressure is applied to the wall, all air entering the cavity through the vented cladding will remain in the cavity to cause the pressure in the cavity to increase. If there is leakage through the air barrier, air will move from the cavity to the interior of the building, and equalization does not occur. The ratio of the air pressure difference across the wall to the air pressure difference across the cladding will depend on the relative tightness of the cladding and the air barrier. Ideally, the air barrier should not leak, both for the rainscreen to function to its maximum level and also to prevent the exfiltration of indoor air and the infiltration of outdoor air.

AREA OF VENT OPENINGS

Pressure equalization depends partly on air movement into/out of the cavity. The rate at which air can move through the cladding depends on the area of openings through the cavity. If only one small opening exists, equalization may be slow, whereas if there are many openings, equalization will occur much faster. Research has indicated that the area of vent openings required depends on the cavity volume and the stiffness of the cladding system and the air barrier system.

CAVITY VOLUME

A larger cavity will require more air to move into or out of the cavity to cause pressure equalization. Therefore, given the same area of vent openings, a smaller cavity will equalize faster than a larger cavity. Thus, in designing a rainscreen wall, consideration must be given to the proportion of vent area in relation to cavity volume.

STIFFNESS OF THE AIR BARRIER PLANE

If the air barrier material is flexible and a positive pressure is applied to it, it will deflect. The result of

this deflection will be an increase in the volume of the
cavity and a larger volume takes longer to pressure equalize. Thus, the more flexible the air barrier, the longer
it will take for the cavity pressure to reach outdoor conditions. This causes the cladding to experience dynamic
loads. Therefore, in designing a rainscreen wall, the air
barrier should be designed to be as rigid as possible.

STIFFNESS OF THE CLADDING

If the cladding is flexible, the cladding will deflect
inwards, reducing the cavity volume, when a positive load
is applied. Thus, the cavity will tend to pressure equalize faster than normal from the compression effects of the
cladding deflection. But, the cladding deflection will
cause the cavity pressure difference to linger longer.
This characteristic of the cladding tends to dampen the
gust loads on the facade. From the result of our pressure
tests, it can be seen that a flexible cladding experiences
a small but longer lasting air pressure difference.

COMPARTMENTALIZATION

In designing a building with the rainscreen approach,
consideration must be given to the pressure variations over
the surface of the building. When the wind impinges on a
building facade, it tends to flow around and over the top
of the building producing variations in pressure on the
surface of the buildings. In some areas the pressure will
be negative. If the cavity behind the cladding is continuous around the building, the pressures on the surface of
the cladding may induce lateral air movement within the
cavity from ingress of air at the front to exit along the
sides and back.

Air will move within the cavity from a region of positive pressure to the region of negative pressure at the
sides of the building; as a result of this movement of air,
pressure equalization will not occur within the stud cavity. Therefore, it is important to "compartmentalize" the
cavity. By Compartmentalization we mean dividing the wall
cavity into smaller individual cavities through the use of
strategically positioned, airtight seals. It is particularly important that these compartments do not extend
around the corner of a building.

In addition it is important to note that compartment
seals are not the same as baffles. Such techniques as
stuffing fiberglass in a crack, or gluing rigid foam pieces
that do not fit tightly is not satisfactory. A compartment
seal may be an elastomeric membrane, a sheet steel angle,
or foamed in urethane insulation.

WIND LOADING

Two conditions of wind must be considered with the pressure equalized wall, the steady state condition and the gust effect. While gusting presents a dynamic loading, it is the time average pressure over the surface which exhibits the most influence on rain penetration. For this reason, water penetration tests were conducted at a steady state pressure while the dynamics of gusting was examined for structural effects.

A SIMULATION MODEL

INTRODUCTION

To design a rainscreen wall the following physical parameter of the wall must be determined and they include; the volume of the cavity, the area of venting, the stiffness criteria of both cladding and the air barrier material and the leakage area of the air barrier system. It is also understood that the cavity volume is bound by compartment seals that must be leak proof.

To assist the designer, a simulation model can be used to determine the pressure equalization performance for the above noted features and characteristics. The simulation model developed predicts the pressure equalization behavior of a wall system in terms of structural air pressure load distribution and pressure equalization time. The simulation model was developed using the fundamental gas laws and basic equations of fluid dynamics.

DEVELOPMENT OF THE MODEL

The simulation model that follows was developed to simulate the behavior of a single cavity compartment, with one plane exhibiting cladding features and one plane exhibiting air barrier attributes. In all simulations it is assumed that the inside pressure is the reference pressure, and various loading rates and initial conditions of cavity pressure are chosen for the simulation.

Previous research has shown that the loading pattern typically exhibited by gusting wind most closely resembles a triangular pulse function. However, to simulate the behavior of the laboratory tests, the model uses an exponential equation to generate the loading on the wall. The rate at which the load is applied can be adjusted by changing the value of the exponent in the equation.

The response of the cavity pressure in a rainscreen wall is a function of the basic gas law:

$$P = \frac{nRT}{V} \quad \dots\dots\dots\dots\dots\dots\dots\dots\dots\dots\dots\dots\dots (1)$$

where P = absolute pressure (Pa)
         V = volume (m^3)
         n = no. of moles of air (moles)
         R = gas constant (J/(mole .°K))
         T = absolute temperature (°K)

In the development of the simulation model, it was assumed that temperature would be constant; a value of 20 °C or 293 °K has been established as the standard condition. It was also assumed that the gas constant would not change significantly.

To understand how pressure equalization occurs, consider the situation where a positive pressure is applied to the wall surface. Pressure equalization will occur when the pressure in the cavity rises or falls to match the applied pressure. Movement of air into the cavity is one mechanism to increase the pressure in the cavity. The mass of air required to achieve equalization depends on the volume of the cavity. The rate at which equalization occurs depends on the rate at which the air can enter the cavity, which is given by the following equation:

$$Q = CA \frac{(2DP)^n}{D} \dots\dots\dots\dots\dots\dots\dots\dots\dots\dots\dots\dots (2)$$

where Q = air leakage rate (m^3/s)
         C = discharge coefficient (unitless)
         A = total area of opening (m^2)
         DP = pressure difference (Pa)
         D = density of air (kg/m^3)
         n = exponent (between .5 and 1)

The rate of air flow into the cavity is constantly changing. As air flows in, the pressure difference across the cavity changes and the pressure difference across the cavity is the driving force which dictates the rate of air entering or leaving the cavity.

Another parameter that causes the pressure in the cavity to increase or decrease is related to deformation of the volume of the cavity. Depending on their rigidity (or flexibility), both the cladding and the air barrier will deflect under the applied load and will change the volume of the cavity. If the cladding deflects more than the air barrier, the cavity volume will decrease and the cavity pressure will increase without the flow of air into the cavity.

In actual situations, a combination of air movement and cavity volume change caused by deflections of the cladding and air barrier will occur. The program attempts to model these simultaneous occurrences. The resulting equation which must be solved takes the following form:

$$Pc = \frac{287 \cdot T \cdot [V_o \cdot d_e + (A_1 \cdot C_d \cdot T_s \cdot \sqrt{2 \cdot de.(Pe-Pc)} - (A_2 \cdot C_d \cdot T_s \cdot \sqrt{2 \cdot de.(Pc-Pi)}]}{V_o - k_1 \cdot (P_e - P_c) + k_2 \cdot (P_c - P_i)} \dots \dots \dots (3)$$

where P_c = absolute cavity pressure (Pa)
         T = absolute temperature ($^\circ$K)
         V_o = initial cavity volume (m^3)
         d_e = density of air (kg/m^3)
         A_1 = area of cladding leakage (m^2)
         C_d = discharge coefficient (unitless)
         T_s = time interval (sec.)
         A_2 = area of air barrier leakage (m^2)
         P_i = interior pressure (Pa)
         k_1 = flexibility constant of cladding (m^3/Pa)
         k_2 = flexibility constant of air barrier (m^3/Pa)

The resulting equation proved too unwieldy to analyze directly so it was divided into smaller segments and solved numerically through a computer program using an iterative procedure. A listing of the computer program will be found in Appendix A. The program is also available on computer diskette, with instructions for use, and will be provided by CMHC upon request.

INPUT PARAMETERS

When the program is executed, the following parameters must be input by the user:

            Height of cavity (m)
            Length of cavity (m)
            Width of cavity (m)
            Flexibility of cladding (m^3/Pa)
            Flexibility of air barrier (m^3/Pa)
            Vent area of cladding (m^2)
            Leakage area of air barrier (m^2)

Each of these parameters is discussed below.

Height of cavity

This is the vertical dimension of the compartmentalized cavity of the wall.

Length of cavity

This is the horizontal dimension of the compartmentalized cavity of the wall.

Width of cavity

This is the width dimension of the compartmentalized cavity of the wall, i.e. the dimension of the space between the air barrier and the cladding.

Flexibility of cladding

This is the flexibility constant of the cladding. A flexibility constant equal to zero represents a rigid cladding which does not deflect under load, such as brick. The units are m^3/Pa and represent the volumetric displacement of a plane of materials subjected to a pressure difference.

Flexibility of the air barrier

This is the flexibility constant of the air barrier. A flexibility constant of 0.00005 m^3/Pa represents a very flexible material, such as 4 mil polyethylene film spanning 405 mm in a wood frame wall.

Vent area of cladding

This is the total leakage and vent area of the cladding. A typical value for an 8 ft. by 8 ft. brick wall vented at the head joints every 24 in. o.c. would be 0.0024 m^2.

Leakage area of air barrier

This is the total leakage area of the air barrier. This value should be zero or very close to zero.

There are a number of other parameters within the program. These parameters were assigned constant values and are described below:

Loading

The program was designed to simulate a wind loading pattern having an a saw tooth pulse of 1000 Pa for a total duration of 0.5 seconds from an absolute positive pressure of 100 000 Pa. Atmospheric pressure is assumed to be 100 000 Pa. The equation for the loading rate takes the following form:

$$P = 1000e^{-nt} \dots\dots\dots\dots\dots\dots\dots\dots\dots\dots\dots\dots\dots\dots(4)$$

where $n = 5$
         $t = time(s)$

Decreasing the variable n reduces the rate of change of pressure or decreases the rate of loading. A value of 5 was selected for the standard value of n because previous research indicated that this loading rate is most represen- tative of a medium speed gust pressure change.

OUTPUT RESULTS

The output from the computer program is the following:
Column 1: Time (sec.)
Column 2: Exterior Pressure (Absolute wind pressure) (Pa)
Column 3: Cavity pressure (Pa)
Column 4: Cladding Load (Pressure difference across the cladding (Col 3 - Col 2)) (Pa)
Column 5: Air Barrier Load (Pressure difference across air barrier (Col 4 - Col 2)) (Pa)
Column 6: Cavity Volume (m^3)
Column 7: Air Mass (Mass of air in cavity) (kg)
Column 8: Vent Flow (Flow of air through cladding) (l/s)
Column 9: A.B. Leakage (Flow of air through air barrier) (l/s)

This data for the absolute wind pressure (EXTERIOR), the absolute cavity pressure (CAVITY) and the pressure dif- ference across the cladding (CLADDING) are graphed for viewing convenience. The maximum cladding load is also indicated for convenience.

The data, for the graph, which are important to de- signers are the time to equalization and the peak load on the exterior cladding. These values can be obtained by scanning Column 3 of the data file. The peak load is eas- ily discernible by scanning this column of data. It is somewhat more difficult to establish the time to equalization.

COMPARATIVE VALIDATION

To validate the simulation model, it was necessary to compare it's output with the measured performance of other systems. The output results of significance are peak load air pressure difference on cladding and equalization time for a particular type and duration of wind gust. The out- put of the simulation model, was compared with the measured performance of a metal and glass curtain wall system. The performance of the latter was reported in a paper in the 1987 CSCE Centennial Conference Proceedings, May 19 - 22, 1987, or IRC/NRC reprint number 1542[3].

From the above noted publication, it was determined that the following features characterized the elements and geometry of the metal glass curtain wall tested. The vol- ume of the cavity was 0.15 m^3, the area of leakage was 0.00023 m^2, no leakage through the back-pan, and an esti- mated stiffness of 0.000002 m^3/Pa for the glass spandrel and

0.000005 m³/Pa for the back-pan. These parameters were input to our simulation model along with an exponential load
exhibiting a 4000 Pa/sec decay. It will be noted from the
comparison of the measured and computed results, that the
results closely approximate each other. There is noted
difference in the slope of decay but the peak loads and
duration times are approximately the same under similar
loading conditions.

Steady State Characteristics

The simulation model was developed primarily to simulate gust loading conditions. However, for steady state
conditions, it was found by experiment, that the pressure
distribution across the cladding (vinyl, stucco, brick) and
the air barrier system (sheathing, gypsum) may be determined from the following equations.

$$CL = \frac{La^2(Pe-Pi)}{La^2+Va^2} \dotfill (5)$$

or

$$AL = \frac{Va^2(Pe-Pi)}{La^2+Va^2} \dotfill (6)$$

where   CL = cladding load (Pa)
            AL = air barrier load (Pa)
            La = air barrier leakage (m²)
            Va = vent area (m²)
            Pe = external absolute pressure (Pa)
            Pi = interior absolute pressure (Pa)

For example, if a sample wall has a .001 m² vent area
through the brick weep holes, and it has .001 m² leakage
area through the air barrier system, the wind load (Pe -
Pi) of approximately 500 Pa would exhibit 250 Pa on the
cladding and 250 Pa on the air barrier system. There would
also be a flow of air corresponding to the actual size of
the leakage, usually referred to as infiltration. It is to
be noted that the flexibility or stiffness of the cladding
or of the air barrier system is of no importance or consequence to the distribution pressures under steady state
conditions, however, the deflections of the cladding components or air barrier systems under steady state loads may
prove unacceptable.

Thus, the steady state pressure distribution in an
exterior wall is easily determined from the known characteristics of leakage areas through the various systems in a
compartmentalized wall, or can be obtained from field measurements of pressure and one other parameter, the leakage

or vent area of the cladding, or the leakage of the air barrier system.

Dynamic Load Characteristics

Dynamic loads on the cladding and the resultant distribution of pressures within the wall is more difficult to predict and is the subject of our simulation model. First, to simulate a gust effect or transient load, experimental testing was conducted in a pressurized chamber by suddenly releasing the pressure by means of a special orifice valve and membrane to cause a rapid change in pressure. The rate of change of pressure of the chamber is set to fast, medium, or slow by means of various orifice sizes and membrane selection. The pressure drop/increase using this method was found to decay along an exponential curve and therefore could be analyzed and simulated.

While simulated gust pattern does not mimic wind behavior, it exhibits all the dynamics of wind effects, and for this reason was deemed suitable to validate the simulation model. Thus, the initial simulation model used an exponential load formula for this purpose. It is to be noted that the simulation now is executed using a triangular pulse load of varying amplitude and frequency. The model could also be modified to use a sinusoidal load of any frequency and amplitude.

A sensitivity analysis of the effect of the parameters is undertaken in the next section. While we believe that the model provides a good first approximation of the dynamic behavior of the cavity pressure for the noted characteristics, it should be compared with the results of other assemblies notably masonry cavity wall systems, precast sandwich wall panels, and similar structural components and elements to determine if size or scale effects exhibit a significant influence.

It is to be noted that the math model does not consider the resonance effects of the air in the chamber or the frequency response of materials in terms of possible dynamic oscillations of the mass of air or other components comprising the metal and glass curtain wall. Measurements made of the laboratory systems have indicated the cavity pressure decayed without any oscillatory behavior.

EXAMPLE SIMULATIONS

To demonstrate the use of the program and the effect of changing the input parameters, a number of example simulations were executed. First, some basic conditions were established. These would be typical of a brick veneer wall 2438 mm by 2438 mm with a 19 mm cavity and a concrete back-

up wall. Both the cladding components and the air barrier
system are assumed to be rigid. The value of the input
parameters used in the simulation are summarized in the
first line of Table 1. Then, each input parameter was varied as indicated in Table 1.

TABLE 1

INPUT PARAMETERS FOR EXAMPLE SIMULATIONS

Example	VOL m3	PFX1 m3/pa	PFX2	VA_1 m^2 x 10^{-4}	VA_2 m^2 x 10^{-4}
Basic Conditions	0.1	0	0	1	0
Cavity Volume Increased	0.5	0	0	1	0
Cladding Flexibility Increased	0.1	$5X10^6$	0	1	0
Air Barrier Flexibility Increased	0.1	0	$1X10^6$	1	0
Cladding Leakage Increased	0.1	0	0	5	0
Air Barrier Leakage Increased	0.1	0	0	1	1

DISCUSSION

     Parametric Analysis Increasing the initial volume sig-
nificantly increased both the peak load on the cladding and
the time to equalization. This result is expected because
the larger volume requires that more air must be exhausted
to attain equalization. However, the fixed vent area limits the rate at which the air can be exhausted from the
cavity.

     Increasing the flexibility of the cladding reduced the
peak load on the cladding but increased the time to equalization. This is attributed to the elastic deformation of
the cladding which cause the cavity pressure to follow the

outside pressure. However, as the load diminishes, the deformed cladding will sustain a difference until it has returned to rest position.

Increasing the flexibility of the air barrier increased the peak load response on the cladding and increased the time to equalization.

Increasing the vent area (or the cladding leakage) reduced both the peak load and the time to equalization. This result was expected because more air could move out of the cavity in the same period of time.

Increasing the leakage through the air barrier decreased the peak loading and lightly increased the time to equalization. In this situation, the cavity pressure decays both outwardly and inwardly in the simulation to accelerate pressure equalization. In a pressure buildup condition, we could expect leakage through the air barrier to have the reverse effect.

The example simulations, although limited in number, demonstrate the sensitivity that model has with respect to each variable.

LIMITATIONS AND FURTHER DEVELOPMENT

Unpredictable results may be output from the simulation when the input parameters are not within realistic limits. The input parameters of leakage area and flexibility coefficient may be difficult to determine when trying to design a wall. More test data is needed to establish typical ranges for these parameters.

Further development of the model could include the following:

1) allowing user to input description of construction materials and let the computer generate the flexibility constants;

2) expand the simulation model to provide conditions using a steady state wind pressure;

3) expand user flexibility with respect to gust rate loadings;

4) develop a single number concept to define the peak load and pressure equalization; response for a rainscreen wall system;

5) Expand the model to include a rain penetration index from the Climatic Data (Weather Index).

72 WATER LEAKAGE THROUGH BUILDING FACADES

6) Develop model further to predict rain penetration index for 15 min., one hour and four hour storms.

REFERENCES:

(1) Garden, G.K., Rain Penetration and Its Control, Canadian Building Digest CBD 40, National Research Council of Canada, Ottawa, 1963.

(2) Inculet, D. and Surry, D., The Influence of Unsteady Pressure Gradients on Compartmentilization Requirements for Pressure-Equalized Rainscreens, Boundary Layer Wind Tunnel Laboratory - The University of Western Ontario, Canada Morrtgage and Housing Corporation, Ottawa,1996.

(3) Ganguli and Quirouette, Pressure Equalization Performance of a Metal and Glass Curtain Wall, Proceedings of 1987 CSCE Centennial Conference, Montreal, 1987 Volume 1, page 127 to 144 or IRC/NRCC Paper 1542, National Research Council of Canada, Ottawa, 1987.

John F. Straube[1] and Eric F. P. Burnett[2]

DRIVING RAIN AND MASONRY VENEER

REFERENCE: Straube, J. F. and Burnett, E. F. P., **"Driving Rain and Masonry Veneer,"** Water Leakage Through Building Facades, ASTM STP 1314, R. J. Kudder and J. L. Erdly, Eds., American Society for Testing and Materials, 1998.

Abstract: Wetting, in particular rain wetting, of walls with a masonry veneer is an important performance consideration for reasons of aesthetics, durability, and utility. Over the past four years, a variety of full-scale clay brick veneer wall systems have been tested in the BEGHUT field test facility. These long-term investigations of the response of wall systems to the southwestern Ontario climate have involved observation of both the exterior and interior environments as well as the performance of the brick veneer.

Standard and non-standard air and rain penetration testing has been conducted. Temperature, vapor pressure, air pressures, and brickwork moisture content have been measured. The contribution of vents of various kinds and the flow characteristics (both air and water) of the region behind the screen has been studied. In the latest project, two weather stations are used to monitor the sun, wind, rain, and driving rain. There are also 14 driving rain gauges mounted on the walls of the facility.

The objective of this paper is to propose a probabilistic model relating the wind, rain, and rain penetration. Driving rain, wetting, and surface drainage are discussed in some detail. Some of the more significant preliminary results of this research and its application to wall performance and rain penetration testing, especially for brick veneers, are presented and discussed.

Keywords: rain, driving rain, masonry, brick, veneers, water penetration

Wind driven rain is the main source of moisture in above-grade walls causing wetting of the cladding. If the exterior of the wall is masonry, particularly brick veneer, driving rain can result in staining, leakage, and freeze-thaw deterioration. Despite the importance of driving rain to building performance, very little is known about the magnitude, duration, and frequency of driving rain deposition on buildings.

This paper examines the mechanisms involved in rain deposition on building envelopes in general and the response of clay brick masonry veneers in particular.

[1] Hankin Chair & Director, The Pennsylvania Housing Research Center, Penn State University, University Park, PA 16502-1408.

[2] Assistant Director, Building Engineering Group, Civil Engineering Department, University of Waterloo, Waterloo, Ontario, Canada, N2L 3G1.

A Wall Classification System

To provide a context for this discussion of rain water penetration of building envelopes consider the classification system shown in Figure 1 [1]. The classification is based on the method by which the wall system controls rain penetration only. This classification system is useful, if only to avoid confusion. Consider, for example, the issue of using the same test procedures intended for mass walls to test screened walls.

Walls are comprised of elements and the joints between these elements. Both wall elements and joints may be classified in the same manner.

The primary classification is whether a wall is a **perfect barrier** (often referred to as face sealed) or an **imperfect barrier**. Because it is very difficult to build and maintain a perfect barrier wall, most walls are designed as, or perform as, imperfect barrier wall systems of either the mass type or the screened type. Some examples of perfect barrier walls are some EIF systems, some window frames, and some metal and glass curtain wall systems.

Mass walls control rain penetration by absorbing and storing rain water which penetrates the exterior surface. In a functional mass wall this moisture is eventually removed by evaporative drying before it reaches the inner surface of the wall. Some examples of mass walls include solid multi-wythe brick masonry and single-wythe block masonry.

Screened walls are also imperfect barrier type wall systems in that this approach acknowledges that some rain water will penetrate the screen. It should be noted that the screen is much more than a rainscreen; it must also resist wind, snow, solar radiation, etc. **Drainage** is the most common and important mechanism by which any water penetrating the screen is removed (diffusive and ventilation drying are others). The dashed lines in Figure 1 indicate that, while undesirable, undrained walls do exist. Supplementary mechanisms, such as a capillary break and a water barrier, are usually employed to resist further inward movement of the water that penetrates the screen. Some examples of screened wall systems include brick veneer, stone veneer, and vinyl siding.

A **cavity** behind the screen provides a capillary break, as well as a clear path for gravity drainage and a path for air flow. A cavity is defined here as any unobstructed space, filled with a porous material or not, that fulfills these functions.

Given a cavity behind the screen, four major sub-classifications relating to air movement and vents are possible:

A **vented** wall system allows some degree of water vapor diffusion and air mixing between the cavity and the exterior. Water can be trapped in the cavity, adhered by surface tension or absorbed by the materials that make up the sides of the cavity, such that it cannot be removed by gravity drainage. Venting (and, to a greater degree, ventilation) provides a mechanism for the removal of water that does not drain from the cavity. Venting, or better still, ventilation, may also remove water vapor that may have diffused outward from the inner wythe.

A **pressure moderated** wall system promotes the moderation of the pressure difference across the screen. The proper choice of venting, i.e., size, number, and location, and the division of the cavity into stiff, airtight compartments are necessary requirements. A relatively small volume of air needs to be exchanged to result in a significant degree of pressure moderation. Although such a wall has heretofore been described as a pressure equalized rainscreen (PER) in Canada, instantaneous pressure equalization rarely occurs in reality and the screen deals with more than rain -- hence the more realistic term, "pressure moderated screened" (PMS) wall, is preferred.

By increasing the flow of air into and through the cavity in periods when it is not raining, a relatively large volume of water vapor can be transported from the cavity. Such a **ventilated** wall will assist the drying of both the inner wythe and the screen. A wall can be both **pressure moderated and ventilated**: this is not only feasible but is to be preferred.

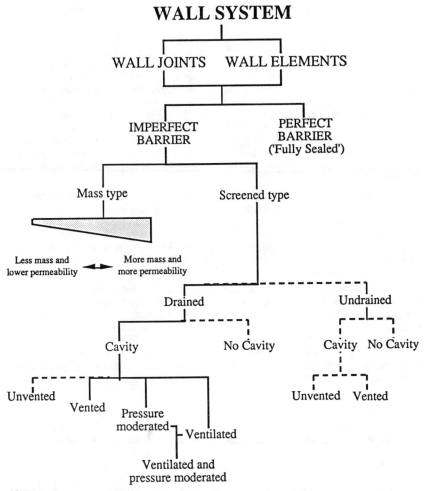

WALL SYSTEM

WALL JOINTS   WALL ELEMENTS

IMPERFECT BARRIER

PERFECT BARRIER ('Fully Sealed')

Mass type   Screened type

Less mass and lower permeability   ⬌   More mass and more permeability

Drained   Undrained

Cavity   No Cavity   Cavity   No Cavity

Unvented   Vented   Pressure moderated ┐ Ventilated   Unvented   Vented

Ventilated and pressure moderated

Notes:

The walls are categorized based on actual behavior, not necessarily design intent.

For the purposes of this classification system, the following definitions are necessary:

Drained: the majority of the water that penetrates the screen is removed by gravity.

Cavity: a clear space or a filled space that facilitates gravity drainage and air flow and resists the lateral transfer of water (a capillary break).

Vented: allows some degree of water vapor diffusion through vents and by air mixing.

Ventilated: allows a significant flow of air largely to promote drying by mass vapour movement.

Pressure-moderated: an approach that moderates air pressure differences across the screen.

Figure 1: Wall Categorization System (by Rain Penetration Control)

RAIN WETTING

Standardised tests (CSA, ASTM) are commonly used to assess the rain penetration resistance of prototype, mockup, and in-situ wall assemblies. These standard tests have two major drawbacks. First, the magnitude and nature of wind pressures and water volumes applied have been based on estimates of likely extreme conditions probably because of the dearth of actual measurements or proven theory. Secondly, these tests implicitly assume that a wall is either of the perfectly sealed type, i.e., any water penetration is considered failure, (e.g., ASTM E331) or of the mass type, i.e., water penetration after a certain length of exposure is considered acceptable (e.g., ASTM E514). Unfortunately, many modern wall designs are screened systems in which water penetration of the screen is a design feature; it is the failure to drain this water that constitutes a failure. Testing of screened wall sytems is not explicitly addressed in any of these standards.

The volume of water deposited on a wall system is the result of the interaction between the wind, rain, the building, and the building envelope. The stochastic natures of the wind and rain, and the many variables associated with the building site and geometry makes the prediction of driving rain deposition on a wall a difficult task. Even if the rate of rain deposition on a building surface were known, the extent of absorption, face drainage, and penetration of water will depend on the cladding material, texture, and previous wetting history.

A probabalistic model of rain-wind-building interaction is proposed in this section. This model is intended as an aid in the understanding and quantification of driving rain. The rain and wind are considered as separate, and statistically independent events. The model separates the wind, driving rain, and building interaction into three parts: the weather at the site, which is unaffected by buildings; building considerations, i.e., how the building interacts with wind and rain; and wall considerations, i.e., how the wall interacts with water deposited on the building envelope. Figures 2 through 4 graphically represent the three stages of the model. Each part is considered in turn, below.

Rain and Wind

Driving rain can be defined as the amount of rain that passes through a vertical plane in the atmosphere. Driving rain is primarily a result of the interaction of the wind speed and rainfall rate, but rain drop diameter also plays a role. As the raindrop diameter increases, the wind is less able to deflect the drop from its vertical fall because of its lower drag coefficient relative to its volume. Best [2], Markowitz [3], and Laws and Parsons [4] all have found that rain drop diameter increases with increasing rainfall intensity.

Lacy [5] conducted the seminal English-language study of driving rain. He proposed a simple equation relating wind speed and rainfall intensity to driving rain :

$$r_v = 0.222 \cdot V \cdot r_h^{0.88} = DRF \cdot V \cdot r_h^{0.88} \qquad (1)$$

where, r_v is the rainfall rate on a vertical plane (mm/m^2/h),

V is the average wind velocity (m/s), and

r_h is the average rainfall rate on the ground (mm/m^2/h).

The proportionality constant in Equation (1) relating rain on a vertical plane (driving rain) to rain on horizontal plane (falling rain) is defined here as the driving rain factor (DRF).

Even recent studies still make use of Equation 1 to generate driving rain information from wind and rainfall information. Some studies assume that this equation will predict driving rain deposition on buildings; this was not its intent.

Equation 1 is often simplified with little loss of accuracy by assuming that driving rain is a simple linear function of wind speed and rainfall rate, i.e.,:

$$r_v = DRF \cdot V \cdot r_h \qquad (2)$$

Using this form of the relationship, Lacy [6] calculated a DRF of 0.208 at Garston, U.K. Based on many years of results, Künzel [7] reported a DRF value of 0.20 for southern Germany, and Choi reported a value of DRF = 0.225 for Australia [8].

It is not precisely correct to assume that the wind and falling rain can be modelled as separate events that only interact at various stages. There is some evidence to suggest that the wind-speed probability distribution is different during rain events [9], and it is well documented that the wind direction distribution is different during rain events [10, 8]. However, the use of wind speed and wind direction probability distributions during rain events is a reasonable approximation since there is no reason to expect that the rate of rain fall influences the wind speed or vice versa.

The exact nature of the rainfall-during-wind and wind-during-rainfall probability distributions are one unknown. It may be possible to manipulate existing meteorological data to generate or approximate the distributions during rainfall. Rainfall-intensity-duration relationships, widely used to design stormwater management systems, are available for most areas of North America, and they can be used to assess the rainfall probability distribution.

The wind speed probability distribution is relatively well known (the average hourly wind speed fits a log-normal distribution), and statistical values have been documented. However, for shorter time scales, the wind speed behaves almost randomly. By transforming the short-term wind speed from the time domain to the frequency domain, research has shown [11, 12] that the wind fits a well-defined distribution, which is a function of only the average wind speed and terrain type. The remainder of the model considers the wind speed and wind pressures in the frequency domain.

The output of this part of the model (Figure 2) is the spectral density function of the wind and a probability distribution of driving rain intensity in the environment for each wind speed and direction. This is site-specific information that is, in itself, very useful design information.

Interaction of Wind, Rain, and the Building

As the wind encounters a building, stream lines and pressure gradients form around the building. While it is clear that driving rain is re-directed by these streams of air, accounting for this effect is difficult.

The second stage of the model (Figure 3) considers a specific area of the building envelope. The smaller the area the greater the model's accuracy. The model employs the aerodynamic admittance function (AAF), commonly used in wind engineering, to transform the spectral distribution of the wind in the environment to wind pressures on the cladding. The AAF is a unique function for a particular building geometry and surrounding terrain and obstacles. Although the AAF is different for each location on the building, with experience, it can be roughly approximated.

A rain admittance function (RAF) has been introduced to transform driving rain in the environment to deposited rain on the building. The RAF is primarily a factor to account for the location of interest on the building, the angle of attack of the wind (wind direction), and wind speed. Although there is no direct link in the model allowing interaction between the wind and rain, the interaction is implicitly contained in the wind

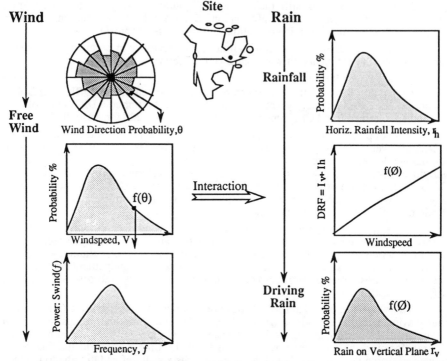

Definitions: r_h rainfall intensity; r_v driving rain intensity, r_{bv} intensity of driving rain deposited on a vertical building surface; V wind velocity, θ wind direction, Ø rain drop diameter, f frequency, $S_{wind}(f)$ spectral density function of wind velocity

Figure 2: Interaction of Wind and Rain

speed and wind direction variables which are included earlier in the model. It is also likely that the RAF is a function of raindrop diameter, although this has yet to be proven.

The literature contains only a few references to simultaneous measurements of driving rain in the environment and driving-rain deposition on a building. Choi [13] has pursued a computational fluid dynamics (CFD) approach to the prediction of driving rain deposition on buildings. The University of Western Ontario has begun wind tunnel modelling of the process [14]. CFD work at the IRC/NRCC has generated encouraging results but this work is not yet complete. Unfortunately, the computer and wind tunnel studies have not yet been validated with real data.

In his studies of driving rain on buildings, Lacy suggested that it might be possible to predict rain deposition on a building surface by applying a simple factor to the driving-rain intensity. The RAF is this factor. The RAF factor accounts for the effect of the building on driving rain in the unobstructed wind. To predict driving rain deposition on a building an extension of Lacy's model of driving rain in the free wind can be written:

$$r_{bv} = RAF \cdot 0.222 \cdot \cos(\theta) \cdot V \cdot r_h = RAF \cdot DRF \cdot \cos(\theta) \cdot V \cdot r_h \qquad (3)$$

$$= RAF \cdot \cos(\theta) \cdot r_v$$

where

r_{bv} is the rain deposition rate on a vertical building surface($l/m^2/h$),
V is the wind speed at the height of interest,
θ is the angle between the normal to the wall and the wind direction, and
RAF is the rain admittance function, where RAF = r_{bv} + ($r_v \cdot \cos(\theta)$).

The RAF has not been reported in most of the literature. However, it can often be calculated from published data. In most cases, the value of RAF is less than 1.0. Sandin [15, 16] reported values of 0.3 (near the lower centre) to 1.0 (upper corners) in studies of driving rain on low-rise buildings. Künzel [17] and Lacy [5] reported values 0.5 for the middle of a low-rise wall over a wide range of wind speeds and rainfall intensities. Henriques [18] measured an RAF value of 0.6 on the centreline of a low-rise building, but the gauge was mounted near the top of the partially-obstructed building at an unreported height above the free-wind gauge. Flori [19] found a RAF value of almost 0.6 and, more importantly, reported increasing values of the RAF factor (up to 1.2) as the wind angle changed from normal to the wall to parallel to the wall.

These values of RAF have been calculated from driving rain measured at the same height in the free wind. Higher up a tall building, the driving rain intensity will be higher because wind speeds increase with height according to a power law. Schwarz [20] measured driving rain deposition on an 18-story building for a seven-month period. The RAF factor was calculated to be 0.5 for the 10 m height. Windspeed increases with height following a power law distribution. Extrapolating windspeed data higher up the tall building studied by Schwarz (using the appropriate power law), one can calculate the

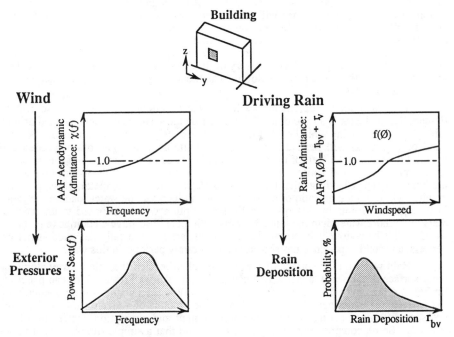

$\chi(f)$ aerodynamic admittance function, $S_{ext}(f)$ spectral density function of wind pressures on exterior of the building.

Figure 3: Interaction of Wind, Rain, and the Building

RAF for other heights on the building from his data. The calculated RAF for the ninth and sixteenth storys was no different than that for the third story at 10 m above grade. The RAF calculated for the upper corners of the building, however, ranged from 0.9 to 1.0. These results (RAF = 0.5 for the centre of a building and RAF = 0.9 to 1.0 for the corners) match Sandin's results for a low-rise building. An important implication of these results is that that driving rain deposition increases with height at the same rate as wind speed. The RAF also appears to be scale-independent, probably in a similar way as mean wind pressures gradients can be scaled for buildings of the same geometry.

Note that all of the measurements reported above are averaged over several rain events, or even over several years. The RAF is likely to vary slightly with the wind speed and rain drop diameters of the individual storm; the existing body of field measurements suggests that these are either not very significant or are averaged out over time. Available CFD results, however, all indicate that the raindrop diameter may be quite important.

Rainwater on Wall

How water behaves once it strikes a wall is very dependent on the nature of the wall and, to some extent, the location of the wall on the building. Some of the most important wall characteristics include the absorbency, the surface texture and, for PMS walls, the degree of pressure moderation.

The nature of surfaces above and beside the area of envelope being considered also play a role since water draining or blown from these surfaces will add to the water on the wall. If water is deposited on a vertical surface at a high rate, a surface film will form and ensure that any extra water will be drained away on the surface (i.e., shed). If a porous building material becomes saturated, it will begin to behave like an impervious material; that is, any deposited moisture will simply be drained away. Therefore, the rate of water deposition, the moisture content of the surface, the duration of the rain event, and the previous wetting and drying history of the cladding will all have an effect on how water behaves on the surface of a building. The model (Figure 4) attempts to account for all of these variables.

The water load supplement is a factor that accounts for some of these effects. Essentially, the factor is a ratio of available water on the surface and the deposited driving rain. Areas of cladding which are below drained areas (e.g., a band of brickwork below a band of windows) will have a high water load supplement. The drainage area and material type above the wall of interest can be used to estimate the value of the the water load supplement., and finite difference formulations may be able to provide useful predictions [21]. Claddings that have very low absorptions (e.g., metal, glass, polished granite) will drain a high ratio of deposited rain and increase the water load on the joints in the system. Joints in systems with little absorption will be exposed to an order of magnitude more water than the joints in walls with more absorptive claddings (e.g., brick, wood). This behaviour is important because joints are still typically designed as perfect barriers, and field experience has shown that they rarely perform in this way.

Rain water on the surface of a wall will either be shed (i.e., flow away along the outer surface of the wall), absorbed by capillarity into the wall material, or can penetrate further into the wall. To account for each possibility, a shedding/absorption/penetration (SAP) fraction is defined; it is a function of the amount of water on the surface, the pressure difference acting, and the moisture content and absorption coefficient of the material. Some computer modelling [22] has found that a simple time-invariant factor (called the rain absorption factor) is sufficient to match measured and predicted results, suggesting that significant simplifications to this model may be possible in certain circumstances. The SAP fraction will need to be measured from laboratory and field tests of different types of cladding, although engineering judgment might also be used to estimate reasonable values.

Pressure-moderated screened wall systems create further complexity because the air pressure difference across the cladding is an important rain penetration mechanism for some types of wall systems. Air pressure differences are generally not a very important water penetration force for permeable walls [23, 24], e.g., masonry veneers. However, for walls with a supposedly impervious cladding, water flow through small cracks, joints, and imperfections driven by air pressure may be the primary water penetration mechanism.

Previous work [25] has developed a promising method for predicting the pressure response of a pressure moderated wall system. A screen admittance function (k_A) can be used to transform pressures on the exterior of the screen to pressures acting across the screen. Three issues need to be resolved. First, a method to predict the value of the

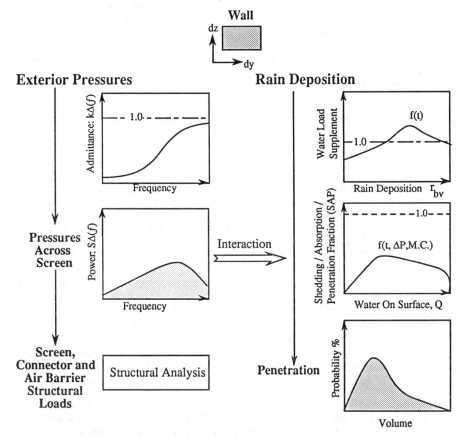

Definitions: $k_A(f)$ screen admittance function, $S_A(f)$ spectral density function of pressure differences acting across the screen.

Figure 4: Interaction of Wind, Rain, Building, and the Enclosure Element

screen admittance (k_A) function has not yet been developed. Although there are some computer simulations available [26], none has yet been shown to accurately model the response of walls in the field. Second, the influence of spatio-temporal wind-pressure variations has been shown [19, 27] to be a crucial factor affecting the ability of walls to pressure moderate. Although the effect of spatial variations can probably be introduced in the screen admittance function, a method of doing this has not yet been developed. Finally, the effect of the duration of a pressure difference on the amount of water penetration through screen materials has not been examined. Transforming the spectrum of pressures across the screen into the time domain may be necessary.

Work is continuing to quantify and further refine this preliminary model.

CURRENT RESEARCH

The Building Engineering Group (BEG) is involved in a research program part of which involves the examination of the process of rain wetting, water penetration, and drying of cladding. Twenty-seven wall test panels, each 1.2 m wide and 2.4 m high, of ten different types have been built, instrumented, and installed in BEG's full-scale, natural exposure and test facilty, the Beghut. Most of the test walls are light-gauge steel- or wood-framed assemblies clad with vinyl, EIFS, or clay brick veneer. The Beghut has standard meteorological instrumentation as well as a total of 14 driving rain gauges on its walls and one in the free wind.

Driving Rain

Although we are at an early stage of monitoring wind and driving rain deposition, some interesting results have already been collected. Several intense, driving-rain storms occurred in the fall of 1995 in the Waterloo area.

A portion of one driving rain event is shown in Figure 5. This event lasted about 12 hours, but rainfall was the most intense for the seven-hour period shown. It can be seen that the peak 15 minute rainfall intensity during the event was 6 mm/hr, about one quarter the 1-in-10 year value for Waterloo. The rainfall intensity remained above about 4 mm/hr for five consecutive hours. The 15-minute average wind speed during this event varied from 3.5 to 6 m/s (average 4.8 m/s) and the wind direction was almost due south.The driving rain collected by the rain gauge in the middle of the south face of the Beghut is plotted in Figure 5 along with the predicted driving-rain deposition using Equation (3) with a DRF of 0.20 and a RAF of 0.5.

It can be seen that the predicted results are generally close to the measured values except for some short-term variations. Over the period shown, the average predicted volume of rain (5.60 l/m^2) was about 10% less than that measured (6.20 l/m^2). This deviation can be expected as a result of natural variability in wind and rain, instrumentation inaccuracies, etc.

The maximum measured rain-deposition rate was about 4 l/m^2/hr. Long-term driving rain measurements in Europe [28] (in areas of high rainfall and wind intensity) have found that rates of more than 4 l/m^2/hr occur in fewer than 10% of driving-rain events. About 80% of driving-rain events can be expected to last for less than 6 to 10 hours. From an analyis of driving-rain measurements and meteorological measurements, researchers at the British Building Research Establishment concluded that a test rate of only 3 l/m^2/hr applied for 6 hours per day for three consecutive days was an extreme but reasonably likely test [29]. These measured rates and durations can be compared to the application rates specified in ASTM standard tests for mass walls (e.g., E514: 139 l/m^2/hr for 72 hours) and for perfect barrier walls (e.g., E331: 204 l/m^2/hr for 15 minutes).

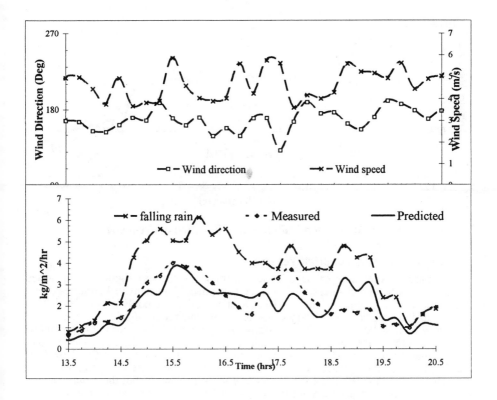

Figure 5: Wind, Rain, and Driving Rain Deposition

Pressure Moderation

Although we have had some success in modelling the response of pressure-moderated walls to spatially uniform dynamic pressures (i.e., dynamic lab tests), the spatio-temporal variations of the wind will govern the performance of most wall systems. We have begun some comprehensive field monitoring of several wall panels in the Beghut. As has been well documented, the degree of pressure moderation is not only a function of the wall characteristics but also of the wind characteristics. The spatial extent of gusts is likely the most important wind charactertistic affecting pressure moderation, but the speed of the gust (i.e., frequency) and to a lesser extent, the magnitude of the gust, also play a role.

Figure 6 presents the measured degree of pressure moderation for a typical brick-veneer-clad wood-framed Canadian house wall with a 38 mm air space and insulated sheathing. The air tight test panel was installed near the centre of the Beghut.

As can be seen from the figure, there is little pressure moderation of high frequency/short-duration gusts (more than 2 Hz). Over the range 0.125 to 2 Hz the degree of pressure moderation averages about 50%. Despite the compartmentalization of the panel (1.2 m x 2.4 m), it was found that the degree of pressure moderation dropped quickly as the wind direction changed from the perpendicular.

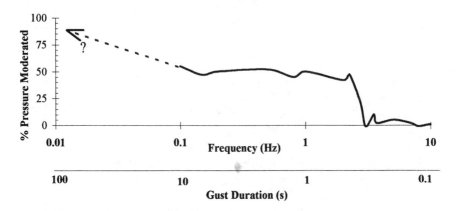

Figure 6: Screen Admittance as a Function of Frequency

Rain Penetration of Brick Veneers

In previous research we have found that brick veneers leak significant quantities of water even when no air-pressure difference is applied. An extensive literature review [27] confirms that there is no scientific basis to support the commonly held belief that air pressure differences are the primary cause of water penetration of brick veneers. This belief may be based on at least three reasons. Air pressure differences are important in mass walls, such as the solid masonry walls. Tests of curtain walls and windows also indicate that air pressure is often the most important penetration force for these face sealed / perfect barrier systems. It has also often been observed that walls leak when it is very windy. Only the last point is relevant to brick veneer walls, but the observation of rain-wind-leak coincidence merely supports the fact that rain is deposited on a wall only when it is windy (when rain is deposited on the wall), not necessarily the assertion that wind pressure is the major cause of rain water penetration.

The interfacial cracks between the brick and mortar are important to rain penetration. Many researchers have observed that water penetration of masonry veneers occurs primarily through the brick-mortar interface at the head joints. Fast drying of the mortar because of low ambient relative humidity, high temperatures during curing, and/or solar exposure will all greatly increase the number and size of the cracks in masonry veneer walls built in the field. Mismatched mortar and brick properties and poor workmanship (unfilled head joints) will also increase the size and number of cracks at the head joints. These lasty two factors are also cited as the major factors influencing the water permeance of brick veneers.

Water on the face of the brickwork will be drawn into small cracks by capillary suction forces. Interfacial cracks are generally in the range of 0.1 and 1 mm [30]. As the surface tension of water is approximately 0.075 N/m, the capillary suction pressure for cracks of this size is in the order of 75 to 750 Pa. Obviously, with such large capillary suction pressures, no applied pressure (either hydrostatic or air) is required to force water into the brickwork. However, the capillary suction pressure also resists the expulsion of the water to the inner face of the veneer. Gravity will build hydrostatic pressure that forces water, drawn and trapped in the cracks by capillarity, to flow back out of the crack. Significant hydrostatic pressures can be built up in the vertical head joint over the height of a brick. A typical brick height of 60 mm suggests a potential hydrostatic pressure of

600 Pa, enough to overcome the capillary suction of a crack 0.115 mm wide.   (It is interesting to note that Grimm [30] states that cracks smaller than 0.1 mm do not appear to contribute to water penetration.) Figure 7 shows an isometric of a likely situation of debonded mortar at the brick-mortar interface and the resulting forces that result in water leakage.

This line of reasoning suggests that rain water can penetrate brick veneers without the benefit of air pressure differences.   While air pressure differences may be of consequence, even instantaneous pressure moderation will not stop water penetration, and may not even significantly reduce it.

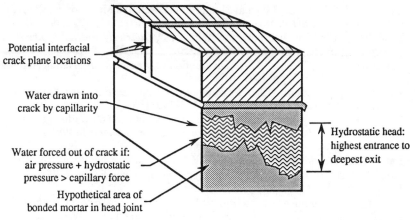

Figure 7: Capillary-Gravity Water Penetration Mechanism in Masonry Veneers

CONCLUSIONS

Driving rain is an important source of moisture in building envelopes and can be the cause of many durability and performance causes. Despite these facts, very little is known about driving-rain deposition or the behaviour of rain water on cladding. Much more research is needed.

The Driving Rain Factor and Rain Admittance Function are useful measures of driving rain that allow driving rain to be studied and compared. These factors, together with rain data, can be used to approximately predict driving rain deposition on buildings.

The abilities of a screened wall to absorb moisture and drain any water that penetrates are critical characteristics; neither is addressed in exisiting test procedures. A review of the literature and preliminary field measurements suggest that driving rain deposition rates of more than 5 l/m^2/hour are only very rarely encountered. Rates applied in ASTM and AAMA tests are far higher than is the case for most real walls. Similarly, pressures applied in standard tests tend to be too high.

Air pressure differences are not the primary force causing water penetration of masonry veneers. Although venting a cavity wall can be very beneficial, a significant amount of pressure moderation is unlikely to occur in service. Even if instantaneous pressure equalization does occur, it may not provide a significant improvement to the control of rain penetration.

ACKNOWLEDGEMENTS

This research is part of the In-Service Performance of Enclosure Walls Project. The Government of the Province of Ontario provided funding through the University Research Initiative Fund. The input and funding of the seven corporate partners (Roxul Insulations, Durisol Materials, Owens-Corning Canada, Sto Corporation, Canada Brick, Brampton Brick, and Celfortec) is gratefully acknowledged.

REFERENCES

[1]   Burnett, E.F.P., Straube, J.F., and Sloof, P.,"The Relative Merits of the Zero-Cavity Wall", *Proc. of Sixth Int. Masonry Symp.*, Calgary, Alta., July 1994, pp. 672-690.

2]   Best, A.C., "The Size Distribution of Raindrops", *Quarterly Journal of The Royal Meteorology Society*, Vol. 76, p. 16-36, 1950.

[3]   Markowitz, A.M., "Raindrop Size Distribution Expressions", *Journal of Applied Meteorology*, Vol. 15, pp. 1029-1031, 1976.

[4]   Laws, J.O., and Parsons, D.A., "Relation of raindrop size to intensity", *American Gephys. Union Trans.*, No. 24, pt. 2, pp. 453-460, 1943.

[5]   Lacy, R.E., Driving-Rain Maps and the Onslaught of Rain on Buildings. *Proceedings of RILEM/CIB Symposium on Moisture Problems in Buildings*, Helsinki, 1965.

[6]   Lacy, R.E., "Driving Rain at Garston, U.K.", *CIB Bulletin*, No. 4, pp. 6-9, 1964.

[7]   Künzel, H.M., *Bestimmung der Schlagregenbelastung von Fassadenflächen.* Fraunhofer-Institut für Bauphysik, Mitteilung 263, No. 21, 1994.

[8]   Choi, E.C.C., "Parameters Affecting the Intensity of Wind-Driven Rain on the Front Face of a Building", *Proceedings of the Invitational Seminar of Wind, Rain, and the Building Envelope*, University of Western Ontario, London, Canada, May 16-18, 1994.

[9]   Lawson, T.V., *Wind Effects on Buildings, Volume 1: Design Applications..* Applied Science Publishers, London, 1980.

[10] Surry, D., Skerlj, P. , Mikitiuk, M.J., "An Exploratory Study of the Climatic Relationships between Rain and Wind," Final Report BLWT-SS22-1994, Faculty of Engineering Science, University of Western Ontario, London, September, 1994.

[11] Van der Hoven, I., "Power spectrum of horizontal wind speed in the frequency range from 0.0007 to 900 cy./hour", *Journal of Meteorology*, Vol. 14, 1957, p. 160.

[12] Davenport, A.G., "The Spectrum of Horizontal Gustiness Near the Ground in High Winds", *Quarterly Journal of the Royal Meteorological Society*, Vol. 87, 1961, pp. 194 - 211.

[13] Choi, E.C.C., "Simulation of Wind-Driven Rain Around a Building", *Journal of Wind Engineering and Industrial Aerodynamics*, Vol 46-47, 1993, pp. 721-729.

[14] Inculet, D.R., Surry, D., "Simulation of Wind-Driven Rain and Wetting Patterns on Buildings," Report BLWT-SS30-1994, Faculty of Engineering Science, University of Western Ontario, London, November, 1994.

[15] Sandin, K., "The Moisture Conditions in Aerated Lightweight Concrete Walls", *Proc. of Symposium and Day of Building Physics*, Lund University, August 24-27, 1987, Swedish Council for Building Research, 1988, pp. 216-220.

[16] Sandin, K., *Skalmurskonstruktionens fukt- och temperaturbetingelser.* Rapport R43:1991 Byggforskningsrådet, Stockholm, Sweden, 1991.

[17] Künzel, H. and Schwarz, B., *Feuchtigkeitsaufnahme von Baustoffen bei Beregnung*, Berichte aus der Bauforschung, Heft 61, Berlin, 1968.

[18] Henriques, F.M.A., "Quantification of wind-driven rain - an experimental approach", *Building Research and Information*, Vol. 20, No. 5, 1992, pp. 295-297.

[19] Flori, J-P., *Influence des Conditions Climatiques sur le Mouillage et le sechalge d'une Facade Vertical*, Cahiers du CTSB 2606, Sept. 1992.

[20] Schwarz, B., "Witterungsbeansphruchung von Hochhausfassaden," *HLH* Bd. 24, Nr. 12, 1973, pp. 376-384.

[21] Hall, C. and Kalimeris, A.N., "Water Movement in Porous Building Materials - V: Absorption and Shedding of Rain by Building Surfaces", *Building and Environment*, Vol. 17, No. 4, 1982, pp. 257-262.

[22] Künzel, H.M., *Verfahren zur Ein- und Zweidimensionalen Berechnung des Gekoppelten Wärme- und Feuchtetransports in Bauteilen mit Einfachen Kennwerten*. Doctoral Dissertation, Fackultät Bauingeneur- und Vermessungswesen der Universität Stuttgart, July, 1994.

[23] Newman, A.J. and Whiteside, D., "Water and Air Penetration Through Brick Walls-A Theoretical and Experimental Study", *Trans. J. Brit. Ceram. Soc.*, Vol. 80, 1981, pp. 27-36.

[24] Newman, A.J., and Whiteside, D.,"Water and Air Penetration Through Masonry Walls - A Device for the Measurement of Air Leakage in-Situ", *Trans. & Journal of Brit. Ceram. Soc.*, Vol. 83, 1984, pp. 190-195.

[25] Straube, J.F., and Burnett, E.F.P., *The Zero-Cavity and DPV Wall Project*. Report for Canada Mortgage and Housing Coporation, Dec. 1995. Unpublished.

[26] Inculet, D.R., *Pressure-Equalization of Rain Screen Cladding*. M.A.Sc. Thesis, Faculty of Engineering Science, University of Western Ontario, London, Canada, 1990.

[27] Straube, J.F., *The Performance of Wall Systems Screened with Brick Veneer*. M.A.Sc. Thesis, University of Waterloo, 1993.

[28] Künzel, H., "Wärme- und Feuchteschutz von zweischaligem Mauerwerk mit Kerndämmung", *Bauphysik* , No. 13, Heft 1, 1991, pp. 1-9.

[29] Whiteside, D., Newman, A.J., Kloss, P.B., Willis, W.,"Full-Scale Testing of the Resistance to Water Penetration of Seven Cavity Fills", *Bldg. and Environ.*, Vol. 15, 1980, pp. 109-118.

[30] Grimm, C.T.,"Masonry Cracks: A Review of the Literature", *Masonry: Materials, Design, Construction and Maintenance, ASTM STP 992*, H.A. Harris, Ed., American Society for Testing and Materials, Philadelphia, 1988, pp. 257-280.

Repair

Raymond L. Delaney[1] and Charles B. Goldsmith[2]

SOLUTION TO MOISTURE, MOLD AND MILDEW PROBLEMS
IN A CENTRAL FLORIDA HOTEL

REFERENCE: Delaney, R. L. and Goldsmith, C. B., **"Solution To Moisture, Mold and Mildew Problems in a Central Florida Hotel,"** Water Leakage Through Building Facades, ASTM STP 1314, R. J. Kudder and J. L. Erdly, Eds., American Society for Testing and Materials, 1998.

ABSTRACT: A 12-story resort hotel in central Florida, built in the late 1980's, has an exterior insulation and finish system (EIFS) facade on steel studs. Interior walls have vinyl wall coverings. There were mildew problems in guest rooms. There were several contributing factors: water in stud cavities from condensation on chilled water lines; leaks into stud cavities from deteriorated exterior sealants; cracks in the EIFS; and condensation at the back of drywall and vinyl during summer. Summer temperature profiles were calculated for the exterior wall assembly based on modified ASHRAE methodology using published local temperature and humidity data. Solutions are preceding.

KEY WORDS: dew point, EIFS, mildew, moisture, mold, vinyl wallcovering

---

Mold and mildew problems on guest room walls in hotels and motels in hot humid climates such as Florida are not uncommon. These problems have been addressed in various conferences and in several publications. This paper describes some of the conditions contributing to moisture-related mold and mildew problems in a 12-story resort hotel in central Florida where some guest rooms had mold, mildew and foul odor. The mold was prevalent behind vinyl wallcovering at exterior walls and partitions. Calculations were made to evaluate the potential condensation in the exterior wall assembly during summer. The impact of other variables, such as HVAC controls and deficiencies in the weather resistive qualities of the exterior wall finish was considered. Recommendations were made to alleviate the problem.

---

[1]Senior Consulting Engineer, C. B. Goldsmith & Associates, Inc., 13303 U. S. Highway 19 North, Clearwater, FL 34624-7294

[2]CEO, C. B. Goldsmith & Associates, Inc.

The subject hotel was built between 1988-89. It is partly 12-stories and partly 8-stories in height.

The exterior steel stud walls from the interior to the exterior consist of the following components:

1. Vinyl wallcovering.

2. Gypsum drywall.

3. Air space.

4. Fiberglass batt insulation with a foil facer touching the sheathing.

5. Gypsum sheathing with screws attached to steel studs.

6. Exterior insulation and finish system (EIFS) with expanded polystyrene foam (EPS) adhered to the gypsum sheathing, reinforced cementitious base, and acrylic modified finish coat with integral color and some painted surfaces.

7. Two-part polyurethane exterior sealant at joints and perimeter of aluminum window walls with operable windows.

The heating, ventilating and air conditioning (HVAC) system was made up of:

1. A chilled water system with fan coil units in guest rooms adjacent to exterior walls.

2. Temperature settings by guests was possible only when the bar bolt on the door was actuated. Otherwise the computer controlled the set point at approximately 78°F (26°C).

3. Fresh make-up air was supplied to corridors which supplied fresh air to guest rooms via the crack under the door. This air was conditioned by a combination of cooling coils, heat pipes and a desiccant dehumidifying system which had to be discontinued in 1995 because its air handler housing had rusted out.

4. Exhaust vents in bathrooms operated continuously.

Historical records from the hotel's maintenance department indicated that from 3% to 5% of the guest rooms had some form of odor, mold and mildew problem at any given time. Usually, these problems were directly related to conditions in the bathrooms but there were also similar problems at the interior side of exterior walls and partitions adjoining the bath rooms. Corrective measures included removing the vinyl wall covering and, at times, removing the gypsum wallboard before reapplication of same materials. In several other guest rooms, the maintenance department used a latex paint instead of vinyl wall covering to reduce mildew. This was an effective solution.

The maintenance department also pointed out that the polyurethane sealants at the exterior window frames had reverted from a rubbery to a gummy characteristic. The mold problems at the guest room exterior walls occurred predominantly under, or adjacent to the window wall jambs where the sealants at the perimeter of the window had failed from loss of adhesion, cohesion (or reversion), or from improper application. Another contributing factor to the mold was from condensation at the chiller lines. These chiller lines contained chilled water at a constant 43°F (6°C) and were located in a chase adjacent to the exterior wall which travelled from floor to floor. Neoprene foam insulation covered the chilled water lines which in time had become swollen and cracked. Condensation formed, escaping through the cracks, and travelled down to the metal firestop at the floor, progressing to the chase below causing mold behind the vinyl wallcovering at the wall of the condenser unit to develop. The upper output louver of the fan coil blew cold air at about 65°F (18°C) against the adjacent exterior wall. Some of the closures of the operable windows were improperly installed and prevented a tight fit against the rubber gasket, causing excess air infiltration. There had not been any problem of water entry from guests leaving the louvered operable windows open. At no time did the hotel install individual dehumidifier units. There was no history of condensate pans or drain lines overflowing or leaking.

A direct-fired desiccant system had been installed in 1992 to provide lower relative humidity (RH) in the corridor air. Although it was effective in reducing mildew and related odors in the corridors and some lower level guest rooms, it lacked effectiveness at the upper level guest rooms. During July 1993 on the 10th floor the average daily room temperature varied from 78°F to 82°F (26°C to 28°C) while the corridor remained almost a constant at 80°F (27°C). During the same period the average daily room RH varied from 50 to 60% while the corridor RH varied from 58% to 78%. In other rooms the average daily temperature and RH varied above and below the corridor temperature and RH. It was not uncommon for the room to reach 80% RH and 80°F (27°C)

Data was not available to indicate the room temperature and RH when occupied and not occupied. It would be reasonable to expect that during summer, the unoccupied guest rooms would have higher temperatures and relative humidities than when occupied.

In March 1995 our firm observed conditions in one guest room during interior renovation which was made necessary because of the extensive mold and mildew behind vinyl wallcovering. This condition caused the vinyl to peel off or be easily pulled off as the mold degraded the wallcovering paste. At the time of our investigation, conditions behind the vinyl and the drywall were dry but must have been wet at an earlier time in order for this condition to occur. Mold was most prevalent below the window sill beside the jamb and at the partition enclosing the fan coil unit.

Here it was noted that condensation had occurred at chiller lines. The resultant moisture in the chase caused metal corrosion and deterioration of the gypsum drywall. Another area of mold was at the vinyl wallcovering at the lower one-third of the height of the bathroom partition wall. Inside the bathroom there were gaps between the tile and the tub at the wall and floor where water had entered and migrated to the cavity in the partition causing the mold. A water test was conducted at the outside of the window with subsequent water entry at the sill and jamb. This leakage was associated with defective sealant at the window perimeter.

Examination of the exterior elevations revealed a pattern of defective sealant at the perimeter of penetrations such as windows and doors. This two-part urethane sealant had reverted to a gummy characteristic in some areas. It is possible that this was caused by improper mixing rather than reversion. There were some stress cracks in the EIFS system at the corners of openings, and the integrally colored EIFS had faded to the point that it impaired the aesthetics.

Since the maintenance department had reported the presence of wet drywall in conjunction with mold and mildew during summer months, we evaluated the potential for condensation from moisture diffusion from outside during hot, humid weather based on weather data published in the Tampa Tribune during July 1993. This newspaper published hourly temperatures and reported relative humidity (RH) for 7:00 a.m. and 7:00 p.m. daily. From this data we derived the corresponding dew points at these two times, using a psychrometric chart from the ASHRAE Handbook of Fundamentals. Vapor pressures were calculated based on a table of thermodynamic properties of moist air as published in the ASHRAE Handbook. Using published thermal resistance data for the wall components and ASHRAE methodology, we used a computer program to calculate and print the temperature profile across the exterior wall for four selected indoor and outdoor conditions. In a similar manner, with known vapor permeance data, we calculated the water vapor transmission rate for a selected "worse case" scenario. Some of these results are included in this paper.

Indoor temperature and RH conditions shown in Table 1 were selected based on what would be considered normal for an occupied guest room during July, 1993.

Table 1 shows four selected outdoor and indoor conditions, labeled A, B, C and D. These conditions were selected to show those conditions in which condensation could and could not occur within the exterior wall cavity or the back of the vinyl or drywall.

Condition A represents a condition of no condensation because the outdoor dew point is lower than the room temperature and the cavity is dry.

Condition B represents a condition where condensation might occur since the outdoor dew point is higher than the room temperature and the cavity is dry.

Condition C is the same as Condition A, but because the cavity is wet, the relative humidity in the cavity could approach 100% and the corresponding dew point in the cavity could be higher than the indoor temperature, resulting in the possibility of condensation at the room side of the cavity.

Condition D represents a dry cavity but the outdoor dew point associated with a moderately cool outdoor temperature is higher than the lower indoor temperature. Thus this unusual Condition D would be more prone to have condensation than Condition A or B which are more normal.

DESCRIPTION	Condition A	Condition B	Condition C	Condition D
Date:	July 20, 1993	July 31, 1993	July 20, 1993	July 2, 1993
Time of Day:	7pm	7pm	7pm	7pm
Outdoor Temperature:	90°F (32°C)	90°F (32°C)	90°F (32°C)	84°F (29°C)
Outdoor Relative Humidity:	58%	66%	58%	80%
Outdoor Dew Point:	74°F (23°C)	77°F (25°C)	74°F (23°C)	77°F (25°C)
Room Temperature:	75°F (24°C)	75°F (24°C)	75°F (24°C)	73°F (23°C)
Room Relative Humidity:	60%	60%	60%	60%
Initial Wall Cavity Condition:	Dry	Dry	Wet	Dry
Outdoor Vapor Pressure:	–	–	–	0.6546 in.Hg.*
Room Vapor Pressure:	–	–	–	0.4910 in.Hg.*

TABLE 1   **SELECTED CONDITIONS**

* In. Hg x 3376 = Pascals

Table 2 illustrates a tabulation of July, 1993 Tampa, Florida daily weather conditions at 7:00 a.m. and 7:00 p.m., and includes highs, lows and averages. It can be seen that as the temperature increases, the RH decreases but the dew point temperature does not change much, since absolute humidity remains fairly constant. Thus the average dew point in July at 7:00 a.m. and 7:00 p.m. are both 73°F (23°C). The data in Table 2 is presented graphically in Figures 2a, 2b and 2c.

Table 3 shows the results of the calculated temperature profile for the exterior wall for Condition A at 7:00 p.m., July 20, 1993. Assuming outside air has free access to all areas of the stud cavity, it can be seen that no condensation potential exists since the calculated temperatures are higher than the outdoor dew point temperature throughout the stud cavity. This lack of condensation potential is indicated in the extreme right column by the word "dry".

Day	Temp. 7a.m.	Humidity 7a.m.	Dew Point 7a.m.	Temp. 7p.m.	Humidity 7p.m.	Dew Point 7.p.m.
1	81 (27.2)	82	75 (23.9)	78 (25.6)	85	74 (23.1)
2	77 (25.0)	90	73 (22.8)	84 (28.9)	80	78 (25.3)
3	72 (22.2)	90	69 (20.3)	85 (29.4)	67	73 (22.5)
4	74 (23.3)	97	73 (22.8)	86 (30.0)	65	73 (22.8)
5	75 (23.9)	94	73 (22.8)	89 (31.7)	55	71 (21.4)
6	77 (25.0)	87	73 (22.8)	88 (31.1)	61	73 (22.8)
7	74 (23.3)	87	70 (21.1)	91 (32.8)	52	73 (22.5)
8	75 (23.9)	87	71 (21.4)	82 (27.8)	77	73 (22.8)
9	71 (21.7)	93	70 (21.1)	86 (30.0)	61	73 (22.5)
10	74 (23.3)	90	71 (21.7)	83 (28.3)	61	70 (20.8)
11	76 (24.4)	87	73 (22.5)	72 (22.2)	87	68 (19.7)
12	72 (22.2)	97	71 (21.4)	91 (32.8)	45	67 (19.4)
13	76 (24.4)	85	72 (22.2)	77 (25.0)	74	68 (20.0)
14	72 (22.2)	90	69 (20.3)	87 (30.6)	61	73 (22.5)
15	75 (23.9)	90	72 (22.2)	79 (26.1)	77	72 (22.2)
16	73 (22.8)	97	73 (22.5)	77 (25.0)	82	72 (22.2)
17	75 (23.9)	94	73 (22.8)	86 (30.0)	63	73 (22.5)
18	76 (24.4)	94	75 (23.6)	88 (31.1)	61	73 (22.8)
19	78 (25.6)	85	74 (23.1)	88 (31.1)	59	72 (21.9)
20	76 (24.4)	90	73 (22.8)	90 (32.2)	58	73 (22.8)
21	83 (28.3)	74	73 (22.8)	86 (30.0)	72	76 (24.4)
22	83 (28.3)	82	77 (25.0)	88 (31.1)	63	75 (23.6)
23	83 (28.3)	77	75 (23.9)	87 (30.6)	68	75 (23.6)
24	82 (27.8)	82	76 (24.4)	86 (30.0)	68	74 (23.3)
25	77 (25.0)	90	73 (22.8)	81 (27.2)	82	75 (23.9)
26	77 (25.0)	85	73 (22.5)	90 (32.2)	58	74 (23.1)
27	79 (26.1)	85	74 (23.3)	88 (31.1)	66	76 (24.2)
29	79 (26.1)	85	74 (23.3)	84 (28.9)	74	75 (23.9)
31	81 (27.2)	88	77 (25.0)	90 (32.2)	66	77 (25.0)

76.7 (24.8)	88.07	72.8 (22.7)	85.1 (29.5)	67.17	72.8 (22.7)

Lowest Figure   Temperature measured in degrees F (degrees C)
Highest Figure   Relative Humidity measured in percent
                       Dew Point measured in degrees F (degrees C)

TABLE 2 - Average Outdoor Temperature and Humidity Conditions - Tampa, Florida
* Data taken from The Tampa Tribune

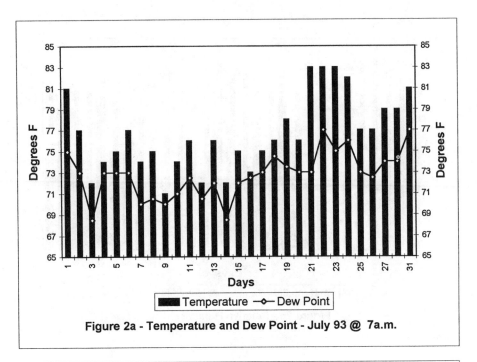

Figure 2a - Temperature and Dew Point - July 93 @ 7a.m.

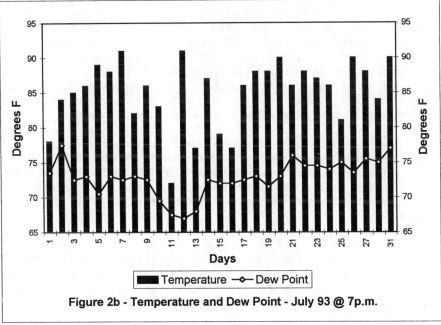

Figure 2b - Temperature and Dew Point - July 93 @ 7p.m.

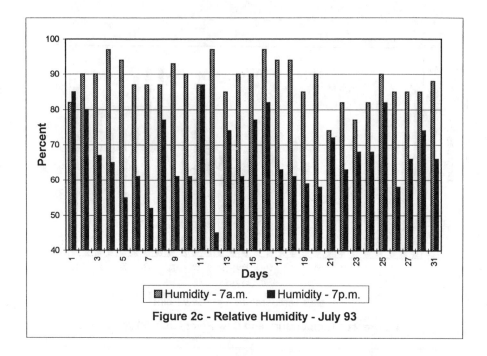

Figure 2c - Relative Humidity - July 93

Figure 3a is a graphic presentation of the results shown in Table 3. It should be recognized that if cold air at 65°F (18°C) blows on the room side of the exterior wall, the dew point behind the vinyl wall covering could be below the outdoor ambient dew point and condensation might occur at that area. When the organic wallcovering paste becomes moist and the temperature in the room increases during unoccupancy, the moisture in the paste is retained because of the low vapor permeance of the vinyl wallcovering. Thus the warm moist conditions in the paste can lead to proliferation of mold, mildew and foul odor as well as delamination of the wallcovering.

Table 4 illustrates the results of the calculated temperature profile for the exterior wall cavity for Condition B at 7:00 p.m., July 31, 1993 with an initially dry cavity. In this case, the selected outdoor dew point of 77°F (25°C) is higher than the monthly average. The data indicates that potential condensation can occur at the back of the gypsum drywall and/or the vinyl wallcovering. This data is shown graphically in figure 4a.

Table 5 illustrates calculated results for Condition C at 7:00 p.m., July 20, 1993 with water present in the cavity. The average temperature in the cavity is 76.5°F (25°C). Since the water in the cavity would generate a relative humidity approaching 100%, the dew point temperature in the cavity would be the same as its temperature. With a room temperature of 75°F (24°C) the temperature behind the vinyl

CONDITION A: [Dry Cavity - No Condensation]
7p.m. - July 20, 1993

TABLE 3

	Bldg. Component	R-value*	R-cumm.	Thickness		Temp.	Dry/Wet?
				inches	mm		
A	Outside Air Temperature					90.00 (32.2)	
B	Outside surface film	0.17	0.17	0.00	0.03	89.83 (32.1)	Dry
C	EIFS - Outside Skin	0.10	0.27	0.13	3.18	89.73 (32.1)	Dry
D	EPS 3/4" Insulation	3.75	4.02	0.75	19.05	85.91 (29.9)	Dry
E	Gypsum Sheathing 5/8"	0.56	4.58	0.63	15.88	85.34 (29.6)	Dry
F1	Foil	0.00	4.58	0.00	0.03	85.34 (29.6)	Dry
F2	Fiberglass Insulation R8	8.00	12.58	2.50	63.50	77.19 (25.1)	Dry
G	Cavity Airspace	0.87	13.45	3.00	76.20	76.30 (24.6)	Dry
H	Gypsum Board 5/8"	0.56	14.01	0.63	15.88	75.73 (24.3)	Dry
I	Interior Finish	0.04	14.05	0.01	0.13	75.69 (24.3)	Dry
J	Inside Surface Film	0.68	14.73	0.00	0.03	75.00 (23.9)	Dry
K	Inside Air Temperature					75.00 (23.9)	

14.73   7.63   193.88   TOTALS

Outside Air Temperature	90.00 (32.2)
Outdoor Relative Humidity	58.00 %
Outdoor Dew Point	73.52 (23.1)
Inside Air Temperature	75.00 (23.9)

Temperature and Dew Point measured in °F (°C)
Relative Humidity measured in percent (%)
* R-value (ft²•h•°F/Btu) x .176 = (m²•K/W)

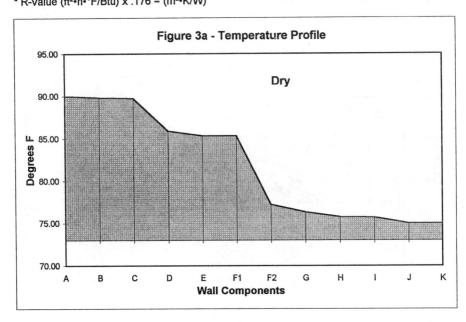

Figure 3a - Temperature Profile

CONDITION B: [Dry Cavity - Condensation]
7p.m. - July 31, 1993

TABLE 4

	Bldg. Component	R-value*	R-cumm.	Thickness		Temp.	Dry/Wet?
				inches	mm		
A	Outside Air Temperature					90.00 (32.2)	
B	Outside surface film	0.17	0.17	0.00	0.03	89.83 (32.1)	Dry
C	EIFS - Outside Skin	0.10	0.27	0.13	3.18	89.73 (32.1)	Dry
D	EPS 3/4" Insulation	3.75	4.02	0.75	19.05	85.91 (29.9)	Dry
E	Gypsum Sheathing 5/8"	0.56	4.58	0.63	15.88	85.34 (29.6)	Dry
F1	Foil	0.00	4.58	0.00	0.03	85.34 (29.6)	Dry
F2	Fiberglass Insulation R8	8.00	12.58	2.50	63.50	77.19 (25.1)	Wet
G	Cavity Airspace	0.87	13.45	3.00	76.20	76.30 (24.6)	Wet
H	Gypsum Board 5/8"	0.56	14.01	0.63	15.88	75.73 (24.3)	Wet
I	Interior Finish	0.04	14.05	0.01	0.13	75.69 (24.3)	Wet
J	Inside Surface Film	0.68	14.73	0.00	0.03	75.00 (23.9)	Wet
K	Inside Air Temperature					75.00 (23.9)	

14.73   7.63   193.88   TOTALS

Outside Air Temperature	90.00 (32.2)
Outdoor Relative Humidity	66.00 %
Outdoor Dew Point	77.41 (25.2)
Inside Air Temperature	75.00 (23.9)

Temperature and Dew Point measured in °F (°C)
Relative Humidity measured in percent (%)
* R-value (ft²•h•°F/Btu) x .176 = (m²•K/W)

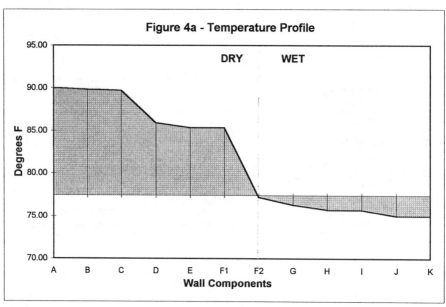

Figure 4a - Temperature Profile

CONDITION C: [Wet Cavity - Condensation]
7p.m. - July 20, 1993

TABLE 5

	Bldg. Component	R-value*	R-cumm.	Thickness		Temp.	Dry/Wet?
				inches	mm		
A	Outside Air Temperature			0.00	0.03	90.00 (32.2)	
B	Outside surface film	0.17	0.17	0.00	0.03	89.83 (32.1)	Dry
C	EIFS - Outside Skin	0.10	0.27	0.13	3.18	89.73 (32.1)	Dry
D	EPS 3/4" Insulation	3.75	4.02	0.75	19.05	85.91 (29.9)	Dry
E	Gypsum Sheathing 5/8"	0.56	4.58	0.63	15.88	85.34 (29.6)	Dry
F1	Foil	0.00	4.58	0.00	0.03	85.34 (29.6)	Dry
F2	Fiberglass Insulation R8	8.00	12.58	2.50	63.50	77.19 (25.1)	Dry
G	Cavity Airspace	0.87	13.45	3.00	76.20	76.30 (24.6)	Wet
H	Gypsum Board 5/8"	0.56	14.01	0.63	15.88	75.73 (24.3)	Wet
I	Interior Finish	0.04	14.05	0.01	0.13	75.69 (24.3)	Wet
J	Inside Surface Film	0.68	14.73	0.00	0.03	75.00 (23.9)	Wet
K	Inside Air Temperature					75.00 (23.9)	

14.73   7.63   193.88   TOTALS

Outside Air Temperature	90.00 (32.2)
Outdoor Relative Humidity	58.00 %
Cavity Dew Point**	**76.75 (24.9)**
Inside Air Temperature	75.00 (23.9)

Temperature and Dew Point measured in °F (°C)
Relative Humidity measured in percent (%)
* R-value (ft²•h•°F/Btu) x .176 = (m²•K/W)
** Average temperature in air space for components F2 & G at 100% R.H.

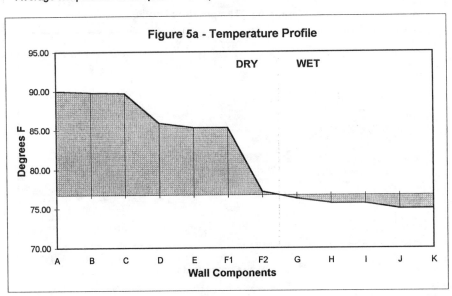

Figure 5a - Temperature Profile

CONDITION D: [Dry Cavity - Condensation]
7p.m. - July 2, 1993

TABLE 6

	Bldg. Component	R-value*	R-cumm.	Thickness		Temp.	Dry/Wet?
				inches	mm	84.00 (28.9)	
A	Outside Air Temperature					84.00 (28.9)	
B	Outside surface film	0.17	0.17	0.00	0.03	83.87 (28.8)	Dry
C	EIFS - Outside Skin	0.10	0.27	0.13	3.18	83.80 (28.8)	Dry
D	EPS 3/4" Insulation	3.75	4.02	0.75	19.05	81.00 (27.2)	Dry
E	Gypsum Sheathing 5/8"	0.56	4.58	0.63	15.88	80.58 (27.0)	Dry
F1	Foil	0.00	4.58	0.00	0.03	80.58 (27.0)	Dry
F2	Fiberglass Insulation R8	8.00	12.58	2.50	63.50	74.61 (23.7)	Wet
G	Cavity Airspace	0.87	13.45	3.00	76.20	73.96 (23.3)	Wet
H	Gypsum Board 5/8"	0.56	14.01	0.63	15.88	73.54 (23.1)	Wet
I	Interior Finish	0.04	14.05	0.01	0.13	73.51 (23.1)	Wet
J	Inside Surface Film	0.68	14.73	0.00	0.03	73.00 (22.8)	Wet
K	Inside Air Temperature					73.00 (22.8)	

14.73		**7.63** **193.88**	TOTALS

Outside Air Temperature	84.00 (28.9)
Outdoor Relative Humidity	80.00 %
Outdoor Dew Point	77.29 (25.2)
Inside Air Temperature	73.00 (22.8)

Temperature and Dew Point measured in °F (°C)
Relative Humidity measured in percent (%)
* R-value (ft²•h•°F/Btu) x .176 = (m²•K/W)

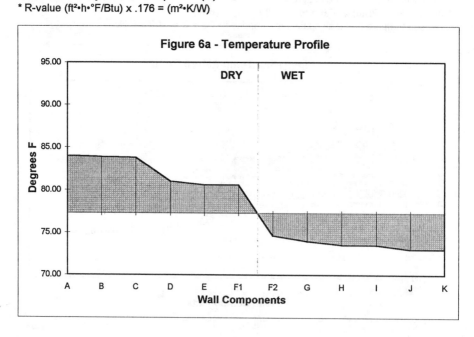

wallcovering and the cavity side of the drywall is below the cavity dew point temperature and condensation is possible at these locations. This data is shown graphically in figure 5a.

Table 6 illustrates calculated results for Condition D at 7:00 p.m., July 2, 1993 with an initially dry cavity. Condensation is possible within the fiberglass insulation and all points toward the room side of the cavity because the calculated temperature at these locations is lower than the outdoor dew point. This data is also shown in figure 6a.

It can be seen from the data that condensation potential changes hourly and daily during summer, depending on changing external and room conditions, as well as the presence or absence of water in the cavity. Of paramount importance is the presence of water in the stud cavity since this condition is conducive to condensation in the wallcovering paste and drywall during summer. The source of such water can be any of the following: condensation, leakage through exterior walls and roofing, lack of proper caulking in bathrooms, condensation on chiller lines, and carpet scrubbing.

Now the question arises as to the rate of diffusion of moisture vapor from the outside inward. Table 1 shows the outdoor and room vapor pressure for the selected Condition D. For this condition, the rate of vapor transfer from the outside to the cavity, and from the cavity to the room, was calculated using ASHRAE methodology and known water vapor permeance of the components. Results indicated that the rate of moisture vapor into the cavity was 0.000043 lb/ft^2.hr (0.21g/m^2.hr), and the rate into the room was 0.0000001 lb/hr.ft^2 (0.0049g/m^2.hr). Thus the higher rate of moisture entry and the potential for condensation at the back of the vinyl and drywall would create a moist condition that could result in mold and mildew as well as deterioration of the gypsum drywall. However, the situation in Condition D is temporary and different conditions at a different time could offset the condensation potential present in Condition D so that the probability of condensation, mold and mildew may not be as great as is indicated by Condition D.

In conclusion, although calculations indicate that there are times during summer when condensation potential at the back of the vinyl wallcovering and gypsum drywall is theoretically possible, the primary causes of this problem are from water entry into the cavity from other sources. Some of these include: defective exterior sealants, cracks in the EIFS facade, condensation at chiller lines, and water getting under bathroom tubs. Once water finds its way into the cavity, water can wick upward and sideways into the gypsum and wallcovering paste. The moist condition created there is trapped by the vinyl wallcovering, and mold and mildew proliferate. This condition is aggravated by the lack of the HVAC system to remove excess humidity, especially during periods of unoccupancy, and is further aggravated by the uncomfortably warm room temperature maintained by the computer to conserve energy. Additional issues which exacerbate the problem are continuously operating bathroom vents and by loose fitting operable windows because they contribute to negative room pressure and infiltration of warm moist air respectively.

The following recommendations were made to alleviate the problem of mold and mildew:

1.   Renovate exterior sealants.

2.   Apply an elastomeric acrylic finish to the EIFS facade to seal and bridge cracks.

3.   Maintain proper caulking at bathrooms.

4.   Prevent cold air from being directed to room exterior walls.

5.   Modify bathroom exhaust vent cycle from continuous to intermittent in order to reduce air infiltration and conserve energy.

6.   Provide a tight fit at operable windows.

7.   Modify the HVAC automatic set-back temperature to a more comfortable level so that the fan coil unit will operate for longer periods and help lower the RH.

8.   Provide a vapor barrier type chiller line insulation to prevent condensation.

9.   Use a mildew resistant, vapor permeable, indoor, acrylic latex paint instead of vinyl wallcovering, at least on exterior walls.

The above recommendations did not include an economic analysis nor priorities.

Paul E. Beers[1] and William D. Smith[2]

REPAIR METHODS FOR COMMON WATER LEAKS AT OPERABLE
WINDOWS AND SLIDING GLASS DOORS

REFERENCE: Beers, P. E. and Smith, W. D., **"Repair Methods for Common
Water Leaks at Operable Windows and Sliding Glass Doors,"** Water Leakage
Through Building Facades, ASTM STP 1314, R. J. Kudder and J. L. Erdly, Eds.,
American Society for Testing and Materials, 1998.

ABSTRACT: In areas with high annual rainfall amounts, such as Florida, water leakage
through operable windows and sliding glass doors is common, particularly at multistory
applications. Although each leak is unique to the product and project, certain trends have
developed. Investigations of water leakage at many projects throughout Florida,
particularly multistory condominiums, have revealed several common water leak sources.
    Observations during storms and field water tests have revealed three typical types
of leaks that most frequently occur. Water percolation between operable members and
the frame occurs during wind driven rain storms. Leakage through the sliding glass door
track or window sill can occur any time water is present in the assembly. Leakage
through perimeter sealants is usually induced during a wind driven rain, but can also
occur if there is standing water next to the assembly.

KEYWORDS: windows, sliding glass doors, water leakage, field water test

---

[1] President, Glazing Consultants, Inc., 8895 North Military Trail, Suite 306-C,
Palm Beach Gardens, FL 33410
[2] Vice President, Glazing Consultants, Inc., 8895 North Military Trail, Suite 306-
C, Palm Beach Gardens, FL 33410

Water leakage through windows and sliding glass doors in areas with frequent wind driven rainstorms occurs in both new buildings and older installations. Many deficiencies that cause the leakage are due to poor workmanship and/or improper installation of sealants. Some leaks are due to the selection and use of improper materials. This could include the entire window or sliding glass door assembly as well as components and sealants.

A pattern in the cause of water leaks has been noted during field investigations at various projects. Water leakage through windows can be caused by many different factors, including static pressure created across an opening, gravity, kinetic energy, surface tension, capillary action, and air currents [1]. Leaks observed during field investigations were typically limited to wind driven percolation of water through areas where operable portions of the assembly interface with the frame or other fixed members, and gravity-induced leakage where water seeps through joints in the assembly or sealants.

It is important to understand how the water control mechanism of windows and sliding glass doors is designed to function. Virtually all are designed to collect water internally and then drain it back to the exterior either through weep holes or other provisions, such as slots in the front of a sliding glass door track [2] [3].

The key to a properly functioning leak-free window or sliding glass door is the ability to manage the water [3]. As rain strikes the assembly, it is collected, usually at the sill, and then diverted back to the exterior. With this concept, there is a reliance on internal seals between metal-to-metal joints. These seals are either applied at the factory as the product is manufactured or in the field as it is installed. In addition, improper selection or application of sealants will usually result in water leakage.

While each instance of water leakage at each project is unique, similar trends have been identified.

TYPICAL TYPES OF LEAKS
Percolation
Percolation occurs during wind driven rain storms and is observed as water bubbling or spraying through the assembly. It is usually located at joints between fixed and operable portions of the assembly, although it can also occur between fixed members.

Most operable window and sliding glass door assemblies internally collect water that is not shed at the outer plane and channel it to the sill or bottom of the assembly where it is collected and drained it to the outside. During a wind driven rain storm, water will raise inside a system to a water head [1]. Wind pressure on an assembly causes a certain level of water to be present in the sill as it drains and additional water is introduced. When air infiltration occurs through a sill with a water head, it causes some of the water to be blown to the inside.

Seepage Through the Sill

Because window and sliding glass door sills are designed to collect and drain water that comes into contact with the assembly, they are the most vulnerable area for leakage [2]. Leakage though the sill usually appears beneath the assembly as a puddle on the floor or stain on the wall. Generally, it does not percolate.

There are several opportunities for water leakage to occur through a sill. Many window sills and virtually all sliding glass door tracks are anchored to the structure with fasteners that penetrate through them [2] [3]. Each fastener requires a hole to be drilled or punched in the sill. Naturally, each of these holes provides an opportunity for water infiltration, if not properly sealed. In addition, frames for window and door assemblies are joined at the bottom corners with a metal-to-metal joint. Again, this provides an opportunity for water infiltration if not properly sealed.

Perimeter Sealant Leaks

Perimeter sealant is located at the interface between the window or sliding glass door assembly and the surrounding structure. Normally, an organic sealant is installed at this location to prevent water from entering. Perimeter sealant leaks usually appear on the wall surface near or below the assembly, on the floor below the assembly, or at the ceiling or window head of a lower floor. They occur when sealants are omitted, improperly installed, or when the sealant material is beyond its useful life and in need of replacement.

SOLUTIONS – CASE STUDIES

The three types of leakage described above have been encountered at several projects. Although different repair methods were used for each project, in each case the leaks were halted. This was confirmed by field water testing the window or sliding glass door assemblies after repairs were completed. The tests were conducted according to ASTM Standard Test Method for Field Determination of Water Penetration of Installed Exterior Windows, Curtain Walls, and Doors by Uniform or Cyclic Static Air Pressure Difference (E 1105). All windows and sliding glass doors that are referenced in the case studies are aluminum frame construction.

Percolation

Six-Story Oceanfront Hotel, Palm Beach County, FL—During field water tests using ASTM E 1105, horizontal sliding windows at this project exhibited severe bubbling in the track that resulted in water spraying inside the hotel room. This occurred at the joint between the bottom of the operable panel and the sill.

Air infiltration was causing the percolation. A solution would be achieved if the air infiltration could be halted. The window had inadequate weather-stripping design and it was not possible to correct the air infiltration using the original window design. Enhancements to the original system design will be necessary to eliminate air infiltration and percolation through the track.

The void between the track and beneath where the fixed and operable panels interlock was the main problem area. Attempts to install additional adhesively applied felt pads in the track beneath the interlocks was not successful in correcting the problem. Next, an aluminum-backed felt pad was attached to the back of the operable panel to extend down inside the track and completely seal all air flow under the panel interlocks.

The pad is similar to the one shown in Figure 1.

The percolation was significantly reduced. However, when field water testing the assembly using ASTM E 1105, the track filled completely with water and even the slightest bubbling caused overflow to the interior. As a result, all windows would not consistently pass the test.

Because consistent results were desired for all windows, the height of the back leg of the track was increased by installing a strip of sheet metal inside the window along the entire length of the track. This allowed for a margin of safety and the windows were successfully tested.

Thirty- Story Oceanfront Condominium, Miami, FL—During wind-driven rainstorms, water was being blown through sliding glass door tracks, damaging interior finishes and contents. Percolation was occurring beneath the operable panel of the sliding glass door, particularly at the interlock with the fixed panel and where the operable panel closes into the frame.

The sliding glass doors did not comply with the standard of quality depicted on the shop drawings. Improper weather-stripping was installed in the bottom of the operable panel and in the frame jambs. Felt weather-stripping pads were omitted in the track beneath the panel interlocks and at the end of the track where it intersects with frame jambs.

Repairs were made to upgrade the sliding glass doors to the condition shown on the shop drawings. Proper weather-stripping and felt pads were installed as required. Field water tests using ASTM E 1105 revealed that the percolation was reduced, but not eliminated. The original design of the product would have to be enhanced to eliminate the percolation.

Aluminum-backed felt pads were installed on the back of the operable panel as described for the six-story hotel above. Figure 1. is a photograph of an installed aluminum-backed felt pad. Further field water testing using ASTM E 1105 confirmed that percolation at the panel interlocks was eliminated. However, percolation continued under the operable panel and from the bottom frame corner where it seated into the frame.

Figure 1 - Photograph of aluminum-backed felt pad.

An aluminum extrusion with wool pile weather-stripping was designed to attach to the back leg of the track so the wool pile connected to the operable panel. Figure 2. is a detail of the new extrusion and weather stripping. A prototype was installed and field water tested using ASTM E 1105. All percolation under and around the operable panel was completely eliminated.

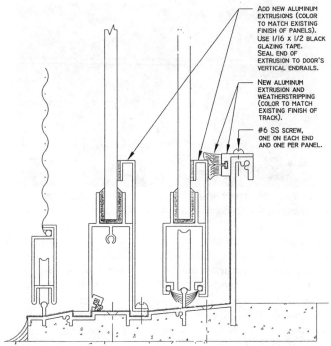

ADD NEW ALUMINUM EXTRUSIONS (COLOR TO MATCH EXISTING FINISH OF PANELS). USE 1/16 x 1/2 BLACK GLAZING TAPE. SEAL END OF EXTRUSION TO DOOR'S VERTICAL ENDRAILS.

NEW ALUMINUM EXTRUSION AND WEATHERSTRIPPING (COLOR TO MATCH EXISTING FINISH OF TRACK).

#6 SS SCREW, ONE ON EACH END AND ONE PER PANEL.

Figure 2 - Detail of the new extrusion and weather stripping.

Seepage Through the Sill

Thirteen-Story Oceanfront Condominium, North Hutchinson Island, FL--The windows and sliding glass doors at this project have a sill pan or trough beneath the track that is designed to collect water and drain it back to the outside. A detail of the sliding glass door sill that is also representative of the window sill is shown in Figure 1.

Fastener penetrations and metal-to-metal corner joints that rely on field seals are located inside the sill pan. This area had proven to be vulnerable during construction. After water leaks occurred, the installer went back to each window and applied additional sealant on top of the existing material. The installer then tested every sill member by plugging the weep holes and filling the sill with water. The test method was similar to the optional water test described in AAMA 502-90 [4]. After the repairs, it appeared the sills were water-tight.

The leaks reappeared several months later because, during the repairs, improper sealant material was used and the installer failed to properly clean old material of dirt and debris before applying additional sealant. Figure 3 shows an improper sealant application that was not properly cleaned. Figure 4 shows holes and gaps in the sealant where it has sagged.

Figure 3 - Improper sealant application. Note that three different colors indicate multiple applications of sealant

Repeated attempts to develop a repair method that would seal the sill fasteners and metal-to-metal joints without disassembling the entire assembly were not successful. Mockups of the repair were tested using ASTM E 1105 and, although there was limited success on some assemblies, consistent results could not be achieved.

It was decided that properly repairing the problem required disassembly of each window and sliding glass door to expose the inside of the sill pan. The existing sealants, dirt and debris were completely removed, the surfaces were cleaned, and new silicone sealant was applied. Before reinstalling the assembly, the weep holes were plugged and the sills were flooded with water to confirm that they were water tight. During the repair process, random testing using ASTM E 1105 confirmed the internal sealant repairs were successful.

Although every effort was made to develop a repair method that would not require disassembling the windows and sliding glass doors, the only successful solution was to remove the deficient seals in the sill pan, clean the surfaces and reinstall the sealant. Had the sealant been properly installed during the original installation, the repair would not have been necessary.

Six-Story Oceanfront Hotel, Palm Beach County, FL—Horizontal sliding windows at this project contained sill flashing with unsealed fastener penetrations and no seals at either end of the flashing. Water was draining from the assemblies to the sill flashing and leaking into the wall cavity. Because surrounding construction was completed, it was not feasible to seal the fastener penetrations and ends of the sill flashing without removing the window and damaging surrounding finishes.

A repair was desired that would not require removal of the windows. The window was capable of performing without using the sill flashing to drain water. A sealant procedure was developed to isolate the window from the flashing, effectively abandoning it. After this was done, leakage occurred at metal-to-metal joints at the bottom corners of the frame, which were not fully sealed.

Figure 4 - Gaps in sealant at frame corners.

A procedure was then developed to seal the faulty joints and the leakage was corrected. This was confirmed by field tests using the ASTM E 1105 method. Although a series of repair steps were necessary, the sill flashing was abandoned and the window was able to perform without it. It should be noted that this is the same project and the same manufacturer of the window discussed in the percolation section, above. These repairs were done in combination with the above-described procedures to eliminate the percolation.

Perimeter Sealant Leaks

Thirteen-Story Oceanfront Condominium, North Hutchinson Island, FL —Much of the perimeter sealant was properly installed and functioning. However, at some sill areas, due to an insufficient joint, the perimeter sealants were partially applied over weep holes. As a result, water draining from the weep holes was migrating behind the sealant to the interior of the building. Figure 5 shows a typical weep hole and perimeter sealant.

The solution for this problem was to remove the perimeter sealant, grind the stucco system to form a proper joint, and reapply the sealant. Figure 1 shows the perimeter sealant blocking a weep hole before the repair. Figure 2 shows the perimeter sealant properly applied at a weep hole after the repair.

Figure 5 - Typical weep hole and perimeter sealant.

Six-Story Hotel, Palm Beach County, FL—Water leakage was occurring through the perimeter sealant joints, which were poorly detailed. The exterior walls of the building were constructed with metal studs, exterior gypsum sheathing, paper-faced wire lath, and stucco. The stucco was terminated at window openings with galvanized "J" beads. The "J" beads were not properly sealed at the corners, and due to their shape, it was not possible to seal them after installation was complete. Figure 6 shows the typical perimeter condition.

There were two repair options: either cut back the stucco and rework all of the window returns, or develop an alternate method to seal the windows to the stucco beyond the "J" beads.

A detail was developed where a break metal shape was attached to the aluminum window frame with silicone. The break metal extended past the "J" bead to the stucco and formed a joint for a new perimeter sealant bead. Thus, the unsealed "J" bead was effectively abandoned and an effective perimeter seal was achieved.

Figure 6 - Typical perimeter condition.

CONCLUSIONS

Unfortunately, in areas with high rainfall amounts, water leakage through windows is common. Multiple repair attempts are often unsuccessful. While some water tests, such as applying water with a hose or flooding the sill with water can be helpful, the only conclusive way to identify and solve the problem is to use ASTM E 1105 both before and after repair attempts [5].

Often, a series of tests and repairs is necessary before a successful repair method is found. However, with the use of a proper test method such as ASTM E 1105, a repair solution can be confidently recommended.

The success of the repairs outlined in this paper were demonstrated at two of the projects by actual weather events. The thirteen-story oceanfront condominium in North Hutchinson Island, FL was struck by Hurricane Erin in August, 1995, after repairs were complete.   Only three leaks were reported in the entire building, as compared to massive leaks throughout the building during each rainstorm before the repairs. The six-story oceanfront hotel in Palm Beach County, FL was struck by Tropical Storm Gordon in November, 1994. This event featured a wind driven rain that lasted about six hours. No leaks were reported.

REFERENCES

[1]   "Water Resistance," Window Selection Guide, American Architectural Manufacturers Association, 1988, p. 4.

[2]   Beers, P. E., "Door Sill Detailing," Progressive Architecture, August 1991, pp. 109-110.

[3]   Smith, W. D., "Water Management - Designing and Installing Storefronts to Prevent Water Leaks," Glass Digest Magazine, July 15, 1993, pp. 46-49.

[4]   "Voluntary Specifications for Field Testing of Windows and Sliding Glass Doors," American Architectural Manufacturers Association, Publication No. AAMA 502-90, 1990, p.1.

[5]   Beers, P. E., "Field Testing Windows for Water Leakage," U.S. Glass Metal and Glazing, August 1990, pp. 52-55.

Richard S. Flood[1]

REMEDIAL REPAIR LEAK PREVENTION IN POROUS STONE FACED PRECAST PANELS - A
CASE STUDY OPTION

REFERENCE: Flood, R. S., **"Remedial Repair Leak Prevention in Porous, Stone Faced,
Precast Panels—A Case Study Option,"** Water Leakage Through Building Facades, ASTM
STP 1314, R. J. Kudder and J. L. Erdly, Eds., American Society for Testing and
Materials, 1998.

ABSTRACT: A proposed leak repair scheme (tested per ASTM) could have
significantly altered the aesthetic appearance of a 42 story, 600 ft.
highrise office tower and adjacent lowrise auxiliary buildings in San
Francisco, California. This case study describes an alternative leak
repair scheme for the 1000+ panels of porous stone faced precast panel
window wall, the objective of which was to retain the existing building
appearance to the maximum extent feasible .
Water from panel perimeters, panel cracks, and stone anchor
locations was leaking into the building around the windows and other
areas. The remedial solution presented here focuses on the water in the
cavity bounded by the porous stone faced pre-cast panel, the flush
mounted aluminum and window frame, and the exterior and interior
silicone sealant joints. The design methodology consisted of first
minimizing water infiltration through the porous stone in a visually
unobtrusive manner and second, channeling and controlling the remaining
infiltrate to both the existing weep system and into newly created
weeped jamb cavity reservoirs.
This option was implemented from the exterior, (using the
building's window washing rig) on a mid-height in-situ panel, (selected
for testing due to prior leak history). Readily available construction
materials and methods were utilized. Upon completion, the repaired
panel passed an extended duration ASTM E-1105-93 test. Substantially
reducing water penetration into the composite panel and then controlling
the remaining infiltrate, this ASTM tested leak repair option provided a
functioning, cost competitive solution to the water intrusion problem
without altering the existing building aesthetics.

KEY WORDS: porous stone, precast panels, parged, silicone sealant, jamb
cavity reservoirs, weeps, leaks, water intrusion, window wall system,
bond breaker.

In the early 1980's, a 42 story, 600 ft highrise office tower and
adjacent lowrise auxiliary buildings were constructed in downtown San
Francisco, CA. The highrise building envelope was comprised of over
1000 porous, stone faced, precast concrete panels. Most of the panels
were rectangular with a window opening cast into the panel.

With the onset of the first storms after completion, numerous
leaks occurred. Extensive investigations by other parties (including
in-situ static air pressure differential testing per ASTM E-1105)
determined several sources of water intrusion.

[1]Senior architect, Ian Mackinlay Architecture, Inc., San Francisco, CA
94105.

The focus of this case study was to provide a remedial repair solution to the water leakage problems under the following constraints:

1.   The remedial repair solution would serve as an optional repair scheme to other parties' face sealed solution.
2.   The remedial repair must be implemented from the building exterior utilizing window washing rigs as the repair platforms.
3.   The repair must be simple (utilizing hand tools and readily available materials) and cost effective.
4.   The existing building aesthetic appearance must be maintained.
5.   The previously obtained water intrusion reports would be utilized as a basis for the design of the remedial work.
6.   The implemented remedial design would have to pass an ASTM E-1105-93 in situ test on one panel, the location of which would be unknown until the test panel remedial work was ready to commence.

EXISTING CONDITIONS

The typical existing porous stone/precast panel was nominally 15'-0" (4572 mm) wide by 13'-1" (3988 mm) high with a window opening 9'-8" (2946 mm) wide by 6'-6" (1981 mm) high. The panel was constructed of 5 layers of materials. These layers were as follows (from the exterior inward, Fig. 1)

1.   Field spray applied organosilane based clear water repellant coating in an ethyl alcohol solution that chemically bonded to the porous stone.
2.   Porous stone (Italian Travertine) in both 3 cm and 5 cm thicknesses.
3.   Porous stone fabricator applied cementitious parging on the back of the stone panels.
4.   6 mil thick polyethylene bond breaker.
5.   5000 psi structural lightweight precast concrete backing panel.

All stone joints within the panel were flush caulked with silicone sealant over an open cell backer rod. All panel to panel joints had two rows of silicone sealant, each over an open cell backer rod. The inner, primary row was at the exterior face of the precast concrete (back of the stone) while the outer row of silicone sealant was flush with the face of the porous stone (Fig. 1).

The panel to aluminum window joint also had two rows of silicone sealant, each over an open cell backer rod. In this instance, the inner row of silicone sealant was positioned at the interior face of the precast panel while the outer row of silicone sealant was flush with the porous stone face and the aluminum window frame (Fig. 1).

Sometime after the panels had been installed, horizontal cracking occurred in the porous stone adjacent to the window jambs, just above the line of the window sill (Fig. 1). The lower jamb area "column" stone cladding cracked because the precast panel backing insidiously deflected (bowed) outward after the panels were placed in the vertical position. The structural design and subsequent fabrication failed to provide adequate stiffening. At the time of this repair effort, the consulting engineering opinion was that essentially all deflection had occurred and the existing bowed panels were now stabilized. This cracking was prevalent throughout virtually all of panels.

WATER INTRUSION

The previous parties' investigation indicated that the primary source of water intrusion was through the edges of the porous stone. The backs of the stone slabs had been parged but the edges had not. The

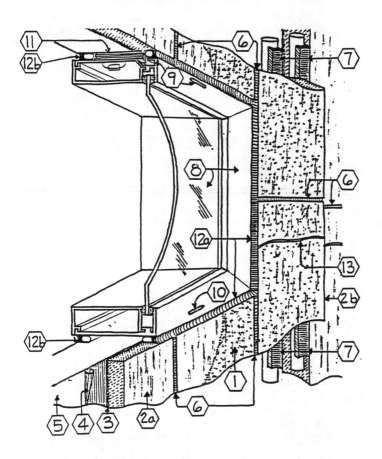

1.   Water repellant sealer
2.   Porous stone 3 cm (2a) and 5 cm (2b) thick
3.   Cementitious parging
4.   Polyethelene bond breaker
5.   Precast concrete - 4-3/4" (12 mm) thick
6.   Silicone stone joint sealant - 1/4" (6 mm) wide
7.   Dual row silicone panel joint with backer rods at offset stone face - 3/4" (19 mm) joint
8.   Aluminum window frame and glass - 2" (51 mm) wide extrusion
9.   Head weep slot and integral gutter
10.   Sill weep slot
11.   Head anchor and shims
12.   Window perimeter silicone joints, outer (12a), inner (12b) with backer rods - 1/2" (13 mm) joint
13.   Porous stone horizontal cracking

FIG.1--Cutaway schematic diagram of existing panel condition.

wind driven rain was able to make an end run around the face silicone sealant, and enter the cavity between the two rows of sealant (panel to panel, panel to window). At the stone joints within the panel, the stone edge intrusion water would run down the face of the polyethylene bond breaker.

The original design intended for most of this water to be intercepted into an integral window head gutter and weeped to the exterior. This did not happen due primarily to silted up gutters, blocked weep slots and anchor shims extending beyond the exterior face of the precast concrete. These conditions forced the intrusion water back over the top of the window head extrusion where the water either overflowed into the jamb cavity or worked its way through sealing imperfections of the head anchors.

At the window jamb cavity, the overflow intrusion water from the head coupled with edge intrusion water from the jamb stone fell down on top of the precast concrete return ledge under the aluminum window sill. This sill cavity had no designed in weepage provisions, although the intrusion water could re-enter the porous stone edge behind the sill sealant joint and work its way out to the face of the stone. The sill cavity ledge ponded water that then worked its way to the interior through shrinkage cracks occurring at the ledge or in the outside face of the precast concrete where intrusion water ran behind the polyethylene bond breaker.

Porous stone edge intrusion water also saturated the small space between the inner and outer seals at the panel joints. Investigation by other parties concluded that the inner silicone seals were all failing due to contractor installation error. It was felt that these inner seals had not properly cured because the outer seals were installed immediately after the inner seals, thereby preventing the required atmospheric air circulation necessary to effect a cured state for the silicone (generally a two to three week average time period). Hence, intrusion water was able to go through or around these inner seals and manifest itself at the interior as leakage.

To exacerbate this edge water intrusion, the horizontal cracks in the porous stone allowed a substantial volume of water to reach the polyethylene bond breaker. These cracks breached three water resistive layers of the five layers of the panel (water repellant coating, porous stone and cementitious parging). All in all, a fair amount of leakage was occurring.

THE REPAIR PLANNING

While all elements and components of the building envelope would have to be addressed to ensure a comprehensive leak repair program, the initial scope of work was limited. It would only address the alternative leak repair program for the typical porous stone faced precast panel.

In order to solve the typical panel leak problems within the constraint framework (retain existing aesthetics, repair from exterior and cost effectiveness), it was decided to implement a remedial repair scheme that would substantially mitigate (in lieu of eliminating) the water intrusion into the core of the 5 layer panel. What water reached the core area would have to be controlled through a weep system and prevented from further migration to the interior. This basic premise was substantially the same as had been contemplated in the original design. The steps to achieve this were as follows:

1.   Repair the cracked porous stone and fill up any visually apparent through voids (mitigate large volumes of intrusion water).

2.   At the panel vertical joints, install weeps to drain the cavity between the inner and outer lines of sealant. Provide roll out type design similar to detail described in Reference 1 (drainage of panel joint stone edge intrusion water).

3.   Provide a new line of silicone sealant just behind the integral gutter of the window head extrusion (prevents intrusion water from entering window head cavity).

4.   Provide a weeped to exterior water collection reservoir at the bottom of the window jamb cavity (provides a means of collecting and drainage of the stone edge intrusion water in the jamb cavity without it overflowing into the sill cavity).

5.   Renew the water repellant coating on the face of the porous stone (further reduces intrusion water).

Our remedial repair scheme was in competition with a previously tested face sealed system. To be considered as a viable alternative, our scheme would have to pass the ASTM E-1105-93 test. There would be no opportunity for fine tuning and retesting if the test wasn't passed the first time.

IMPLEMENTATION

Now that the remedial plan was established, all that had to be done was implement it. For most of the items this was a relatively straight forward process as follows:

1.   The roll out weeps from the panel joint sealant cavity would only require removing a portion of the outer sealant, cleaning the joint and installing the roll out silicone sealant from the inner sealant line (which had been previously replaced at our test site) to the outer sealant line (Fig. 2). After 14 to 21 days of curing, the outer sealant line would be replaced, and allowed to cure. The weep would be in the vertical panel joint below the level of the horizontal panel joints (Fig. 3).

2.   The new line of silicone sealant behind the window head gutter required removing the outer, face silicone seal between the stone and aluminum (Fig. 4). At this point, the extended head anchor shims (Fig. 4) would be ground back to 1/2 inch (12 MM) inboard of the face of the precast concrete. Bond breaker tape would be placed over the ends of the ground shims, backer rod installed elsewhere, the existing integral head gutter and weep baffles cleaned and the new line of silicone sealant installed (Fig. 5). The new line of silicone sealant would roll out at the jambs and mate with the existing line of vertical silicone stone joint sealant above the head/jamb intersection. The backslope of the rollout bead will divert most of the stone joint intrusion water into the end of the window head gutter (Fig. 5). As it turned out, this work had been previously done at the test location.

3.   Renewing the water repellant sealer posed a material selection problem as the original sealer was no longer in production. The new proprietary product was formulated for use on calcareous surfaces as the porous stone involved in this case. It would be applied to a dry surface after the sealant and epoxy work was fully cured.

4.   The porous stone cracks and voids would be filled with a 2 part epoxy adhesive conforming to ASTM C881, Grade 3, trowel application. Finishing the cracks would utilize ground up porous stone particles (200 sieve or finer) mixed in a cream colored, knife grade epoxy adhesive. The epoxy adhesive would rebond the porous stone to regain its previous strength and waterproof the crack (Fig. 8). The finishing epoxy mixed with porous stone sand would allow blend finishing for color and appearance matching.

5.   The tough nut to crack was the jamb cavity reservoir. The solution came in a brainstorming roundtable discussion - use a hand held disc grinder and cut a vertical slot in the precast concrete sill ledge return at each jamb. The slot would not damage the porous stone facing

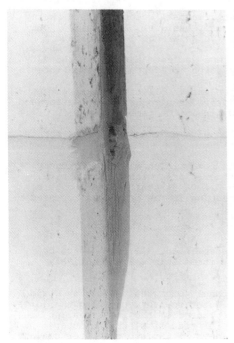

FIG. 2--Offset panel joint (±3/4"-19 mm). Roll out sealant starting at inner sealant line (top), roll out sealant (middle) and outer sealant (extreme bottom). Note 3/4" (19 mm) horizontal panel joint sealant.

FIG. 3-- Completed panel (±3/4"-19 mm) joint weep. Open cell backer rod from upper outer sealant line is exposed to provide a baffled weep below the 3/4" (19 mm) horizontal panel joint.

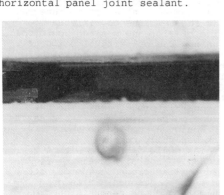

FIG. 4--Existing (±1/2"-13 mm high) window head cavity with extended shims at far left (sealant removed).

FIG. 5--New sealant line (±1/2"-13 mm high) behind window head integral gutter rolled out to mate with vertical stone joint (±1/4"-6 mm wide) sealant (not yet installed).

as it would be within the existing vertical stone to stone joint. The nominally triangular shaped slot (hypotenuse leg being curved per the grinding disc radius would be at least 1/4" (6 mm) wide. During the actual installation, the stone joint and slot were widened to ±3/8" (9.5 mm) at the top, tapering to the existing joint width of the ±1/4" (6 mm) below the weep exit. The slot's back and sides would be waterproofed with a thin coating of silicone sealant. A plastic weep tube with foam baffle would drain the slot reservoir. A 1/4" (6 mm) inside diameter weep tube was actually installed. The weep tube opening to the exterior would be 7 inches (178 mm) minimum below the window sill cavity to provide both sufficient reservoir capacity for jamb cavity intrusion water and adequate water head pressure to ensure positive drainage and not allow the reservoir to overflow back into the sill cavity area (Figs. 6, 7, 8).

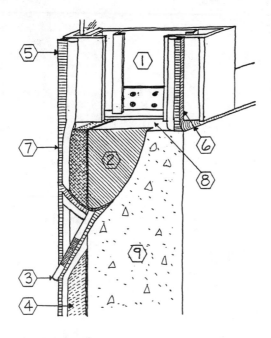

1.   Existing window jamb cavity - 2" (51 mm) wide extrusion
2.   New disc grinder cut slot reservoir with silicone sealant coating at back and sides
3.   New plastic weep tube with reticulated polyurethane foam block set in silicone sealant
4.   Porous stone edge of 3 cm stone
5.   Window to porous stone outer silicone sealant line and backer rod
6.   Existing window to precast concrete inner silicone sealant line and backer - 1/2" (13 mm) joint
7.   Stone to stone silicone sealant
8.   Existing sill cavity
9.   Precast concrete - 4 3/4" (121 mm) thick

FIG. 6--New weeped jamb cavity reservoir

FIG. 7--Jamb sealant (1/2"-13 mm joint) and stone sealant removed. Slot reservoir cut in joint (widened to 3/8"-9.5 mm at top tapered down to existing 1/4"-6 mm joint width ± 9"-229 mm below sill). Note horizontal crack in porous stone.

FIG. 8--Installed reservoir weep tube. Tube exit is 7" (178 mm) below sill sealant joint.

TEST LOCATION AND TIME FOR REPAIR

When we were informed where our in-situ test location was to be, we were not too surprised. This mid-height building location already had been used to perform ASTM E-1105-93 testing. It had an in-place pressure chamber as well as a thoroughly documented leak history and identified leak location survey. The bonus to us was that the inner panel joint sealant lines had been replaced and the new window head sealant behind the integral gutter had also been installed. Once the remedial repair work started, the actual swing stage time was relatively short, 4 half days. Due to scheduling, fall storms, and needed curing and drying times, the calendar time ran about two months until testing could be scheduled.

THE TEST AND TEST PROTOCOL

Upon arrival at the test site, a testing protocol briefing was given to all the observers. For the first time, we were informed that the ASTM E-1105-93/AAMA 502-90 test was going to be modified for an extended duration and the initial 4.86 lb/ft² (23.73 kg/m²) differential pressure test deleted. It was explained to us that this modified protocol was the protocol used to test the competitive face sealed system. The modified protocol was as follows:

1. Water would be sprayed uniformly on the test wall at a rate of 5 gal/ft²/hr (203.72L/m²/hr) for 2.5 hours.
2. The first 30 minutes would be run at a differential pressure of 6.24 lb/ft² (30.47 kg/m²).
3. The next 60 minutes would be run a differential pressure of 8.0 lb/ft² (39.06 kg/m²)
4. The last 60 minutes would be water only, without any differential pressure.

The test was run and monitored by a representative from a certified independent testing laboratory. He applied a white paste to some areas of known leakage. This paste turns bright red in contact with moisture.

FIG.9--Water deluge from spray rack
during ASTM E1105-93 test

The test commenced mid-morning with the 6.24 lb/ft² (30.47 kg/m²) increment (Fig. 9). About 10 minutes into the test, one small area of the paste showed a barely perceptible shade of pink. No water penetration was observed. At the end of 30 minutes, the differential pressure was increased to 8.0 lb/ft² (39.06 kg/m²). During the next 60 minutes, the pink spot remained unchanged and no water penetration was observed. About 10 minutes before this test increment ended, a borescope was inserted into the jamb cavity (Fig. 10). The view through the borescope showed jamb cavity intrusion water dripping into the reservoir at the rate of 1 drop of water every 5 seconds. The intrusion water was fully controlled and weeped to the exterior.

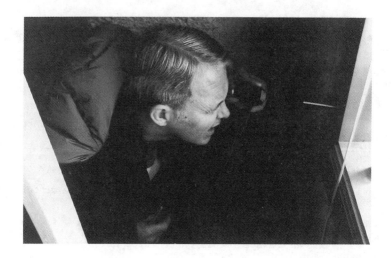

FIG. 10--Author viewing intrusion water drip into
new jamb cavity reservoir during ASTM E1105-93 test.

At the 90 minute mark, the differential pressure was reduced to
zero (atmospheric). The water spray then continued to flow over the
test wall for another 60 minutes. Again, no water penetration was
observed.
Our repair scheme passed the test without any interior leakage
after taking about 20 inches (508 mm) of equivalent rainfall over the 2-
1/2 hour test duration and a maximum wind speed of 57 mph (91.74 km/hr)
for an hour.

COST

The remedial repairs were bid by 6 contractors. The cost range
for all remedial items (except for the clear sealer) ranged from $580 to
$800 per panel with an average of $695. This met our goal of about $650
to $700 per panel for cost effectiveness.

PERSPECTIVES

The following comments were made during peer review of this paper.
They are presented here to provide the profession with the benefit of
these opinions and data.

1. The face sealed scheme is the repair solution currently being
implemented on the building. The scheme presented in this paper will
not be implemented.
2. Regarding decision to mitigate: "the decision to mitigate
rather than reject water from system is in this reviewer's opinion a
serious mistake. Any water penetrating to the core of the panel system
has an increased probability for penetrating the remaining two layers
through stone anchor penetrations, mis-lapped polyethylene, and precast
cracking. Water can be held between the concrete and polyethylene and
potentially cause rebar rusting int he long term exposure".
3. Regarding controlling core area water: "Controlling water
once it has reached the core of the curtainwall system is extremely
difficult. The fact that the repair approach mimics the original design
does not validate the repair".
4. Regarding epoxy adhesive: "Filling the existing cracks with
an epoxy adhesive without providing other means of stress relief will

leave the marble subject to additional cracking from dynamic movement, thermal cycling and the stone limit state". "The use of trowel-in epoxy to repair the cracked stone panels does not follow generally accepted practice".

5. Regarding plastic weep tubes: "Plastic weep tubes are subject to UV degradation and cracking over time. The reservoir would probably be more useful if the weep tube were omitted".

6. Regarding plastic weep tube placement: ".....while the weep tubes at a non-moving joint such as the jamb reservoir are fairly benign, inserting weep tubes into working joints is a prescription for failure. Insertion of a weep tube into a working joint diminishes the effective width of the joint. Typically, these type of joints fail from over extension and from degradation of the weep tubes".

7. Regarding design complexity: "Although the presented window repair was installed and tested, such a repair, in the reviewer's opinion, is overly complex, is applicable only to the windows and has a better than average potential for installation failure and high maintenance requirements.

8. Regarding reuse of the design: "Emulation of the described repair by the uninitiated or inexperienced designer would be likely to lead to an incomplete and unsuccessful repair".

CONCLUSION

In this instance, this remedial repair option proved itself to be a viable and cost effective system. It is hoped that this paper will provide impetus to the profession to thoroughly examine and evaluate all potential solutions to a problem. Who knows, the "Off the wall" approach utilizing creative thinking and unconventional methods may prove to be the winner.

ACKNOWLEDGEMENTS

(1) I wish to thank the principal and staff of Ian Mackinlay Architecture, Inc. and the ASTM peer reviewers for their advice, critique and support in preparing this paper.

REFERENCES

[1] Ruggiero, S.S. and Myers, J.C., "Design and Construction of Watertight Exterior Building Walls", Water In Exterior Building Walls, STP 1107, T. A. Schwartz, Ed., American Society for Testing and Materials, Philadelphia, 1992, pp 11 - 39.

Case Studies

Ian R. Chin[1] and Edward A. Gerns[2]

LESSONS LEARNED FROM INVESTIGATION OF WATER LEAKAGE THROUGH PRECAST AND CAST-IN-PLACE CONCRETE FACADES

REFERENCE: Chin, I. R. and Gerns, E. A., **"Lessons Learned from Investigations of Water Leakage Through Precast and Cast-In-Place Concrete Facades,"** Water Leakage Through Building Facades, ASTM STP 1314, R. J. Kudder and J. L. Erdly, Eds., American Society for Testing and Materials, 1998.

ABSTRACT: Rain water is expected to penetrate through joints in building facades. Consequently, a secondary line of defense is recommended in facades that contain frequent joints to collect, divert, and drain the water to the exterior. Concrete facades have historically been designed without this secondary line of defense because concrete walls have very few joints and it was believed that water would not penetrate concrete. However, due to shrinkage cracks in concrete, improper design, sealant joint failure, wall profile, and condensation water leakage has occurred through concrete facades. This water leakage may be controlled and be prevented from leaking into the interior of the building by a secondary line of defense. Details of a secondary line of defense against water leakage in concrete facades are presented in this paper.

KEYWORDS: Condensation, flashing, sealant failure, shrinkage cracks, water leakage, weepholes

---

The exterior envelope of a building is perhaps the most critical component of a building when considering environmental comfort and aesthetics. Historically, exterior walls were typically load bearing walls that support their own weight, the weight of the floor(s) and roof of the building and wind and seismic loads. Current construction techniques typically utilize non-load bearing walls which support only their own weight and resist wind loads. From a serviceability standpoint, both load bearing and non-load bearing walls are the primary barrier which help maintain the interior spaces at comfortable temperature and humidity levels and perhaps more importantly they prevent water penetration into the interior.

Generally, the element of the wall that is closest to the exterior provides the first line of defense against water penetration. In brick, concrete, and small panel stone masonry walls, rain water is expected to penetrate through the many joints in these wall systems regardless of the quality of workmanship. Of course water penetration is reduced with

---

[1]Vice President, Principal, and Chicago Unit Manager, Wiss, Janney, Elstner Associates, Inc. (WJE), 29 North Wacker Drive, Suite 555, Chicago, IL

[2]Senior Architect/Engineer, Wiss, Janney, Elstner Associates, Inc. (WJE), 29 North Wacker Drive, Suite 555, Chicago, IL

improved design and workmanship. Consequently, these wall systems are designed with a secondary line of defense to collect, divert, and drain the water that has penetrated the exterior veneer harmlessly back to the exterior of the building. This secondary line of defense includes flashing, weepholes, drainage cavities, drainage gutters, and inner wall components that are watertight.

Systems which employ larger components such as metal and stone panels have significantly fewer joints than small unit systems such as brick. Joints between panels in the larger component systems are typically sealed with sealant in lieu of mortar. These wall systems are often designed with a secondary line of defense against water penetration because improper design and/or construction of the joints, and deterioration of the sealant will allow water to penetrate the system and leak into the building, and because the consequences of water leakage in buildings can be significant from both an economic and reputational standpoint.

Concrete facades, both conventional and precast, have historically been designed without a secondary line of defense against water penetration because it is generally assumed that the following conditions exist in these walls:

1.   Rain water does not penetrate solid concrete elements.
2.   Sealing of perimeter joints of openings in concrete facade elements is sufficient to prevent water leakage through these joints.
3.   Sealing of control, construction, and expansion joints in concrete facades is sufficient to prevent water leakage through these joints.
4.   Perfect design and workmanship are used to design and construct concrete facades.
5.   Condensation does not occur on the back side of the wall.

If only these conditions are considered, then it may be adequate to design a concrete facade without a secondary line of defense. In this case, the owner of the building should be informed that the inevitable deterioration of sealant in the perimeter joints of window, door, mechanical, and other openings in the wall may result in water leakage. Consequently, a proactive sealant maintenance and replacement program is necessary to reduce the water leakage.

However, in reality, the following conditions individually or in combination, have resulted in water leakage through concrete facades on buildings investigated by the authors and their colleagues:

Cracking of Concrete Facades Due to Shrinkage of Concrete

Shrinkage of concrete occurs as it cures. This shrinkage continues at a decreasing rate for several months after the concrete is poured. Shrinkage of concrete can be reduced by using the smallest amount of water and cement in the mix to achieve the desired strength and workability. If proper curing techniques are followed, cracking of the concrete can also be further minimized. However, regardless of the efforts taken, generally, shrinkage and subsequent cracking of the concrete cannot be entirely eliminated.

Concrete members that are free to move will not be affected internally by shrinkage. However, in poured-in-place concrete structures, beams are usually rigidly connected to supporting columns and walls and they cannot contract freely to accommodate the shrinkage of the concrete from curing or thermal effects. This restraint results in tensile stresses developing in the beams which cause the beams to crack when the stresses exceed the tensile capacity of the concrete, as shown in Fig. 1. Similar shrinkage type cracks can also occur in precast concrete wall units, as shown in Fig. 2.

Fig. 1 -   View of shrinkage cracks in poured-in-place concrete structure

Fig. 2 -   View of shrinkage cracks in precast concrete wall units

The size of shrinkage cracks in concrete members can be minimized by using reinforcing steel in the members to counteract the shrinkage and to distribute the cracks uniformly. Control joints also control the location and profile of cracks. Water penetration can occur through cracks that are wider than 0.004 in. (0.1 mm)[1]. Shrinkage cracks in concrete walls and beams that are wider than 0.004 in. (0.1 mm) have been observed in buildings investigated by the authors and their colleagues, as shown in Figs. 3 and 4. Water that penetrates cracks in concrete walls and beams can leak into the interior of buildings, as schematically shown in Fig. 5.

Fig. 3 -   View of crack in concrete wall

Fig. 4 -   View of crack in concrete wall

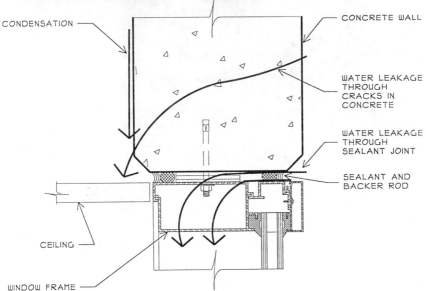

Fig. 5 -   Section through concrete wall at window head showing potential *paths of* water- leakage.

Improper Design of Concrete Members

Reinforced concrete members that are designed without control joints, expansion joints, and other provisions to accommodate shrinkage and other movements can develop cracks that allow water to penetrate into the building. Decorative grooves are often formed in precast concrete panels. These features create weak planes which can develop cracks, as shown in Fig. 6

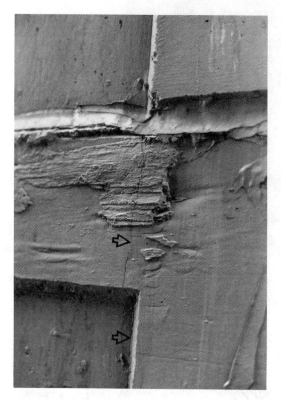

Fig. 6 -   View of crack in concrete wall
at decorative grooves

Sealant Joint Failure

Adhesive failure of sealant joints, the separation of the sealant from the joint substrate, as shown in Fig. 7, and cohesive failure, splitting of the sealant, as shown in Fig. 8, allow water to penetrate through the joint into the interior of the building, as shown in Fig. 5.

Fig. 7 -   View of adhesive failure of sealant joint

Fig. 8 -   View of cohesive failure of sealant joint

The following guidelines should be followed to minimize the likelihood of sealant failures:

A proper joint design, as shown in Fig. 9.
A sealant should be selected which will bond to the joint substrate materials.
Proper mixing of sealant and joint substrate preparation.
Installation of sealant should be performed in strict accordance with the sealant manufacturer's recommendations.
Refer to ASTM C1193, "Standard Guide for Use of Joint Sealants" for additional sealant joint requirments [2].

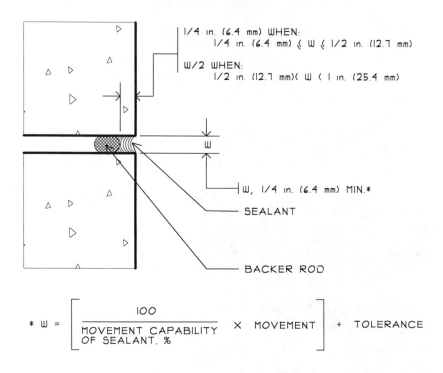

$$* W = \left[\frac{100}{\text{MOVEMENT CAPABILITY OF SEALANT, \%}} \times \text{MOVEMENT} \right] + \text{TOLERANCE}$$

Fig. 9 -   Width to depth relationship of sealant joint

In reinforced concrete buildings separation of sealant from the concrete members can also occur due to the presence of form release agents on the concrete joint substrate. These agents prevent proper bonding of sealant. In addition, exposed aggregates at the joint substrate prevent complete bonding of sealant to the substrate.
When sealant joints in an exterior facade are the only line of defense against water penetration, as shown in Fig. 10, water from rains will penetrate through openings in the sealant joints caused by weathering, deterioration, and/or workmanship and leak into the building. Pressure differential between the interior and exterior of the building and wind forces contribute to allowing water to penetrate the system.

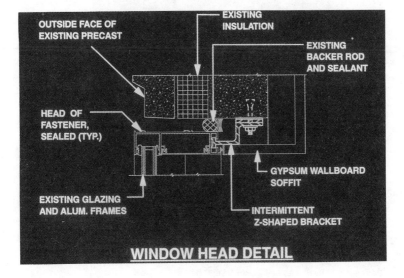

Fig. 10 -   Section through window head
             showing sealant joint as
             the only line of defense
             against water penetration.
             Sealant in joint was installed
             from the interior of the
             building.

Sloped Wall--Sloped reinforced concrete walls allow water on the wall
to readily flow through cracks in the walls and through separations and
splits in sealant joints. Fig. 11 is a view of a sloped concrete wall
that is cracked.

Fig. 11 -   View of a sloped
             concrete wall that is
             cracked

Condensation--When the interior side of an exterior reinforced concrete wall is allowed to reach its dew point temperature, condensation will develop on the interior side of the wall. The condensation will damage interior finishes if there are no provisions to collect and control such condensation.

SECONDARY LINE OF DEFENSE IN CONCRETE WALLS

The above conditions can result in water penetration through reinforced concrete walls and subsequent leakage into the building. A secondary line of defense against water penetration should, therefore, be considered in concrete facades. This secondary line of defense should include flashings with end dams and weepholes, or an extension of the window head to form a flashing, as schematically shown in Figs. 12 and 13, respectively. To avoid puncturing of the flashing by window head anchors the following options are possible:

1.   Use windows that can be anchored at the jambs.
2.   Fabricate flashing with window anchor points at dimples that are above the level of the flashing drainage plane.

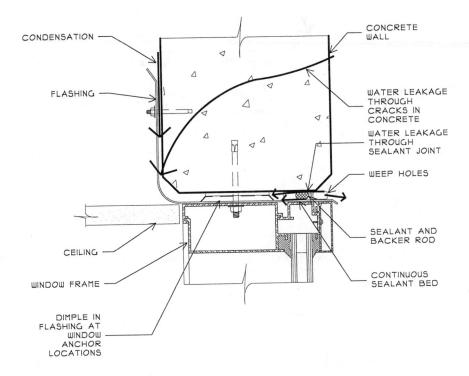

CONDENSATION

FLASHING

CEILING

WINDOW FRAME

DIMPLE IN
FLASHING AT
WINDOW
ANCHOR
LOCATIONS

CONCRETE
WALL

WATER LEAKAGE
THROUGH
CRACKS IN
CONCRETE

WATER LEAKAGE
THROUGH
SEALANT JOINT

WEEP HOLES

SEALANT AND
BACKER ROD

CONTINUOUS
SEALANT BED

Fig. 12 -   Section through concrete wall at window
head showing effect of flashing and weep
system

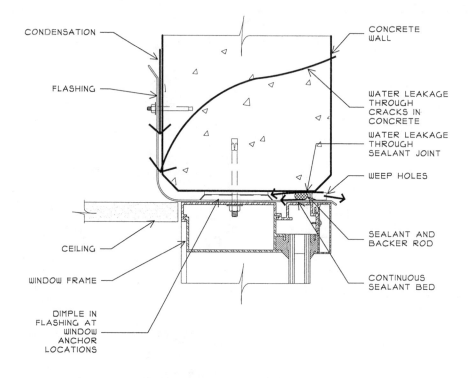

Fig. 13 - Section through concrete wall at window head showing
effect of window head extension flashing

This secondary line of defense should be supplemented by:
  a.   Avoiding the use of sloped concrete facades.
  b.   Locate properly designed and constructed control joints in
        walls to reduce the potential of unanticipated and
        uncontrolled cracking of concrete.
  c.   Seal all construction joints on walls.
  d.   Follow concrete durability recommendations of the ACI which
include, proper concrete cover, mix and air entrainment.

CONCLUSIONS

     Concrete facades on buildings are not immune to water penetration.
Water can enter the building through cracks that develop in the walls and
through sealant joints which are improperly designed, constructed and/or
deteriorated.
     To prevent damage at the building interior from water that penetrates
the facade, a secondary line of defense against water penetration, such as
a flashing and weep system, should be incorporated into the wall system.

REFERENCES

[1]   Birkeland, O., and Svendsen, S.D., in <u>Symposium on Masonry Testing</u>, <u>ASTM STP 320</u>, American Society for Testing and Materials, 1963, pp. 171-177, in Grimm, C.T., "Water Permeance of Masonry Walls: A Review of the Literature," <u>Masonry: Materials, Properties, and Performance</u>, <u>ASTM STP 778</u>, J. G. Borchelt, Ed., American Society for Testing and Materials, 1982, p. 178.

[2]   American Society for Testing and Materials, ASTM C1193 "Standard Guide for Use of Sealants," <u>Annual Book of Standards, Vol. 04.07</u>, 1995, pp. 278, Philadelphia, PA.

Gary L. Zwayer[1], David F. Cook[1], and Joan P. Crowe[1]

LEAKAGE AT INTERFACE BETWEEN MULTIPLE FACADE COMPONENTS

REFERENCE: Zwayer, G. L., Cook, D. F., and Crowe, J. P., ''**Leakage at Interface Between Multiple Facade Components,**'' Water Leakage Through Building Facades, ASTM STP 1314, R. J. Kudder and J. L. Erdly, Eds., American Society for Testing and Materials, 1998.

ABSTRACT: Buildings clad with multiple facade components perform well when they are properly designed and constructed. When water leakage does occur, typically it happens at the interface of the different components. The authors have performed numerous field investigations regarding water leakage of buildings and will discuss, through case studies, reasons for the leakage at the interface and examine how it could have been avoided. Additionally, design principles will be discussed regarding better water resistance performance of these interfaces. Problems with water leakage can be avoided if designers, manufacturers and installers perform a thorough study of each material and it's interface with adjacent materials. Through the cooperation of these parties in the development of a complete understanding of each component and its interface with the other components, proper design and detailing, pre-construction meetings with all parties, pre-construction mock-up testing, on-site field observation, and quality control testing, water tight buildings can be erected.

KEYWORDS: interface, design, installation, failures, cause

The combinations of building materials for wall construction are limitless. The aesthetic and functional choices that architects and owners have allows them tremendous freedom to create building imagery. With this freedom comes technological challenge. Unique combinations of material may make a building visually appealing, but if the interface between those materials is not properly designed and installed, the building facade may function poorly. It is not unusual to have different trades (and disciplines) working together on the exterior of buildings. The interface between trades' areas, or between different systems, is a likely place to expect problems. Even though the interface between one material and another is where one system's responsibility ends and another system's begins, it is the responsibility of many parties to insure that the various materials are joined properly and function well with each other. Only through careful study and understanding of the function and requirements of each material by the architects, material manufacturers and installers can successful transitions be achieved.

Prior to the advent of the curtain wall, construction techniques incorporated various building materials in thick structural walls designed to shed water away from the exterior wall surface. Thick walls provide a barrier due to their mass and the distance that water must travel to penetrate them. Overhangs, eaves, sloped window sills,

---

[1] Senior Consultant, Architect/Engineer II, Architect/Engineer II, respectively, Architectural Unit, Wiss, Janney, Elstner Associates, Inc., 330 Pfingsten Road, Northbrook, Illinois 60062-2095

water tables, and drip edges of thick walls not only added visual interest to the exterior of a building, they also functioned to shed water. These details were often located at critical intersections of different building elements.

Recessing windows from the exterior surface of the building protected this vulnerable element from water which may run down the face of the building. Providing an overhang at the top of a wall not only protected the top of the wall, but, during periods of slight wind, provided shelter for the entire wall. One of the most effective methods to reduce water leakage through the exterior wall was, and still is, to reduce the amount of water that is in contact with the surface.

With the use of modern materials, exterior walls became less massive. Since the components of exterior wall construction became lighter and thinner, the distance and path water had to travel from the exterior surface to the interior was reduced and straightened. Each element of the building cladding became a highly engineered system in itself. Stone, masonry, glass, metal, wood, plaster, EIFS, and many others are all component systems for cladding the exterior of the buildings.

The manufacturers and suppliers of each of these component systems have developed details, test methods, certification procedures, and performance expectations for their products. However, these standards of performance stop at the edges of the product that they test. Manufacturers prepare installation instructions which delineate the proper installation methods and procedures for their system. Many times they do not detail how to interface their product to adjacent construction

The authors of this paper have performed numerous field investigations regarding water leakage of buildings. Often the reasons for the observed leakage are improper detailing and installation at building component interfaces. This paper will discuss, through case studies, the reasons for the observed leakage and examine how it could have been avoided. Additionally, design principles will be discussed regarding better water resistance performance of these interfaces.

CASE STUDY #1

The interface between exterior brick veneer and aluminum window frames is common in commercial construction. Improperly installed or detailed, this typical interface can produce sources of water leakage. One example of an improperly installed joint between brick veneer and aluminum window framing was observed on a 10-story building. The exterior cladding consisted of an aluminum frame ribbon window system with brick veneer spandrel panels. The 5-ft high x 10-ft. (1.5 m x 3 m) wide masonry spandrel panels were installed in a panelized system consisting of a steel framework, steel studs, gypsum sheathing, and brick veneer. The panels were shop fabricated, including the brick veneer, with a drainage cavity, membrane flashing over the steel lintel, and weep holes. They were transported to the site, hoisted in place and attached to the building structure.

Two separate sources of water leakage were identified at the intersection between the head of the aluminum frame ribbon windows and the bottom of the masonry panels. One was caused by the failure to join the membrane flashing over the lintel from one panel to another. The panelized construction compounded this problem in that the shelf angles also terminated at the ends of each masonry panel. These aligned openings in the flashing and lintels allowed water which penetrated through the brick veneer to penetrate directly to the window framing and interior of the building every 10 ft. (3 m). See Fig. 1.

A second source of water leakage created at the interface between the windows and the masonry panels was caused by the attachment of the window frames to the bottom of the steel lintels. The attachment was made by fastening the window head receptor to the bottom of the steel lintel with power-actuated fasteners. The fasteners penetrated through

Fig. 1--Open flashing joint at window lintel joint

the horizontal outstanding leg of the steel lintel and the outstanding leg of the lintel flashing. The fastener penetrations in the lintel flashing created a path for water to leak through the flashing.

Compounding the above two problems, sealant was installed in the joint between the bottom of the brick and the top of the steel lintel. This sealed the intended drainage path of the masonry cavity above the lintel. The sealant did not seal to the lintel flashing, leaving a path for the water to flow under it and into the window head.

As a result of these and other construction deficiencies, water leakage occurred on the interior of the building prior to the completion of construction. Gypsum board soffits, particle board sills, and knee walls were all damaged. Since there were numerous holes in the membrane flashing caused by the intermittent fastening of the window head receptors to the steel lintels, all of the lintel flashing had to be removed and replaced. The repair required that the steel lintel be exposed, cleaned, primed and painted. A new prefinished metal flashing with an integral drip edge was installed over the steel lintel. The back edge of the metal flashing was sealed to the gypsum board sheathing with a flexible membrane. The joint between the bottom of the drip edge and the top of the window receptor was sealed covering the toe of the outstanding leg of the shelf angle.

During our investigation, it was determined that the anchorage of the window head to the building structure was inadequate to sustain design wind loads. The window attachment was also modified. Adequate attachment was achieved by fastening the window head receptor to the bottom of the steel lintel with self tapping metal screws prior to the installation of the masonry flashing. These fasteners were then cut off flush with the top of the steel lintel prior to the installation of the new lintel flashing. See Fig. 2.

These problems were caused by a lack of understanding of the interface of the systems and their fasteners which were being used to clad this building. The architect, masonry contractor, window and sealant installers could have avoided these problems if all of the parties understood the relationship between the systems.

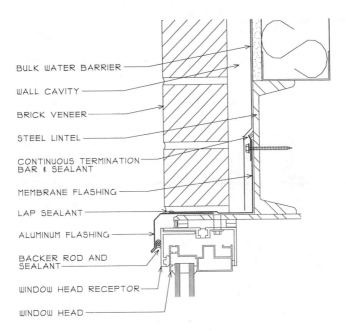

BULK WATER BARRIER

WALL CAVITY

BRICK VENEER

STEEL LINTEL

CONTINUOUS TERMINATION
BAR & SEALANT

MEMBRANE FLASHING

LAP SEALANT

ALUMINUM FLASHING

BACKER ROD AND
SEALANT

WINDOW HEAD RECEPTOR

WINDOW HEAD

Fig. 2--Section detail at lintel flashing repair

CASE STUDY #2

        A second case study demonstrates a problem which can occur when
installing a building component which was not manufactured to
accommodate adjacent construction. A common example of this problem is
where perimeter sealant interfaces with aluminum frame windows. The
manufacturers of these components should recognize that the perimeter of
their product will generally abut a sealant joint. Many conventional
head, sill and jamb extrusions are a C shape with the legs of the C
facing the perimeter. These extrusions provide minimal surface area for
the proper installation of a backer rod and sealant.
        An example of this was observed on a masonry veneer clad building
in Chicago. The exterior wall construction was masonry veneer over a
1 1/2 in. (38 mm) cavity with bulk water barrier on plywood sheathing on
steel studs. The fenestration consisted of aluminum frame windows and
doors. The aluminum frame windows were installed with the exterior edge
of the windows minimally overlapping the interior edge of the brick
veneer. The combination of the hollow C aluminum jamb and the air space
behind the brick veneer provided insufficient surface area for the
adhesion of sealant. In addition, backer rod placed within the joint
easily fell back into the void between the portion of the extrusion and
the masonry air space. See Fig. 3.
        Once this occurred, it was impossible to tool the sealant with
adequate pressure to achieve sufficient contact with the adjacent
substrates. To prevent water leakage through the perimeter joint
around the windows at this installation, the perimeter sealant must be
installed properly. As is evident from the detail, (Fig. 3) a different
position of the window relative to the masonry would not eliminate the
problem.
        The profile of the hollow jamb would still provide minimal surface
area for both sealant adhesion and backer rod support. If the window
manufacturer had fabricated the window extrusions with a profile which
would facilitate the installation of a typical sealant joint with backer

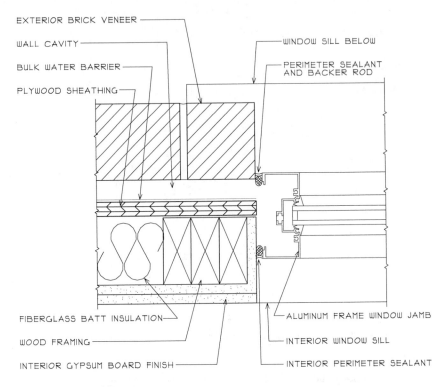

EXTERIOR BRICK VENEER

WALL CAVITY

BULK WATER BARRIER

PLYWOOD SHEATHING

WINDOW SILL BELOW

PERIMETER SEALANT
AND BACKER ROD

FIBERGLASS BATT INSULATION

WOOD FRAMING

INTERIOR GYPSUM BOARD FINISH

ALUMINUM FRAME WINDOW JAMB

INTERIOR WINDOW SILL

INTERIOR PERIMETER SEALANT

Fig. 3--Plan detail at window jamb

rod, the perimeter sealant could have been installed properly to avoid
failures.

Many different repairs could have been implemented to reduce the
amount of water leakage that was occurring around the fenestration at
this building. Some of them would be similar to the options available
during the original construction noted above. One way to improve the
interface for a proper sealant installation at this intersection, would
be to have the windows installed with a receptor system. These systems
include an additional aluminum extrusion at the head, jambs and sill of
the window opening. The exterior surface of the receptor system is
generally flat and will provide a larger area for the proper
installation of a perimeter sealant joint. The sill extrusion can also
include a weeped flashing to direct water out of the wall beneath the
window.

The bulk water barrier could also have been sealed to the exterior
surface of the window frame receptors. See Fig. 4. This would have
provided a secondary defense against water penetration through the
perimeter sealant joints. Another option would be to have installed a
perimeter seal in the wall cavity to prevent air and water, which may
have been in the adjacent wall cavity, from entering the building
through the window penetration in the bulk water barrier. See Fig. 5.

All of these repairs would have required that a substantial
amount of work be performed on the building. Since the building was
occupied, the owners and builders made a joint decision that it would be
undesirable to remove and replace the windows in this building or
perform a substantial amount of work on the exterior masonry. This

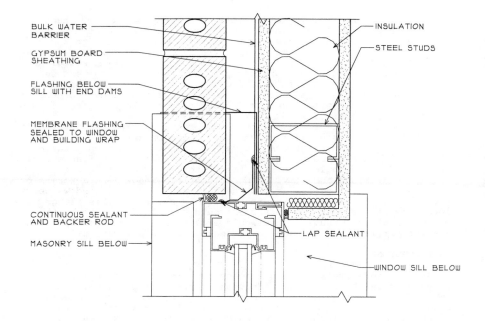

BULK WATER BARRIER

GYPSUM BOARD SHEATHING

FLASHING BELOW SILL WITH END DAMS

MEMBRANE FLASHING SEALED TO WINDOW AND BUILDING WRAP

CONTINUOUS SEALANT AND BACKER ROD

MASONRY SILL BELOW

INSULATION

STEEL STUDS

LAP SEALANT

WINDOW SILL BELOW

Fig. 4--Window jamb with bulk water barrier seal

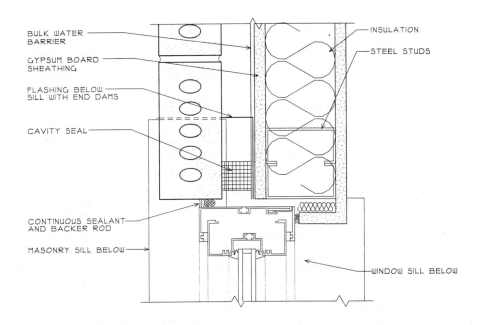

BULK WATER BARRIER

GYPSUM BOARD SHEATHING

FLASHING BELOW SILL WITH END DAMS

CAVITY SEAL

CONTINUOUS SEALANT AND BACKER ROD

MASONRY SILL BELOW

INSULATION

STEEL STUDS

WINDOW SILL BELOW

Fig. 5--Window jamb with cavity seal

eliminated the possibility of installing a receptor system, changing the relationship between the window perimeter and the adjacent masonry, sealing the wall cavity or sealing the bulk water barrier to the exterior of the window frames. The repair that was implemented was the application of a fillet bead of sealant over the existing hourglass shaped sealant bead. Bond breaker tape was applied to the exposed surface of the existing sealant, and it was used as a form of joint backer. While this repair procedure did not eliminate every theoretical leakage path associated with the fenestration on the building, it did eliminate the observed water leakage on the interior.

A need for the improvement of the profile of the perimeter of the window frame extrusion to receive sealant and backer rod was noted above. Other improvements can be made at the intersection between a window and other building systems. An integral flashing flange could be fabricated which could be easily tied into the adjacent bulk water barrier. Aluminum and vinyl clad residential window manufacturers often incorporate a nailing fin around the perimeter of their windows serves such a purpose. If the moisture barrier is sealed to this flange, the integrity of the bulk water barrier could be maintained around the perimeter of the window. This would provide a second layer of defense against air infiltration and water leakage at this location.

CASE STUDY #3

The proper relationship between adjacent building components is often critical to the proper function of the entire system. It is important that everyone involved with the creation of the interface between two adjacent components be fully informed as to the requirements of the adjacent systems. A case which illustrates this idea was observed on a mid-rise residential building.

The window manufacturer incorporated a reglet in the front face of the vinyl clad windows. This reglet was placed in the frame cladding extrusion in order to facilitate the joining together of two separate units and accept frame extending trim panning. The reglets continued across the face of the frame members into the perimeter edge surfaces where perimeter sealant was typically expected to bond. During this investigation, we observed that the perimeter sealant around the windows was not held back behind the back of the reglet as discussed below.

On this project, the exterior wall was constructed of EIFS on gypsum board sheathing on wood studs. The windows were set in factory made triple units. The typical installation details produced by the window manufacturer showed the perimeter sealant to be held back from the face of the window frames. See Fig. 6. On this particular window system, the reglets continue through the window corners. It was important to recess the sealant line back behind the reglet in order to prevent water from migrating from the reglet behind the perimeter sealant at the open corners.

They did not specify that the sealant should be held back behind the back of the reglet, nor did they give any set-back dimension. The vinyl extrusion used to join two units together was typically less than 1/8 in. (3 mm) thick. The perimeter sealant contractor evidently did not have access to the window shop drawings, and he did recess the sealant behind the back edge of the reglets.   He installed the sealant flush with the face of the window frames. As a result, water was ₡ channelled behind the perimeter sealant through the reglets, and there was substantial water leakage around the perimeter of the windows.

A second problem related to the perimeter sealant installation was also observed on this project. Contract Documents were not available for review, however, the window shop drawings showed a space between the window and the EIFS to receive sealant. The EIFS contractor did not leave a recessed joint around the perimeter of the windows. In many locations, the EIFS finish abutted the window perimeter leaving insufficient space for a proper recessed perimeter sealant joint.

The recommended repair for these deficiencies was to remove and properly replace portions of the EIFS around the window perimeter,

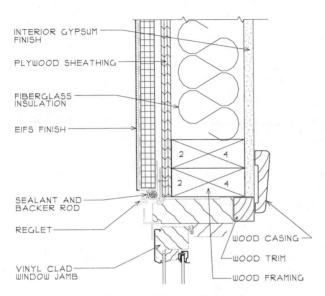

INTERIOR GYPSUM FINISH

PLYWOOD SHEATHING

FIBERGLASS INSULATION

EIFS FINISH

SEALANT AND BACKER ROD

REGLET

VINYL CLAD WINDOW JAMB

WOOD CASING

WOOD TRIM

WOOD FRAMING

Fig. 6 - Detail at window jamb

allowing space for a proper sealant joint. Once there was sufficient space for the sealant joint, it was installed well back from the face of the windows behind the rear of the reglet.

As it was shown above, it is important to properly locate the perimeter sealant joint to insure satisfactory performance of the sealant, and the adjacent building components. Typically, sealant installers do not provide shop drawings for the size, profile, and location of the sealant joints that they are going to install on a project. It is often practical for the architect to merely show idealized perimeter details and sealant joints on the contract documents because the manufacturers of the components have not been selected. Perimeter profiles of components from different manufacturers often have different profiles, and perimeter sealant requirements.

Shop drawings are typically required from component manufacturers. These drawings should include the relationship of the component to any other adjacent building element. They should also include the size, shape and location of all sealant joints in contact with the perimeter of the components. These drawings are typically reviewed by the architect and general contractor. Both of these parties should have a full level of understanding as to the function of the different components involved and require that they are properly shown and coordinated. Once the shop drawings have been accepted by all parties, they can be used to delineate the location of the perimeter sealant around the components.

CASE STUDY #4

The intersection between a horizontal water proofing membrane and a masonry drainage wall is another typical detail. It is important for the designer and specifier to fully understand how each system controls

water in order to properly detail this intersection to prevent water
leakage. It is also important for the workmen to understand how their
system performs in relationship to the entire wall system in order to
achieve a water tight installation. Two separate cases were
investigated which demonstrate the necessity for understanding by all of
the parties involved.

A case which demonstrated the necessity for the architect to
understand the proper function of the two intersecting systems occurred
at the base of a set back masonry-clad tower above a roof-deck plaza.
The wall consisted of an exterior wythe of brick veneer over No. 15 lb
building felt on gypsum board sheathing on steel stud back-up with
flashing and weeps at the base of the wall. The roof deck plaza was
installed as part of a remodelling program at the building. The
waterproofing membrane for the plaza was a loose laid Polyvinyl Chloride
(PVC) membrane. The membrane was attached to the pre-existing masonry
cavity wall with a surface-applied aluminum termination bar. The top
edge of the membrane was sealed to the face of the brick veneer with
sealant. None of the parties involved with the installation of the
plaza waterproofing membrane appeared to have recognized the fact that
water could be expected to be behind the surface of the exterior wythe
of brick veneer. No provision was made to eliminate any water from
within the wall cavity above the roof deck membrane termination. As a
result, water which penetrated the brick veneer above the top of the
roof deck termination was trapped behind the waterproofing membrane.
Water leakage was reported in the parking garage beneath the roof plaza
within a year of the installation of the plaza membrane. Subsequent
water penetration testing demonstrated that the brick veneer was porous
and allowed substantial water penetration to the wall cavity.

The recommended solution to this problem was similar to the detail
that should have been installed along with the roof plaza membrane.
This was to install a three-piece through-wall flashing above the plaza
membrane termination. The purpose of this flashing is to collect water
which penetrates the brick veneer above the plaza membrane and conduct
that water out of the wall cavity above the membrane termination before
it is trapped within the wall. The prefinished aluminum flashing was
installed at the first bed course above the existing membrane
termination bar. It incorporated a removable piece which continued down
over the top of the existing termination bar and served as a
counterflashing to the existing membrane. Prior to the installation of
the new flashing, the existing termination bar, fastening, and sealant
joint at the top of the plaza membrane was inspected and repaired as
necessary. The interior edge of the aluminum flashing was sealed to the
existing wall sheathing with a flexible membrane flashing. A second
termination bar and sealant should be used to seal the top edge of the
membrane portion of the flashing to the gypsum board sheathing. The
No. 15 building felt was lapped over the top of the membrane
termination. See Fig. 7.

Even when the intersection is properly detailed, problems can
result as a result of improper installation. Another case at a similar
intersection between a masonry cavity wall and a horizontal roof
membrane demonstrated the necessity for the proper integration of
flashings installed by separate contractors on the exterior of the
building. This case occurred at an intersection between a set back
brick veneer clad tower and a roof deck. The exterior walls were
constructed of a single wythe of brick veneer with a drainage cavity and
a moisture barrier over sheathing on steel studs. The roof system was a
ballasted, loose-laid Ethylene Propylene Diene Monomer (EPDM) membrane
on a layer of tapered rigid insulation on a concrete roof deck. Water
leakage was observed dripping from cracks and penetrations in the
concrete roof slab above the ceiling beneath the roof deck at numerous
locations away from the perimeter of the brick clad tower.

Water penetration testing isolated the problem to failures associated
with the masonry wall drainage system.

Inspection openings revealed gaps, discontinuities, and missing
end dams in the through wall flashing. Similar to the flashing problems
cited above, these deficiencies at the exterior wall set backs allowed
water within the wall cavity to bypass the interface between the wall

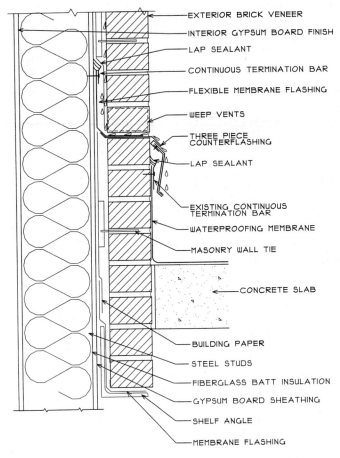

EXTERIOR BRICK VENEER
INTERIOR GYPSUM BOARD FINISH
LAP SEALANT
CONTINUOUS TERMINATION BAR
FLEXIBLE MEMBRANE FLASHING
WEEP VENTS
THREE PIECE COUNTERFLASHING
LAP SEALANT
EXISTING CONTINUOUS TERMINATION BAR
WATERPROOFING MEMBRANE
MASONRY WALL TIE
CONCRETE SLAB
BUILDING PAPER
STEEL STUDS
FIBERGLASS BATT INSULATION
GYPSUM BOARD SHEATHING
SHELF ANGLE
MEMBRANE FLASHING

Fig. 7 - Wall section detail at roof deck plaza membrane repair.

and roof flashing and migrate to the interior. While it is very likely
that these gaps and discontinuities were present through out the
building, they were not the source of reported water leakage since the
water continued downward until it was interrupted by the roof slab.
    Since the majority of the existing masonry wall flashing appeared
to be intact, the recommended repair utilized as much of the existing
flashing as possible. A few courses of brick veneer were removed at
wall corners, window and door jambs, and flashing laps. The flashing
was exposed, cleaned and properly lapped.
    The above example demonstrated the need for workmen to fully
understand how their system functions. Experienced workmen can install
their systems for years without fully understanding how it works. It
may be that only when they are presented with a critical detail where
all of the components of their system must function properly in order
for the entire exterior enclosure to work will the error of their

installation be brought to light.

CASE STUDY #5

There are fundamental differences between the way that a brick
veneer drainage wall system and an EIFS wall prevent water leakage into
a building. Since that is the case, special care must be exercised when
detailing a joint between these two systems.

An EIFS wall relies on a relatively thin impervious surface to
prevent water leakage to the interior. Since water penetration behind
the exterior surface is not expected, there is generally no secondary
means of defense against water penetration designed into the wall
system. This means that for an EIFS wall component to be effective at
preventing water penetration, all of the water must be stopped at the
exterior surface.

Brick veneer drainage walls typically rely on two means of defense
against water leakage. The first level of defense is the exterior
surface of the wall itself. This surface serves as a rain screen,
shedding the vast majority of water. However it is generally recognized
that this surface is porous and can contain numerous paths for water
penetration. Cracked bricks, and cracked or unfilled mortar joints are
all potential sources where water may penetrate behind the brick
surface. Wind, gravity, internal building pressure, and even capillary
action can cause water to penetrate the surface of the brick veneer. In
a properly detailed drainage wall system, this water is collected by the
wall flashing and directed out of the wall at the base of the wall or
above penetrations such as windows and doors.

When a combination of both an EIFS and a masonry system are
present on the same facade, aesthetic and structural considerations
often dictate that the lighter appearing EIFS material is located above
the masonry. This relationship is not generally a cause for water
leakage. However, where the relationship between these two elements is
reversed and the brick veneer is above the EIFS or they abut one another
side by side, the joint between these two systems must be properly
detailed in order to prevent water leakage. Unless the EIFS backup is
designed to accommodate the water from the brick veneer cavity, and
direct it to the exterior of the building, the water which can be
expected in the masonry cavity must not be allowed to migrate behind the
EIFS.

A case which demonstrates the necessity for proper detailing of
this condition was investigated recently at a residence in Chicago. The
exterior facade was composed of alternating EIFS and brick veneer
panels. The EIFS panels consisted of a polymer based synthetic stucco
system on expanded polystyrene insulation board on plywood sheathing.
The adjacent brick veneer drainage wall consisted of exterior brick
veneer with a 1 1/2 in. (38 mm) air space over a bulk water barrier on
plywood sheathing. At the base of the masonry wall a metal flashing was
installed to direct water from the drainage cavity to the exterior
immediately above the roof membrane counterflashing The masonry wall
flashing was sealed to the top of the counterflashing. The roof
counterflashing continued beneath the base of the EIFS panel. The
perimeter sealant around the EIFS panels was sealed to the top of the
roof counterflashing. At the joint between the EIFS and masonry
drainage wall, there was no separation between the two systems, and no
means to prevent water within the masonry cavity from penetrating behind
the EIFS panels.

During the first year after the building was occupied, water
leakage was reported at the first floor ceiling beneath a second floor
set back wall. Water penetration testing eliminated the roof membrane,
flashing, counterflashing, EIFS and it's adjacent sealant joints as
sources for the water leakage. The testing demonstrated that the source
of the water leakage was through the brick veneer. When the masonry
wall drainage system was isolated from the EIFS and tested for water
leakage, no water leakage was observed. Only when water from within the

masonry cavity was allowed to migrate behind the EIFS, was water leakage observed.

The recommended repair for this condition was similar to the detail that should have been installed during the original construction. It required that the masonry wall drainage cavity be isolated from the EIFS backup. A metal end dam was soldered to the metal masonry flashing. This prevented water from migrating from behind the masonry cavity to behind the EIFS panels. See Fig. 8.

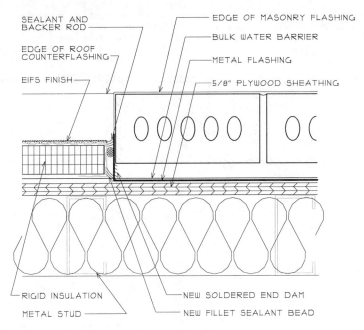

SEALANT AND BACKER ROD

EDGE OF ROOF COUNTERFLASHING

EIFS FINISH

EDGE OF MASONRY FLASHING

BULK WATER BARRIER

METAL FLASHING

5/8" PLYWOOD SHEATHING

RIGID INSULATION

METAL STUD

NEW SOLDERED END DAM

NEW FILLET SEALANT BEAD

Fig. 8--Plan detail at joint between masonry drainage wall and EIFS

The installers of the two systems did not separate the different functions of the two separate systems. The importance of the interface between the two systems was ignored by all of the parties involved, and an easily preventable condition resulted in serious damage to the interior.

CONCLUSIONS

The above cases demonstrate some of the problems which can result when the intersection between various exterior wall components are not designed and installed correctly. This paper has discussed some of the causes of these problems and proposed ways that they could have been avoided.

Through cooperation, understanding and improved detailing, the construction industry can improve the performance of joints between various building components. Owners, architects, general and sub-contractors all become frustrated, lose time and spend money when buildings leak and repairs have to be made. It should be the responsibility of each architect to understand the function of the various systems which are incorporated into the facade of a building and develop the Contract Documents accordingly. It should be the

responsibility of each general contractor to coordinate the work on
their projects to enable their subcontractors to properly install their
materials in manner which will allow for the proper interface of the
systems and function of the entire facade. It should be the
responsibility of each supplier to completely communicate to their
buyers and installers the requirements of their system and how they
relate to adjoining materials. Finally, it should be the responsibility
of each installer to understand the function of each element of a
building that he or she is asked to install and how it will be effected
by adjoining construction. Only through the thoughtful process of
learning and understanding the various functions of the adjacent systems
can intersections between systems be properly detailed and installed.

Marcus J. Dell[1] and Sean B. Liaw[2]

PERFORMANCE OF STUCCO-CLAD WOOD-FRAME BUILDINGS IN A TEMPERATE RAIN
FOREST

REFERENCE: Dell, M. J. and Liaw, S. B., "Performance of Stucco-Clad Wood-Frame
Buildings in a Temperate Rain Forest," Water Leakage Through Building Facades, ASTM
STP 1314, R. J. Kudder and J. L. Erdly, Eds., American Society for Testing and
Materials, 1998.

ABSTRACT: The use of stucco cladding on wood-frame buildings is common
construction for low-rise condominiums on the southwestern coast of
Canada, a mild climatic region with heavy rainfall (temperate
rainforest). This paper is a case study of severe deterioration that
has occurred due to water ingress and resultant fungal attack at a
condominium in Vancouver. The condominium was built in 1987 and
consists of 3, four-storey buildings interconnected by exterior
walkways. All buildings and walkways are of wood-frame construction,
and the exterior walls are clad in conventional stucco. The causes of
the water ingress and the subsequent deterioration are numerous,
including: poor waterproofing membrane application; improper flashing
terminations; and substandard stucco application. The following key
issues will be illustrated in this case study: the implications of
applying elastomeric coatings to wood structures already infected by
fungi; the importance of proper waterproofing details in a wet climate;
the implications of using waferboard sheathing as opposed to plywood;
and techniques for repairing deteriorating wood-frame structures.

KEYWORDS: stucco, wood-frame structure, fungi, flashing, waterproofing
membrane, elastomeric paint

The condominium in this case study was constructed in 1987 and
consists of 3, four-storey buildings interconnected by exterior
walkways. The buildings are of wood-frame construction with stucco
cladding. Each building has a flat roof system with controlled drainage.
The flat roofs cover all exterior walkways and stairwells, but do not
overhang the footprint of the building. The design intent was that the
stucco cladding and underlying sheathing membrane (building paper) would
protect vertical structures from moisture. Membranes and metal cap
flashings are used to waterproof horizontal surfaces of the structure
(walkways, balconies, etc.). Because the wood-frame components were not

---

[1]M.A.Sc., P.Eng., Manager, Building Science Division, Levelton
Associates, #150 - 12791 Clarke Place, Richmond, British Columbia, Canada,
V6V 2H9.

[2]M.Eng., P.Eng., Building Science Division, Levelton Associates,
#150 - 12791 Clarke Place, Richmond, British Columbia, Canada, V6V 2H9.

intended to be wetted, the governing code did not require them to be constructed with pressure-treated lumber.

This building was selected for a case study because its construction and water ingress problems are typical of those occurring throughout the southwestern coast of Canada.

The climatic conditions in this region are unique in comparison to the remainder of the country. Environment Canada defines the climatic region as a temperate rain forest; the average winter temperature remains above freezing and the annual precipitation averages 1.4 m [1]. During the winter months, precipitation is persistent. The climatic conditions on the southwest coast of Canada are very similar to those in Seattle, Washington.

This paper is organized into sections based on distinct phases and categories of remedial work conducted. In each section, the following will be discussed: the deficiency or damage requiring remedial work; the possible causes of the deficiency or damage; and the remedial work conducted. The buildings are referred to in this report as south, northeast, and northwest.

INITIAL INVESTIGATION - 1991

Initially, the Owners were concerned about water ponding on the exterior walkways and water penetration into the elevator core. The Owners were also considering painting the stucco cladding with a high-build elastomeric acrylic paint to improve the aesthetics of the building and to seal cracks in the stucco. Our firm was retained to review the water ponding and penetration problems. It was quickly determined that the water entering the elevator core was the result of an exterior planter that had not been waterproofed.

Brown staining below stucco-clad structural wood columns and walls was observed while on site. This type of staining is indicative that the wood is, or was, wet. Wet wood is susceptible to fungal attack (Figure 1).

FIG. 1--Typical staining indicative of wet wood.

At completion of the initial examination, a report was submitted to the Owners providing details for remedial repairs to the planter. It was also recommended that further examination be conducted to determine the cause of the brown staining and that the building not be painted until all sources of water ingress and resultant deterioration were identified and corrected.

The planter membrane was re-waterproofed, and the water entering the elevator subsided. However, the Owners elected to proceed with painting of the structure against our recommendations. Specifically, two coats of elastomeric acrylic paint were applied to all stucco wall surfaces.

Painting of the stucco would not seal all the possible sources of water entering the walls. We, therefore, had the following concerns:
• The acrylic paint would reduce the drying potential of the wall. The paint manufacturer promotes the product as breathable (water vapour permeability @ 20 mils = 10.1 grams/m²/24 hours as per ASTM Test Methods for Water Vapour Transmission of Materials [ASTM E 96]); however, application of the paint to the stucco decreases the permeability of the cladding.
• The paint hides the stains and discolouration that are indicative of wood deterioration. Hidden problems are less likely to be corrected.
• The paint would be damaged if remedial work was conducted to correct other possible sources of water ingress.

SECOND INVESTIGATION - 1993

In 1993, the structure was re-examined because a significant amount of water was entering the underground parking structure. The water was entering the parking structure due to membrane failure in numerous planters (not the planter repaired in 1991). During our investigation of the planters, it was observed that staining was worsening at the base of the stucco-clad structural wood columns and at other locations. It was also reported that water was continuing to leak through the wall and ceiling of a ground-floor suite at the northeast corner of the condominium complex.

A significant investigative and remedial program was initiated. The approach to the investigation and the subsequent remedial repairs was affected by the following factors:
• It is difficult to evaluate the condition of wood-frame components behind/below stucco without removing the stucco. The Owners elected not to have holes/openings cut in the stucco throughout their building.
• Areas of deterioration that posed a safety issue (e.g., deteriorated exterior walkways and stairways) had to be corrected as they were identified.
• The financial limitations of the Owners significantly affected the approach to the investigation and remedial repairs.
• The building had to remain occupied while the investigation and remedial repairs were implemented.

Early in the investigation, it was determined that the structural columns and beams used to support the exterior walkways on the south building were significantly deteriorated. Because the walkways are the only means of egress from the buildings, it was decided that immediate repairs were required.

Northeast and South Building Walkway Repairs

The uppermost walkways are covered by the main roof, while the lower walkways are protected by the walkway above. However, because the walkways are bordered by walls on only one side, they are subjected to

wetting from wind-driven rain. The original construction of the
walkways consisted of:

   • Fifty to 75 mm of exposed aggregate concrete topping, with wire
mesh reinforcement;
   • Ninety-pound granulated roofing felt protection sheet;
   • Bitumen-modified polyurethane waterproofing membrane;
   • Plywood deck;
   • Joists.

   The joists are simply supported between the exterior wall of the
building and beams that span between exterior columns. There is an
approximately 125 mm high curb along the outer perimeter of the walkways
that is covered with metal flashing.
   In 1993, removal of sections of the curb flashing uncovered
significant deterioration of the wood curb. Removal of concrete topping
at adjacent areas revealed that the deterioration had spread to portions
of the plywood walkway deck and to the header beams located under the
curb (Figure 2). The ends of the joists fastened to the header beams
were also deteriorated. Deterioration was also discovered in the
sheathing and wood members of virtually all columns that support the
walkways (Figure 3).

FIG. 2--Typical header beam deterioration.

   The damage at the walkways occurred for the following reasons:

   • The original waterproofing membrane was not well bonded to the
plywood deck at many locations and was poorly adhered to the scupper
drains. Also, the membrane terminated on the inside face of the curbs;
it should have been brought over the top of the curb and down the facia
of the walkways.
   • At several locations, the waterproofing membrane was
unacceptably thin and had been damaged.
   • Wood strips used as control joints in the concrete topping had
been nailed through the waterproofing membrane; this is unacceptable
workmanship.

FIG. 3--Typical column deterioration.

• The drainage slope on the walkways was poor. The slope of the
concrete topping ranged from level to approximately 0.7% toward the
outer edge of the walkways. The plywood deck sloped approximately 1.4%
towards the building. While some water is shed from the surface of the
concrete topping, inevitably, water will pass through the topping at
cracks and at the edges of the topping. Water will then collect between
the topping and the waterproofing membrane on the plywood deck and drain
towards the building.
• A significant amount of water entered the structure at the
junction between the curb metal flashings and the columns. The
flashings were merely butted up against the stucco on the columns and
caulked. Not surprisingly, wood deterioration was typically
concentrated at walkway curbs and columns (Figure 4). Sealant is not
effective at this location because the joint is of the wrong
configuration to accommodate thermal movement of the flashing.
• The walkway curbs were constructed of waferboard, and
waferboard was used as walkway column and facia sheathing.
The Canadian Wood Council (1990) defines waferboard as a
structural panel made from thin, short poplar wafers that are bonded
together with a waterproof phenolic adhesive, usually arranged randomly
throughout the panel [2]. The product conforms to CSA Standard
CAN3-0437.0, "Waferboard and Strandboard" [3]. In our opinion, the
random orientation of the wood fibres in waferboard allows water to be
drawn into the material; capillary action draws water along the long
direction of the fibres into the core of the sheet. Because water

penetrates into the sheet, significant amounts of water can be retained and the drying process is slow.

FIG. 4--Wood deterioration is often concentrated at the metal flashing tie-in to columns.

Remedial work conducted from 1994 to 1995 included:

• All deteriorated wood members were removed and replaced. However, if a single wood member had less than 10% material loss, the deteriorated wood was removed down to sound wood, and the surface was treated with copper napthenate to deter fungal growth. Adjacent wood surfaces that were still sound were also treated with copper napthenate.
    • Plywood, not waferboard, was used to reconstruct walkway curbs and for walkway facia and column sheathing.
    • Proper slope and drainage are critical to eliminating water ingress. The slope on the walkways was corrected to promote drainage to the scupper drains and to ensure that water did not enter the building. Slope was achieved by installing tapered shims over the existing plywood and laying new plywood over the shims. An average grade of 3% and a minimum grade of 2% was attained.
    • New bitumen-modified polyurethane waterproofing membrane was applied over the walkway decks. The membrane was brought up and over the curbs on the outside perimeter of the walkways and extended down the entire facia of the walkways. It is acceptable to install a waterproof membrane on the exterior face of the walkway facias because both sides of the facia are at the same temperature and relative humidity. By utilizing a continuous waterproof membrane along the full length of the walkway curbs, it does not matter if the joints in the metal cap flashings leak. The metal cap flashings are only required to keep the sun off the membrane. A "trowel-on" grade of membrane was selected for this application because it is easy to apply over the difficult configuration. A polyester reinforcement was used in conjunction with the membrane to ensure that the membrane could withstand some substrate movement.
    The column bases were coated all around in membrane up to a height of approximately 300 mm. The membrane is 120 dry mils and

200 dry mils thick in the field and at deck seams, respectively. Seams
and upturns were reinforced with fabric. The manufacturer's recommended
minimum membrane thickness for a plywood substrate is 60 wet mils in the
field and 120 wet mils at seams.
  • New copper scupper drains were installed at the outside edge of
the walkways at every bay (more drains then had originally been
present). These drains were manufactured with flanges to give the
waterproofing membrane sufficient surface to bond to. The drains were
also staggered so that the upper drains do not drip onto the lower
drains and splash water back onto the walkways. The original scupper
drains did not have flanges to allow a proper tie-in to the
waterproofing membrane.
  • All metal cap flashings on the walkway curbs were replaced.
The new flashings were constructed with standing seam joints and 75 mm
upturns at the ends which abutted the columns. These upturns were
tucked behind the sheathing membrane and stucco on columns or walls
(Figure 5). The upturns are intended to protect the junction between
the curb and the column, which is a particularly vulnerable location for
water entry. The flashings were installed with a 5% slope toward the
walkways. Good slope on the flashings reduces the potential for water
to penetrate the flashing joints, and stops water from draining onto the
face of the building and causing staining.
  • Epoxy aggregate was used as the walking surface of the
walkways, replacing the original exposed aggregate concrete topping.
Epoxy aggregate is more permeable than concrete topping, thus, allowing
more water to drain through rather than pond on the surface. It also

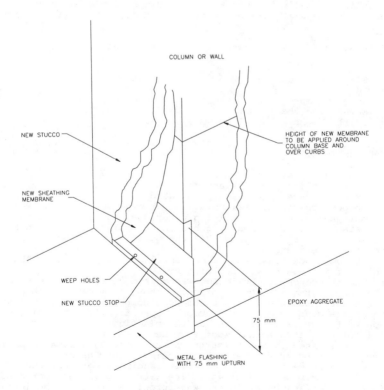

FIG. 5--Walkway curb and column or wall
       intersection.

can be applied more thinly than concrete topping, therefore, allowing
the installation of a properly sloped plywood deck on the walkways.
   • Drip flashings were installed through the stucco at each floor
level. The flashings will direct water that is draining down the face
of the sheathing membrane back to the exterior. Water has less
opportunity to penetrate into the structure if it is removed from behind
the stucco at each floor level than if it drains down behind the stucco
for the full height of the building.
   • Spun-bonded polyolefin sheathing membrane, with taped seams,
was used instead of organic building paper at walkway facias and
columns. It is believed that inorganic sheathing membrane will not
deteriorate as rapidly with exposure to moisture. Care was taken to
ensure all joints were properly lapped to shed water.
   • Stucco was re-applied to walkway facias and columns. Care was
taken to ensure the stucco thickness was at least 22 mm, as required by
City of Vancouver Building Bylaws. Weep holes of 6 mm diameter at
300 mm on centre were drilled in stucco stops to allow water that does
penetrate the stop to drain out (Figure 5).
   • All fasteners through the stucco (e.g., walkway railing
fasteners) were sealed. This included injection of caulking into pilot
holes before the insertion of fasteners. Polyurethane caulking was used
for this purpose.

Southwest Stairwell Repair

   During performance of the remedial work described in *Northeast and
South Building Walkway Repairs*, extensive wood deterioration was
discovered in the walls (Figure 6) and landings of the southwest
stairwell. The majority of the stairwell had to be rebuilt from 1994 to
1995.

   Both sides of the stairwell walls were of the following
construction:

   • Elastomeric paint;
   • Stucco;
   • Asphalt impregnated organic building paper;
   • Waferboard sheathing;
   • Thirty-eight mm by 89 mm wood studs.

   The following items most likely contributed to the damage at the
southwest stairwell:

   • The stucco was observed to have cracked significantly before
1991 (prior to application of elastomeric paint). It is probable that
water entered at these cracks and penetrated the building paper and wet
the wood components of the stairwell. In our experience, light-weight,
asphalt-impregnated, organic building paper does not provide long-term
water resistance when continually subjected to moisture. During the
remedial work, it was determined that the building paper was
significantly deteriorated.
   • At some locations, the stucco thickness was less than that
required by City of Vancouver Building Bylaws.
   • The stucco on all buildings was coated in elastomeric paint in
1992. The application of such a paint, without eliminating other
avenues for water to enter and wet the wood components of the building,
may have accelerated wood deterioration. Specifically, the paint will
have reduced the overall permeance of the cladding, reducing the
potential for the wet internal wood components to dry.
   • As discussed in *Northeast and South Building Walkway Repairs*,
water penetration occurred where the flashings abut the stucco.
   • No drains were provided at stair landings, nor were the
landings sloped to promote drainage. The lack of drainage increased the
significance of deficiencies in the waterproof membrane on the landings.

FIG. 6--Typical stairwell wood
deterioration.

• The stair stringers were built tight to the walls of the
stairwell. Water may have penetrated behind the stucco at the junction
between the stringers and the walls. The rot patterns confirmed this
source of water ingress (Figure 7).
• The base of the stairwell is supported on a concrete curb that
was level with the surrounding courtyard concrete topping, thus allowing
the sill plates of the stairwell to be easily wetted. The curb should
have been higher to ensure the wood components were well above the water
drainage surface (200 mm recommended).
• The original bitumen-modified polyurethane waterproofing
membrane on stair landings was poorly bonded. The membrane only
extended up the sides of the landing approximately 50 mm. The generally
accepted building practice is 200 mm.
• The pattern of deteriorated wood exposed by removal of the
stucco clearly indicated that water was not penetrating the roof or roof
flashings (Figure 6).

Remedial work conducted from 1994 to 1995 included:

• All the stucco was stripped from the stairwell. Complete
removal of the stucco allowed for identification of all areas of
deterioration. Also, because a comprehensive rebuild of the stairwell
was required, it was not cost-effective to save select areas of stucco.

FIG. 7--Wood deterioration at stair
stringer.

• The concrete curb supporting the walls of the stairwell was
raised so that the top of the curb is 100 mm above the concrete topping
in the courtyard (200 mm above the membrane surface). This ensures that
ponded water in the courtyard does not wet the sill plates of the
stairwell.
• All the landings on the stairs were sloped at 3% to promote
drainage. This was a difficult task because the building code does not
allow a variance in the rise and run of stairs.
• New bitumen-modified polyurethane waterproofing membrane was
applied on all stair landings and down the full length of the facia
below the landing. It was also applied on the top of all stair landing
guards to provide extra waterproofing protection under the metal cap
flashings.
• As described in *Northeast and South Building Walkway Repairs*,
all curb metal cap flashings had standing seam joints and 75 mm upturns
at their ends. These upturns were tucked behind the sheathing membrane
and stucco on walls.
• The stairs were redesigned so that the stringers were set off
of the stucco-clad walls, allowing water to drain freely between the
stringers and the walls. Originally the stringers were built tight
against the wall and intercepted water that was running down the face of
the wall. Metal stringers were required to facilitate this change.
• As described in *Northeast and South Building Walkway Repairs*,
spun-bonded olefin sheathing membrane, with taped seams, was used

instead of building paper. Stucco was applied in accordance with City
of Vancouver Building Bylaws, and weep holes were drilled into stucco
stops.

Repair to Balconies

     Because brown staining was observed, which is indicative of wet
wood, and because of leakage at ground-level suites, remedial work
proceeded at several balconies in 1994. Upon removal of the metal cap
flashings on balcony guards, adjacent stucco, and the vinyl
waterproofing membrane on the balcony deck, severe wood deterioration
was discovered in the balcony guard, deck, joists, beams, and columns
(Figure 8). Remedial work included complete reconstruction of six
balconies and portions of exterior walls adjacent to these balconies.
     The original construction of the exterior walls consisted of:

  • Elastomeric paint;
  • Stucco;
  • Asphalt-impregnated organic building paper;
  • Waferboard sheathing;
  • Thirty-eight mm by 89 mm wood studs, infilled with fibreglass
batt insulation;
  • Six mil polyethylene vapour barrier;
  • Interior drywall.

FIG. 8--Typical wood deterioration at
balconies.

     The following items contributed to the damage at the balconies and
exterior walls:

     • The balconies were waterproofed with a 40-mil vinyl membrane
that was fully adhered to the plywood substrate. The vinyl membrane
installation was not deficient except for poor bond of the vinyl to
flangeless scupper drains (Figure 9). Water leakage behind the membrane
at the scupper drains contributed to deterioration of the wood.

FIG. 9--The vinyl membrane was not well bonded to flangeless
balcony scupper drains.

• Metal cap flashings are installed on the top of balcony guards.
As discussed in *Northeast and South Building Walkway Repairs*, a
significant amount of water had penetrated into the wood structure at
the junction between the metal cap flashings and the stucco. The top
surface of the cap flashings were not sloped to promote drainage from
the junction with the stucco. Water ingress at this location resulted
in wood deterioration down the full length of the wall and horizontally
a distance of approximately 3 m. The deterioration also rose vertically
approximately 0.9 m to 1.2 m above the highest point of water entry.
The disbursement of the deterioration from the point of water entry may
be indicative of the distance water is drawn through the waferboard by
capillary action.

The remedial repairs conducted to the balconies were similar to
those conducted on the northeast and south building walkways. The
following requirements were emphasized during the repair:

• All new sheathing was plywood not waferboard.
• The balconies were well sloped (3% average) to the drains. The
new scupper drains were fabricated with 75 mm flanges to allow proper
tie-in of the membrane.

• The new vinyl membrane was extended up the building walls a
minimum of 200 mm, and the new polyolefin sheathing membrane was lapped
over the vinyl membrane a minimum of 100 mm.
• The tops and outside faces of the perimeter guards were coated
in a trowel-on grade, bitumen-modified polyurethane membrane that was
fully reinforced. The intent of the membrane is to protect the wood
from any water that penetrates the metal cap flashings or stucco at
these prone locations.

CONCLUSIONS

The design intent of the buildings was that all elements exposed to rain had to be waterproof. Unfortunately, poor quality construction and detailing allowed water ingress through numerous sources. In our opinion, buildings designed for a wet climate should utilize roofs and overhangs to reduce the amount of rain striking exterior walls and walkways. If an open-style building is to be constructed, the waterproofing details must be very carefully designed and constructed to ensure water ingress does not occur.

Water penetration through the building envelope can result in significant deterioration of wood-frame structures. In this case study, approximately $300 000 worth of remedial work was conducted from 1994 to 1995. It is estimated that an additional $250 000 to $400 000 worth of remedial work remains to be completed.

The reasons for the extensive wood deterioration can be summarized as follows:

• The waterproofing membrane application on walkways and in planters was of poor quality.

• The extent of the deterioration may have been less had plywood sheathing been used instead of waferboard. Regardless of the care taken, some water will always penetrate the stucco and building paper cladding system resulting in wetting of the sheathing. The sheathing should be able to dry out quickly enough so that the environment is not conducive to fungal growth.

• Detailing at the termination of metal cap flashings on walkway curbs, stairwell guards, and balcony guards was improper. Extensive water ingress occurred at these locations. Caulking of the joint between flashings and stucco is not an acceptable practice because thermal movement of the flashing will result in failure of the caulking. Also, the joint configuration is not correct for a caulking application.

• Light-weight, asphalt-impregnated, organic building paper is not acceptable for application behind stucco because it deteriorates with long-term exposure to moisture.

• The seal of the vinyl membrane to scupper drains on balconies was poor. All scupper drains must have proper flanges for adhesion of the membrane.

• The stucco application was inferior. Stucco must be applied to the correct thickness and must be properly cured.

• Coating of the stucco in elastomeric paint, without eliminating other avenues for water to enter and wet the wood components of the building, may have accelerated wood deterioration.

• The inadequate drainage slope on walkways and balconies increased the severity of deficiencies in the waterproofing membranes. Proper drainage is essential to long-term performance.

REFERENCES

[1]   Canadian Commission on Building and Fire Codes, 1995, National Building Code of Canada, National Research Council of Canada, Ottawa, Ontario, Canada.

[2]   Canadian Wood Council, 1990, Wood Design Manual, Ottawa, Ontario, Canada, pp. 16.

[3]   Canadian Standards Association, CAN3-0437.0, "Waferboard and Strandboard", Rexdale, Ontario, Canada.

Dean A. Rutila[1]

INVESTIGATION AND REPAIR OF LEAKAGE PROBLEMS IN RECENTLY CONSTRUCTED CURTAIN WALLS

REFERENCE: Rutila, D. A., **"Investigation and Repair of Leakage Problems in Recently Constructed Curtain Walls,"** Water Leakage Through Building Facades, ASTM STP 1314, R. J. Kudder and J. L. Erdly, Eds., American Society for Testing and Materials, 1998.

ABSTRACT: Waterproofing problems with recently constructed curtain walls illustrate that some, well understood, principles of waterproofing continue to be violated during wall construction. The author finds that divided or fragmented responsibility for the design often leads to the lack of understanding of the waterproofing requirements. New problems are being invented/discovered during the design and construction of these curtain wall systems due to the lack of understanding of the design requirements. Design specifications, workmanship, and the management of construction all contribute to recent problems. This paper presents the author's experience investigating and repairing waterproofing problems in newly constructed curtain walls. The author presents examples of design, workmanship and construction management problems that contribute curtain wall leakage problems, and presents a summary of the repair design and implementation.

Designers must understand the difference between barrier (surface sealed) curtain wall systems and cavity wall systems. The design must reflect the selected concept(s) consistently through the details, and it must anticipate a reasonable level of workmanship. Contractors and construction managers contribute to waterproofing problems in modern curtain walls through their lack of understanding of the design principles and, therefore, their lack of knowledge of what is important to the waterproofing performance. When the managers and oversight professionals fail to understand the construction, their direction or lack of direction to the workers contribute to problems.

KEYWORDS: Curtain wall, leakage, design, construction, management, mock-up, testing.

As a building envelope consultant and structural engineer, the author finds the lessons of design responsibility for curtain wall waterproofing and

---

[1] Associate, Simpson Gumpertz & Heger Inc., Consulting Engineers, 297 Broadway, Arlington, Massachusetts 02172, U.S.A.

building structures related. Because of the intense public and professional interest in structural collapses, the causes of these collapses are carefully evaluated and debated. One thread /that runs through the review of collapses is the way in which problems are created by fragmented or divided responsibility for the design, and the resulting lack of understanding of the design by the design and construction professionals [1 and 2]. This lack of design understanding can, as the examples illustrate, be applied to curtain wall leakage.

CENTRAL FLORIDA COURTHOUSE

A ten-story courthouse had leakage problems that began before it was completed, but the owner, design professionals and contractors were unable to agree on causes or resolve the problems. The building has a reinforced concrete frame with concrete masonry in-filling the frame at exterior walls. Low, stepped roofs on three-story wings butt into the ten-story center tower (Photo 1). Walls are clad with brick veneer supported on steel angles at each story (Fig. 1). Aluminum framed casement windows with insulating glass are set into "punched" openings in the wall cladding. The roof was originally covered with clay roofing tiles.

The design team consisted of regional firms with some experience with building envelopes of the type built. The general contractor was a large, nationwide firm with many significant projects of greater complexity and cost within its experience. The owner retained a clerk-of-the-works who was experienced in that role, although he was unknowledgeable about the waterproofing requirements of the curtain wall system used on this building. The owner appeared willing and able to fund a project consistent with its goals.

Photo 1 -- Central Florida Courthouse, With a Ten-Story Tower and Three-Story Wings

Description of the Problems

During the first year after construction, leakage continued and was widespread, mildew began to grow behind vinyl wall paper on exterior walls, and ceiling tiles sagged and collapsed. In general, mildew growth did not initially appear to be related to leakage locations, except below expansion joints separating the tower from low roofs. The Owner reported leakage that was related to the curtain wall at the following locations:

• Through the ceiling into the first and second floors below rising, set-back walls on stories above. This leakage recurred in fixed locations around the building. Occupants associated it with heavy wind driven rain falls.

• Through the ceiling into the first, second, and third floors below the expansion joints and roof flashing that join the rising tower with low roof areas. This leakage occurred along the roof-to-wall intersection, and traveled down through interior expansion joints from story to story. Occupants considered this leakage the most common, occurring with most rainfall.

• Below the rising dormer walls that penetrate the high roof. The brick clad dormers house elevator shafts and equipment, and provide for air supply and exhaust penetrations.

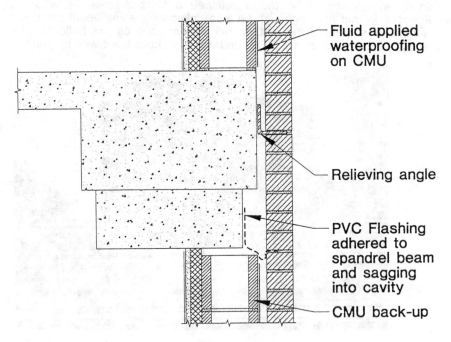

Fig. 1 -- Typical exterior wall construction at Central Florida Courthouse

The owner identified mildew growth through pink, orange, and black stains showing through the vinyl wall paper that covered most interior wall surfaces. Stains first occurred in areas away from reported leakage near the ceiling at the first floor perimeter, at piers between windows; this exterior wall is recessed 10 feet from the roof eave, below a canopy at the perimeter of the first level roof. Later, mildew growth also occurred below areas of masonry and window leakage.

Other problems identified by the owner included extensive cracking of the brick veneer.

In an effort to identify the causes of the leakage and mildew problems, and to determine responsibility, the owner's attorney assembled a team of engineers with specialties in project management, litigation support, building envelope design, construction and investigation, and HVAC systems. In general, this paper presents the work of the author's firm, and omits descriptions of the work of others, except where their results are needed to understand curtain wall issues.

Contract Documents

The contract documents were prepared with an architect as lead designer with sub-consultants for the structure, site, mechanical, and electrical systems. The form of the construction contract was based on a standard lump sum contract. Most of the design of components related to the building envelope was prescriptive, giving specific details, materials, and procedures to be followed, but many key waterproofing instructions were given as performance requirements. Some structural components related to the envelope were performance in nature, requiring separate contractor design.

The drawings showed several important details that were related to the author's findings on leakage:

• The typical window details showed metal sill flashing formed to provide through-veneer flashing below exposed brick sills. Jamb details show brick veneer cladding over concrete and concrete masonry back-up with wood framing filling the rough masonry opening to the window frame; no waterproofing or dampproofing is shown on the back-up materials to protect against water that penetrates the brick veneer.

• Details for the windows at low roofs show the typical sill flashing one course above roofing flashing, with the roofing let into a metal reglet embedded in the brick veneer. Most of these windows are spaced about 400 mm apart (16 in.), creating a continuous through-wall flashing above the roof line.

• The window flashing detail above the expansion joint is similar to other windows close to low roofs. This detail is also the detail for the more general condition along the expansion joint away from windows. Absent are details at roof-to-rising wall conditions away from windows; this condition is rare at low building areas, but is the most common condition were the low roofs meet the rising tower and at the tower roof dormers.

The roofing and expansion joint flashing along the tower terminated at a surface mounted detail on the brick.

Absent from the drawings were details showing flashing at shelf angles mounted at each floor to support the brick; structural drawings detail the angles with a gap (soft joint) below the angles but the brick is shown schematically in dashed outline. Details at spandrel beams also show a gap between the bottom of the beams and the top of the concrete masonry in-fill/back-up, with the gap closed with sealant and backer rod. The drawings also show details related to the structural support of the masonry, including continuous shelf angles bolted to the spandrel beams using adjustable inserts, continuous bent plates supporting brick over 20 ft openings, and brick hung from the bottom of the horizontal leg of lintel angles and bent plates.

As a result of the limited curtain wall waterproofing information shown on the drawings, the curtain wall waterproofing design relies heavily on a few key specification requirements. The specifications require dampproofing on the back-up material, but do not describe the full range of back-up materials on the building including concrete, concrete masonry, and wood. The specifications require metal flashing at bottoms of walls and at supports. Flashing at windows is required to be watertight and is to be coordinated with the air and vapor seals. The specifications also described the type and spacing of anchors for various back-up conditions, including an addendum adding cast-in-place anchors at beams and columns.

Submittal Documents, Shop Drawings, and Contractor Changes

In general, the files of submitted documents represent a common limited level of effort by the contractor, and as such were incomplete on many building envelope items. A few shop and erection drawings showed flashing components, but without coordination between trades. The flashing details specified but not drawn by the architect were not developed as erection details or questioned by the contractor. The files were full of items for the structure, major architectural envelope systems such as roofing, window, and masonry materials, architectural finish items, and mechanical and electrical components, but few details of the implementation and interpretation of the curtain wall design. Noteworthy was the shop and erection drawing for the brick support angles which were faithful to the design, although incomplete regarding anchorage and final dimensions.

A design proposed by the contractor changed the copper flashing in the masonry system to polyvinyl chloride. The record on this change was never resolved to the author's satisfaction, but the change may have facilitated agreement between the contractor and designer on the scope of through-wall flashing specified for the masonry. The agreement to change flashing materials did not include any changes to reflect the installation difference between a flexible sheet membrane and the much stiffer sheet metal material.

One detail that was developed by the contractor during the construction was in response to the contractor's difficulty in sealing the joint at the bottom of spandrel beams. The contractor proposed to seal the gap with polyvinyl chloride sheet membrane adhered to the beam and concrete masonry below the beam. This design change was never adopted.

Construction

The construction of the building envelope was generally deficient, with all components having substantial defects, and with general coordination problems. As background, but not directly related to leakage, the author found the following defects:

- the concrete masonry back-up wall had widespread missing reinforcing, it was unreinforced, it was ungrouted where reinforced, and it was not anchored to the structure;

- the concrete masonry back-up was sporadically dampproofed. Areas of masonry near windows were often coated while areas a few feet away were not. The concrete masonry returns at window openings were not coated;

- the shelf angles had adjustable inserts in the concrete beams and field cut oversized holes that did not engage the bolts in bearing or otherwise provide reliable support;

- rolled angles with flexible strap hangers were substituted for the designed and much stiffer hung angles over large openings, allowing large rotations of the angles and supporting brick;

- no horizontal gaps (soft joints) were installed in the brick below shelf angles, but a few joints were painted on the brick with sealant;

- windows were installed with thick wood shims, not continuous blocking which is necessary to receive dampproofing, and the powder driven fasteners spalled the concrete masonry around the openings;

- the roofing underlayment had holes in it, the roof deck was damaged by construction abuse and had manufacturing defects, and the gutter at the roof perimeter leaked.

Investigation Results

Review of the design, the owner's complaints, and the documents describing possible causes of the building leakage lead us to a general investigation of the building waterproofing system, including masonry, roofing and window systems. We used the methods described by Cole [3] to water test wall and window systems, using tests with applied air pressure and without. Workers were directed to cut openings through exterior components to view concealed conditions, revealing the following defects in the construction that were related to curtain wall leakage:

- Flashing at window sills was laid flat below the windows, not panned up at the inboard leg nor at jambs. Window leakage was not identified by the owner in his comments to us, but the stains at widows, the locations of leaks, and the condition of the flashing suggested windows as a possible source that should be investigated. Our tests showed rapid leakage that was readily absorbed into the concrete masonry before leaking behind finishes to the floor. Two years after our investigation, as remedial work was being readied, extensive mildew growth began to form at window sill areas.

- Flashing, installed at the base of walls with a continuous arrangement of windows and piers, was sagging into the cavity due to mortar droppings, creating a gutter-like condition that directed water to unsealed corners and joints in the flashing (Fig. 2). Leakage through unsealed joints in the flashing corresponded to the locations of recurrent leakage into first and second floor areas below these rising walls.

- Through-wall flashing was missing at the base of tower walls along the expansion joints, at rising dormers, and at similar details with low roofs. As described above, the design detail for the flashing along the expansion joint was at the non-typical condition of a window near the joint. This detailed showed through-wall flashing a few courses above the expansion joint, a detail that could allow some leakage, but much less than if no flashing exists. Roof flashing that was fastened to the surface of the brick veneer provided no protection to the interior for water infiltrating the veneer cavity.

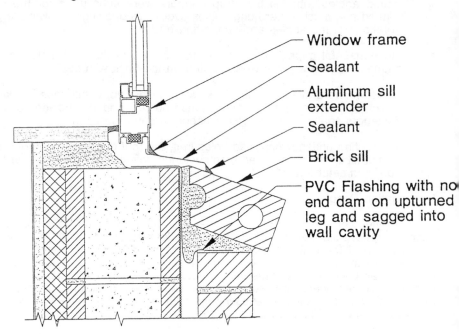

Window frame

Sealant

Aluminum sill extender

Sealant

Brick sill

PVC Flashing with no end dam on upturned leg and sagged into wall cavity

Fig. 2 -- As-built window flashing at Central Florida Courthouse

Extensive cracking of the masonry veneer increased the amount of leakage. Cracking was caused by defects in the attachment and positioning of support angles, the lack of soft joints below angles and the lack of vertical joints in the brick, necessary to allow differential movement between brick expansion and concrete frame shortening (creep), and the lack of veneer anchors.

Flashing was also missing at support angles for the brick veneer (Fig. 1), although no water leakage to the interior was directly caused by this lack of flashing. The long-term durability of the non-galvanized bolts, nuts and angles (most were hot dip galvanized) was questionable. Flashing was installed several courses below the angle, in the position of the sheet membrane air seal proposed but not accepted as a change for the sealant joint between the top of block and bottom of spandrel beam; the author remains uncertain of the reasons for the decision to install the flashing in this position, but as installed it provided no protection because it sagged into the cavity, pulled off the back-up, and had unsealed joints and corner laps.

Repair Program

Most of the widespread wall waterproofing problems, taken individually could be addressed with spot repairs. The author's firm prepared design concept documents for the repair of the building before the results of the engineering review of the air conditioning system and the widespread scope of the reinforcing problems of the concrete masonry back-up were known. In general, the preliminary repair concept included flashing and masonry joints installed where missing and defective, with anchors and supports repaired. The owner was concerned about the appearance of the building with some aesthetic loss in exchange for saving the cost of re-cladding.

The combination of the needed inspection of all areas of concrete masonry back-up, the missing dampproofing in the wall cavity, and the need for a vapor retarder to resist the central Florida humidity led us to the conclusion that the brick veneer should be completely stripped and re-constructed. The reconstruction included some upgrades (items that the owner did not buy the first time) including lead coated copper flashing and a combined vapor retarder/ waterproofing barrier on the back-up (Fig. 3). The need for the widespread repair was demonstrated with the development of mildew throughout the building between the time of the author's initial investigation, when the building was about one-year old, to the time when the preliminary design was completed two years later.

Evaluation of the Causes of Leakage

The designer failed to present a clear description of the waterproofing system, instead relying on individual specification items which required experience to interpret. The design showed a non-standard detail of the expansion joint along the tower, but relied on the specification for the general case. The drawings showed no details for corners or transitions in flashing and no details at shelf angles supporting the brick, again relying on the specification. The designer approved the change from metal flashing, which could span a cavity with some dropping of mortar, to polyvinyl chloride which could not, without comment on the significance of the change.

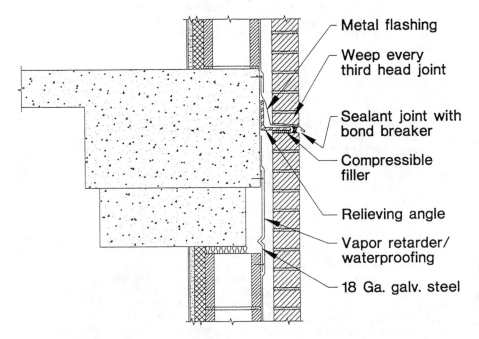

Fig. 3 -- Typical repair detail at Central Florida Courthouse

The sub-contractors did not have a clear understanding of the water-proofing system, as shown by the missing through-wall flashing at roofs and relieving angles, by the modification of the air seal at the top of walls, and by the window sill flashing installation. The sub-contractors did not have a clear understanding of the waterproofing materials being used, as shown by the sagging flashing caused by mortar dropping on the unsupported sheet system.

The construction management, provided by the general contractor failed to coordinated the activities of the several subcontractors. Each subcontractor provided their own access scaffolding. The mason permitted the waterproofing contractor to use staging when convenient, but other wise the waterproofing contractor leaned out windows to waterproof back-up masonry that could be reached and skipped areas unreachable by this method.

As is common, the general contractor divided the responsibility for the waterproofing system among subcontractors representing different trades. Masons installed concrete masonry back-up, brick and polyvinyl chloride flashing. A waterproofing contractor installed the dampproofing on the back-up wall. Carpenters installed the window anchorage bucks. A window erection contractor installed the aluminum windows. Roofers installed metal flashing at roof-to-curtain wall intersections. However, these subcontractors worked independently with little or no coordination of the waterproofing system. As a result, there was virtually no continuity of one waterproofing element to the next.

There was no mock-up or sample of a typical wall area constructed to allow the designer, contractor, and subcontractors to review the design intent, including the waterproofing concept of the wall system. Such a mock-up is a practical method of bringing the fragmented "design" provided by each contractor and subcontractor together. It allows missing submittal items to be identified and resolved, and it establishes general understanding of the design concepts. This understanding was never developed by the architect's on-site personnel, the owner's clerk, and the general contractor's supervisory staff. None of those present saw, or saw the significance of the defective work as it progressed.

CENTRAL OHIO COURTHOUSE

This twenty-seven-story building is clad with exposed aggregate, precast concrete panels and a one and two-story tall aluminum curtain wall window system. The building has low, six-story tall areas, and several facade setbacks with intermediate height roofs. Windows are surrounded by precast panels, rather than punched through the panels.

The designer is a nationally known designer of high-rise office buildings. The building was built using a joint-venture construction manager with multiple prime contractors. The building structure and envelope were let to one prime contractor to provide coordination and responsibility for the performance of the system. The curtain wall system was specified with performance requirements for joint sealants, precast concrete, aluminum framed windows, and louvers and grilles. The prime contractor was required to provide engineering design of the precast panels and their attachment to the structure, and engineering design of the aluminum framed window system. Sealant performance was specified in terms of leak free performance. A full scale mock-up was specified to verify the contractor's design and execution, including structural performance, water resistance, and air infiltration resistance.

Description of Problems

Leakage occurred through the curtain wall from the time of occupancy and continuing for over a year. Sealant repairs were performed under warranty by a subcontractor but provided no resolution.

The owner identified widespread leakage based on complaints by office workers and stains on the interior frames of many windows. The owner offered a general description of leakage events as occurring during frequent spring and summer rain storms. The owner's main complaints centered on certain high profile windows in public lobbies that had highly visible stains; however, these stains were minor compared to more typical stains in offices.

Contact Documents

The design documents use performance requirements for most elements of the curtain wall system, showing general selection of materials, arrangement of components and aesthetic requirements on drawings and specifying structural and weather resistant performance.

Drawings show two color precast concrete panels covering columns and spandrel areas. Most concrete panels are rectangular, 150 mm (6 in.) thick, 600 to 900 mm (24 to 36 in.) wide, and one to two stories tall at columns and one to three windows wide at spandrel beams. Panels make returns at a few recessed windows, louvers and grilles, at parapets, and some building corners. Parapet coping panels are shown with membrane flashing beneath them.

Windows are shown as a one and two-story high aluminum curtain wall system that is mounted to the interior face of the precast concrete panels. Windows are shown approximately flush with the exterior surface of panels, with perimeter sealant joints between concrete panels and window frames. Concrete panels provide flat sills below windows, without sill flashing.

Louvers are set behind aluminum grilles that have extruded shapes similar to windows. Some louver details typically show sill flashing pans, but flashing corners are neither detailed nor described. Watertight flashing is specified for louvers. Some openings have aluminum grilles matching those at louvers, but with "blank off plates"; grilles are shown on drawings, but are not described in the specifications.

Performance requirements in the specification give structural and waterproofing design responsibility for precast concrete panels, windows, and louvers to the respective manufacturers. Precast panels are to have exposed granite aggregate, in two different colors and are to be free of cracks larger than 0.25 mm (0.01 in). Sealant joints, including those between panels and at window perimeters, are required to be leak free for five years and are to be guaranteed jointly by the sealant manufacturer and installer.

Submittal Documents and Shop Drawings

Submittal correspondence includes some exchanges on the exposed aggregate finish of the concrete panels, including the designer's request to keep a steel formed finish on corner chamfers but off panel edges. The correspondence never resolves the issue with agreement between the designer and contractor. The discussions do not include any technical discussions of the manufacturing process of applying a concrete cure retarder to the forms to allow the removal of paste from the face of the panels after the panels gained sufficient strength to have forms striped and panels lifted and turned.

Shop drawings for panels show the details of steel reinforcing, anchors, and panel dimensions, but do not describe the method of placing concrete or cure retarder at panels with returns at recessed window, louvers, parapets and corners. The location of cold joints at these corners is not shown.

Window submittals show the sizes, shapes and arrangement of windows, and notes describe in ambiguous terms the sealing of corners and the erection of the system. The field work procedures are neither described nor shown.

Louver shop drawings show the arrangement of the louvers and show a sill cross section of the flashing. The louvers and grilles are provided by a different contractor than the one providing windows. Drawings of grilles at louvers were submitted, but no drawings of grilles with blank off plates were submitted.

Mock-up Testing

After approval of window, precast concrete panels, and sealant for mock-up testing, a two-story typical area was constructed at a testing facility. The mock-up included a typical two-story window, two one-story windows, surrounding precast concrete, and sealant between these elements. The precast concrete panels included a plan offset in the vertical face of the building, including a vertical corner panel that is L-shaped in plan. Workers from the contractors who would later perform the work on the building erected the panels and windows, and sealed the joints. The mock-up was tested for air and water leakage and structural performance.

The mock-up leaked during all five static and one dynamic water tests. Initial tests identified leakage through cracks in the precast concrete, through glazing pocket joint sealant, and through perimeter sealant joints. These problems were "repaired" with additional application of sealant and the mock-up re-tested. Leakage persisted and was finally determined by the designer to be "not leakage" because of the limited quantity. The test report and the author's interviews failed to satisfactorily resolve the nature of the accepted leakage beyond "drops of water on the inside face of the frame. The mock-up was accepted by the designer with the repeated comment to avoid exposed aggregate at sealant joints.

This mock-up was witnessed by representatives of all members of the project team including the designer, construction manager, envelope prime contractor and envelope sub-contractors. The report was distributed to senior individuals in all organizations, but was greeted with shock by the owner when found after the author's investigation.

Construction

The curtain wall was built in general conformance to the design, including submittal documents, shop and erection drawings, and mock-up test. The precast panels and windows were erected without scaffolding the building. The window installer used a cantilevered erection stage suspend through window openings to hoist fully assembled two-story curtain wall units out through an opening for erection, with all connections performed from the interior. The sealant contractor used two-point cable suspended scaffolding (swing staging) for access during joint sealing. Sealants were installed from early spring through late fall of one year. The sealant installers report that they (two workers) used the staging for the full, typical day, with no representatives from the design or construction team monitoring their work, except to review their progress against the schedule. These workers further report that work proceeded in "marginal" weather, but not when it was precipitating.

Louvers with grilles were installed with aluminum sill flashing that had upturned legs to form pans. Corners of the pans were sealed with sealant. The exterior of the pan stopped at the sill perimeter sealant joint, and the sealant was installed with no weep holes to allow drainage off the pans. The grilles with blank-off plates were installed without sill flashing. The same installers installed the windows and louvers, even though the two tasks were contracted separately.

Many precast concrete panels with return legs at recessed openings had a crack at the corner of the vertical ashlar face and the return (Fig. 4); most of these cracks appear to be along cold joints caused by the two stage casting operation which was necessary to produce exposed aggregate concrete on two faces of L-shaped panels. The cold joints were necessary to allow the concrete cure retarder to be applied to horizontal form surfaces at right angles to each other. The design required this producer, given the producer's capabilities, to use a two-stage casting process, although the process was not described by the designer or contractor. Other cracks or cold joints were formed on flat panels at perimeters. These cracks are at cold joints between placement of a surface concrete containing more costly granite chips and back-up concrete using less expensive aggregate.

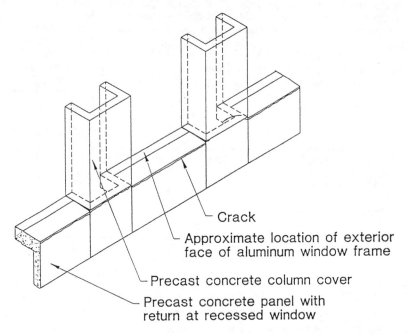

Crack

Approximate location of exterior face of aluminum window frame

Precast concrete column cover

Precast concrete panel with return at recessed window

Fig. 4 -- Precast concrete panel cracks at Central Ohio Courthouse

A separate prime contractor was responsible for interior finishes, including the installation of glass fiber insulation that has an interior foil liner that probably acts as a vapor retarder. This liner is a reinforced, aluminum surfaced, asphalt coated kraft paper that is fastened to the concrete panels with adhered "stick pins."

Investigation Results

Our investigation included occupant interviews, a survey of many areas of the building, and water testing those areas that represented the different conditions and leakage patterns found during the survey. Based on the survey and available offices, the author surveyed the exterior of the curtain wall. After the survey, we tested windows using test methods described by Cole [3], with and without an interior air pressure chamber. After testing, workers from the window subcontractor disassembled units for inspection. The testing demonstrated the following:

- Leakage occurred at sealant defects at the top horizontal mullion of one- and two-story aluminum curtain wall units (Fig. 5). The water flowed onto the top of the horizontal mullion, and followed a variety of paths to the interior. At some locations, the water traveled to the vertical joints at the window perimeter and flowed down to floors below. The interior, aluminum face on the insulation provides a significant barrier to leakage in many locations, diverting water from one floor to another. This aluminum facer obscured the pattern of leakage, acting like a flashing without a weep to the exterior. Interior stains showed past leakage had collected at most interior window stools, with highly varying intensity.

- More severe leakage dripped to the interior at the top of windows units below louvers and below grilles with blank-off plates. Louvers and grilles with blank-off plates occurred on the twenty seventh and seventh, mechanical equipment floors. Water tests showed that louver sill pans leaked as they filled and overtopped the inside upturned legs of the pans. Pan corners also leaked, but to a lesser degree. The perimeter sealant applied at grilles in front of the louvers prevented the pan from draining. Grilles with blank-off plates leaked through the perimeter sealants and through the panel "glazing" into the frames.

- Severe leakage occurred through cracks (Fig. 4) in precast concrete panels at the twenty sixth and twenty seventh floors. These panels have returns at deeply recessed window and louver openings. The water penetrating the cracks flows down joints between windows and concrete panels before being diverted to interior spaces at the windows at the upper floors (typically floors 22 through 26).

- Water running down joints between precast concrete panels bypassed surface termination details where low roofs meet the high-rise walls. The water entered the joints between panel through sealant defects at windows and away from windows.

- Small amounts of water leaked from intermediate, horizontal mullions when tested under negative interior pressure. On disassembly, the author found holes in the sealant used in the glazing pocket to seal frame corners. This leakage appeared to be the same leakage identified during the mock-up that was accepted by the designer, and it was the cause of the high profile leakage that had so concerned the owner.

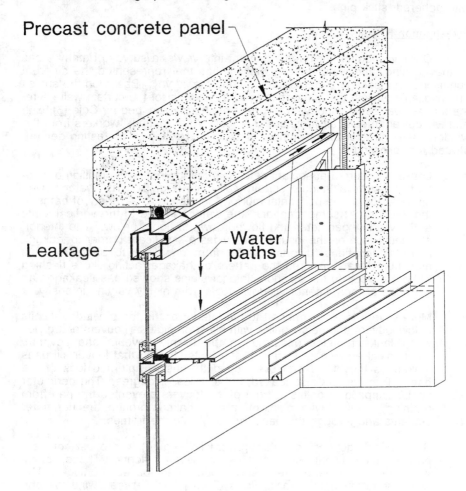

Precast concrete panel

Leakage

Water paths

Fig. 5 -- Window/concrete panel configuration at Central Ohio Courthouse

The survey of the building exterior showed the following:

• Widespread failure of the bond between the two-part polyurethane sealant and the painted aluminum window frame. Primer was generally found on the sealant, showing that the primer failed to bond to the paint. The cause of the primer failure remains unknown because of the difficulty in showing the presence or absence of surface contaminants after the joint failed and was exposed to leakage.

- Precast concrete panels at the twenty sixth and twenty seventh floors were cracked at corners of deep returns at window and louver openings.

Repair Program

The prime contractor responsible for the building envelope organized repairs under terms of its warranty. This work included the sealant contractor and manufacturer, the precast concrete contractor, and the louver contractor. In general, the prime contractor and individual contractors worked to meet the performance requirements established by the design documents and refined during the mock-up test.

The sealant contractor and the sealant manufacturer replaced the failed polyurethane sealant with a silicone sealant, and installed weep holes at louvers. The precast concrete panel contractor routed and sealed cracks, as had been done during the mock-up, and injected cracks with epoxy, based on his experience with the crack type. The louver contractor inspected and repaired flashing. Flashing was not installed at grilles with blank-off plates under the prime contractor's repairs since this work was not specified. Windows with leakage of the type accepted during the mock-up were not repaired. This work was monitored by the prime contractor to minimize the likely recurrence of additional warranty claims.

Evaluation of the Causes of Leakage

The project team was sophisticated and they adopted a contracting approach intended to provide good coordination between the building structure and curtain wall, avoiding problems with tolerances and assignment of tasks, and providing a waterproof building. The design intends for the concrete panels, windows, and sealant to provide a watertight barrier. In spite of the attempts to provide a watertight barrier, the approach failed, initially.

Most of the leakage occurred because the sealant did not meet the performance specified and precast concrete panels had cracks or separations at cold joints. It is clear that the leakage will recur when the sealant fails again, and if significant cracks or joints open again. The lack of weeps at the louvers, unsealed louver corners, and lack of a flashing design at grilles with blank-off plates are errors by the sealant contractor, louver contractor, and designer, respectively. The sealant contractor did not make the necessary adjustment from a completely surface sealed or barrier waterproofing design to the one location were the design employs a drainage cavity and requires sealant weeps. Similarly, the window/louver installer and designer failed to make adjustments in their work between surface sealed components (the largest part of the work) and areas requiring a drainage cavity (louvers and grilles).

Although the leakage problems are resolved, for now, several larger issues remain.

- The sealant leakage was both inevitable and premature. The author is uncertain what the owner's expectations are, but the design provides a building that will remain vulnerable to minor sealant defects and will require ongoing sealant repairs. At the same time, the five year warranty requirement in the contract and the results of the mock-up did not serve as an adequate notice to the sealant contractor, sealant manufacturer, and prime contractor that the sealant joints, as designed were vulnerable to defects and the water resistance of the wall system depended on the sealant performance. Had they understood the consequences of their actions, the author questions wether the sealants would have been, as they apparently were, installed when it was cold and moisture was likely present.

- The mock-up was competently conducted and completely successful in that it identified problems that later plagued the building. At the same time, the lessons of the mock-up went, apparently, unlearned by the project team making the mock-up less successful.

- The mock-up included only the most standard conditions and several key non-standard conditions leaked, such as the louvers and grilles, and the precast concrete at window returns.

By relying on performance specifications, the designer fragmented the design responsibility for the waterproofing. The precast contractor was effectively the waterproofing designer for the panels, the window manufacturer the designer for the window waterproofing, and the sealant installer and manufacture the designer for the sealant waterproofing. The prime contractor was to have overall responsibility and the construction manger had oversight duties, but neither was sufficiently involved to see the obvious gaps in the waterproofing system.

The project documents do not acknowledge the method of casting the precast concrete panels with deep returns were a two-stage casting process is likely. The documents suggest a lack of understanding on the application of a cure retarder in the discussion of the exposed aggregate on chamfers and corners. The author is uncertain if the designer was aware that cold joints were likely in the design. Similarly, the designer seemed to include louvers with grilles, not realizing that the prime contractor separated the work. The designer seemed to group grilles with louvers which had flashing and a drainage cavity and the contractor grouped them with the surface sealed window/wall system. The small, non-standard nature of the grilles allowed then to be forgotten during the shop drawings.

The lessons of the mock-up went unlearned, in part because they were poorly recorded and in part because the schedule was driving the project team's thinking during the mock-up. We found no record of the locations where sealant repairs were applied to windows during the test. We had to rely on memories of three-year old events to reconstruct the mock-up.

CONCLUSIONS

The author's experience with recent investigations into curtain wall leakage, two of which are summarized herein, shows that failures of the "checks and balances" of traditional forms of construction contracting contribute to leakage. Widespread and systematic leakage through curtain walls can be attributed to:

- failure of designers, contractors, mangers, and oversight professionals to understand the waterproofing design principles [4],

- failure in the communication of the waterproofing design through contract documents and contractor produced design and submittal documents,

- failure to verify the design through shop and erection drawings, testing and inspection, and

- fragmentation of responsibility that is not coordinated.

RECOMMENDATIONS

The design of a curtain wall system should include identified waterproofing concepts, identified waterproofing components, including barriers, flashing, cavities, and seals, and the design should describe the intended installation and integration of the components.

The contractor, through submittal of shop drawings and erection drawings, should confirm its understanding of the waterproofing concepts and the intended execution of the details.

All members of the curtain wall construction team should understand the waterproofing principles of the design, the proposed construction methods, the performance requirements of the system, and the significance of test results. Team members who lack understanding of any of these issues cannot adequately serve the interest of the owner, who is usually paying them, and cannot adequately serve their own business interests. An informed curtain wall construction team serves the owner and themselves by oversight of each other. While responsibility may or may not be identified and may be limited by contractual duties, all members are at risk when the system fails to perform, whether due to one or all of their errors.

The designer, contractor and mangers should understand the importance of performance testing and the need to schedule time for tests that fail; those who focus on the scheduled completion and acceptance of the testing without critically evaluating the conclusions of the testing agency and designer, are not providing an important project service.

The construction manager and designer should monitor the contractor's compliance with the submittal and testing requirements, and performance evaluation requirements for the work. It is inadequate for the manager and designer to point to the contractor's non-compliance with contract requirements after leakage problems occur.

The benefits of knowledgeable monitoring of the work by designers, construction managers, and inspectors retained by the owner should be considered. Contemporaneous identification of defects allow contractors and designers to resolve problems inexpensively compared to addressing the results after leakage occurs.

ACKNOWLEDGMENTS

The author thanks the principals and associates of Simpson Gumpertz & Heger Inc. for their support in writing this paper.

REFERENCES

[1]   Heger, F. J., "Public-Safety Issues in Collapse of L'Ambiance Plaza," *Journal of Performance of Constructed Facilities*, Vol. 5, No. 2, American Society of Civil Engineers, May 1991.

[2]   Gubbe, L. W., "Divided We Fall," *Civil Engineering*, November 1995.

[3]   Cole, G. G., and Schwartz, T. A., "Establishing Appropriate Field Test Pressures for Investigation of Leakage Through the Building Envelope," *Water In Exterior Building Walls, STP 1107*, American Society for Testing and Materials, 1992.

[4]   Ruggiero, S. S., and Myers, J. C., "Design and Construction of Water-tight Exterior Building Walls," *Water In Exterior Building Walls, STP 1107*, American Society for Testing and Materials, 1992.

Michael J. Scheffler[1] and Christopher J. Sass[1]

WATER LEAKAGE THROUGH SLOPED GLAZING AND SKYLIGHTS: CASE STUDIES

REFERENCE: Scheffler, M. J. and Sass, C. J., **"Water Leakage Through Sloped Glazing and Skylights: Case Studies,"** Water Leakage Through Building Facades, ASTM STP 1314, R. J. Kudder and J. L. Erdly, Eds., American Society for Testing and Materials, 1998.

ABSTRACT: This paper will describe two case studies of water leakage through sloped glazing and skylights. The authors have investigated and developed construction documents for the repair of numerous buildings with sloped glazing and skylights. Construction types examined include metal and glass systems.

KEYWORDS: sloped curtain wall, water leakage, sealant, flashings, water testing

---

Sloped curtain walls and skylights present special problems for the designer and particularly the installer to construct wall systems that are water tight. Sloped wall systems have complex geometries and complex internal water drainage paths. Tolerances become more critical in sloped curtain wall applications because gaps between horizontal, vertical and sloped mullions allows internally weeped water to exit the system.

Sloped systems are extremely difficult to diagram and detail and are even more difficult to construct. Often many aspects of the design are not completely detailed prior to construction and the most difficult to construct components are dependent on the ability of the installer to improvise or "design" in the field.

Trying to rectify deficiencies in sloped wall systems is very difficult after construction is completed, particularly because of access limitations for both exposing concealed components and getting men and materials to the sloped areas. Also, after the sloped wall is constructed it is usually not feasible to dismantle the system or gain access to concealed components and often the only cost effective repair solution is to modify the original design of the system by covering over elements or altering the way internal components work. Frequently performed inspections and maintenance is often required to maintain a repaired system's integrity, and it is likely that systems that have been repaired will have overall performance and component longevity that may not be as good as the expected for the original system.

---

[1] Consultant and Senior Architect respectively, Wiss, Janney, Elstner Associates, Inc. 29 N. Wacker Drive, Chicago, IL 60606

This paper describes investigations performed to determine the causes of water leakage through two sloped curtain wall systems at two different buildings and the repairs employed to correct identified deficient conditions. These examples illustrate why sloped curtain walls are different than vertical curtain walls and some of the difficulties involved in designing and constructing this type of facade.

CASE STUDY NO. 1

Background

The building of case study No. 1 is a 45-story steel frame office building in a Midwestern city, completed in 1984. The 40th through the 43rd floors and the 45th floor have a sloped curtain wall at the east elevation. The 44th floor has a vertical curtain wall. (Fig. 1.) The sloped curtain wall at the 40th through the 43rd floors consisted of vision glass, granite panels, and aluminum panels. The sloped curtain wall at the 45th floor was not a part of this investigation. The four southern bays create a sawtooth configuration in plan, as shown in Fig. 2. The investigative work described below was performed approximately six years after the building was completed at the request of the owner. Prior to the authors' investigative work, remedial sealant repairs were performed in an attempt to stop the water leakage; however, water leakage was continuing to occur through the sloped glazing during rains.

The sloped curtain wall on this building is a commonly-used vertical curtain wall, installed in a sloped application. The curtain wall was designed with primary and secondary water protection systems; the curtain wall itself being the primary system. (Fig. 3). This primary system consists of structural steel tubes (rafters) which span from slab edge to slab edge. Spanning between and anchored to the rafters are steel angles at the top and bottom of the granite panel and an aluminum rail with integral trough at the head of the glass. The steel angles support the granite panels. Aluminum panels and a gutter system are supported by a continuous steel channel anchored to the slab edges. The glass and the window washer track are supported by the rafters. At the glass locations, a two-piece aluminum cover with integral condensate troughs is anchored to and surrounds each rafter. Aluminum pressure plates in both directions secure the edges of the glass and aluminum panels. The sides of the granite panels are an exposed butt joint filled with backer rod and sealant.

The gutter system consisted of individual 1.52 meter long gutter sections, each section connected to the adjacent section with a short length of pipe. The system was designed to carry water from section to section until it reached the internal downspout located at the end of the last gutter section.

The design intent was to have the curtain wall prevent water from entering the building; however a secondary system was designed to accommodate water which penetrated the curtain wall and vapor condensation. The possibility of condensation occurring on the aluminum rafter covers was addressed with condensate troughs which would collect the water and deposit it into the secondary water protection system. The secondary water protection system consisted primarily of a two piece aluminum sill at the base of the aluminum panels and other components. Water which collected on the upper sill was to weep out through

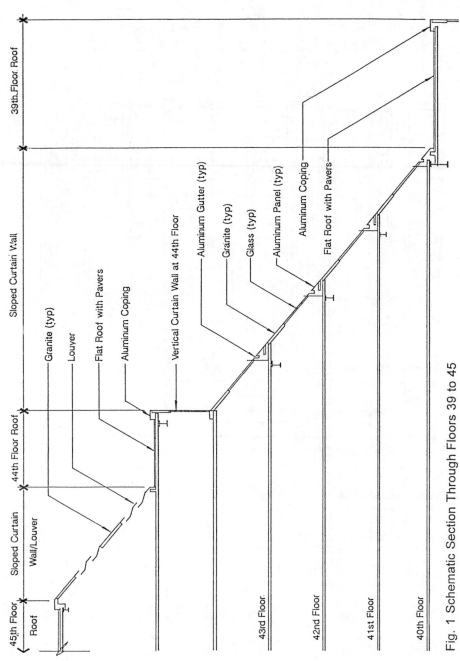

Fig. 1 Schematic Section Through Floors 39 to 45

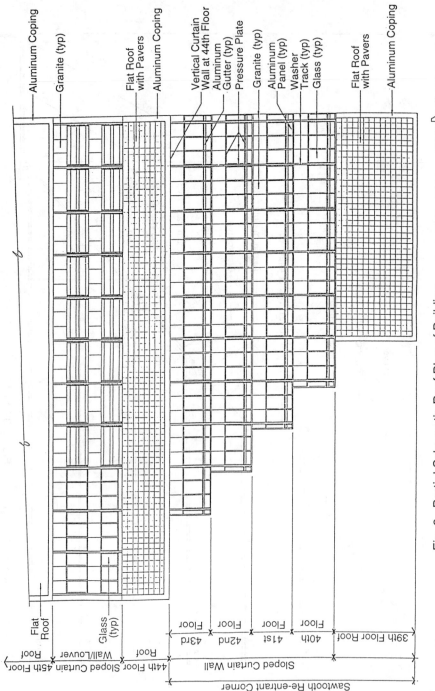

Fig. 2   Partial Schematic Roof Plan of Building

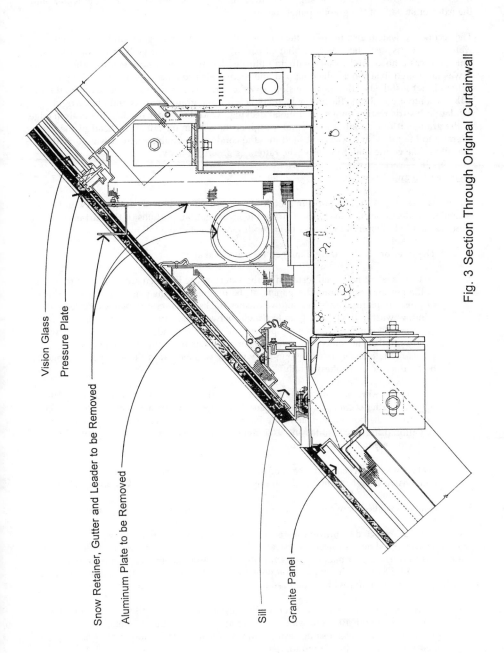

Vision Glass

Pressure Plate

Snow Retainer, Gutter and Leader to be Removed

Aluminum Plate to be Removed

Sill

Granite Panel

Fig. 3 Section Through Original Curtainwall

holes onto the lower piece of the sill. The lower sill was to be sloped to direct the water onto the exterior surface of the granite panels below.

The secondary system also included flashing to collect water which penetrated the curtain wall. A stainless steel sheet metal L-shaped pan was installed at the ends of the floor slabs. This pan was a horizontal surface with an upturned leg at the back side (towards the interior). It was fabricated in sections which lapped and were sealed to adjacent sections. The pan, although not installed with a positive slope, was to direct water across the edge of the floor slab and onto a membrane flashing which lay beneath the granite panels and above rigid insulation boards resting on a sloped metal decking. Once the water reached the bottom edge of the granite, it flowed into the integral trough of the aluminum rail at the head of the glass, laterally to the rafter, and was deposited into the condensate trough where it was carried to the sill via the condensate troughs at the rafters as described above.

Investigation and Testing

Water was leaking to the interior due initially to sealant failure in both the primary and secondary water protection systems. During the investigation, portions of the curtain wall were dismantled. Observations of as-built conditions revealed the following:

1.   The interior finishes were damaged by water leakage.

2.   Silicone sealant had been installed at the exterior face between adjacent granite panels, at the perimeter of aluminum panels, at the perimeter of the glass, along the perimeter of pressure plates, between window washer tracks and pressure plates, between window washer tracks and granite panels, between pressure plates and gutters, between the upper and lower sill pieces, and over the heads of screws. Sealant was deteriorated at the joints between adjacent granite panels, at pressure plates and pressure plate fasteners and along the window washer tracks. The sealant exhibited both adhesive and cohesive failure.

3.   The gutters were built up of multiple pieces with sealed joints. The connecting pipes between gutter sections, which were located in the ends of each section, were 19.05 mm above the bottom surface of the interior of the gutter sections. This 19.05 mm elevation difference resulted in 19.05 mm of water which could not flow into the adjacent section and was constantly retained in the gutters.

4.   Sealant was observed at the base of mullions on the interior of the system where the condensate troughs terminated, although sealant at this location was not specified.

5.   Sealant installed between the sections of the L-shaped pan exhibited adhesive failure.

The sealant was expected to prevent water from penetrating the systems, however the water protection systems should protect against water leakage in the event of sealant failure. The testing was performed in a manner that evaluated the entire system and then proceeded to test subsystems and eventually individual components to understand how the systems functioned with the sealant intact and with sealant failures. The testing revealed the following:

1.   Water was sprayed onto the exterior surfaces of the curtain wall using a calibrated spray nozzle with 10 psi of water pressure at a distance of 0.406 meters from the exterior surface. This testing resulted in water leakage at the top of the granite panels and the bottom of the aluminum panels.

2.   Water was poured into the aluminum rail at the head of the glass after the cover and

gaskets were removed from the joints between the glass and the granite. This testing resulted in water leakage at the bottom of the condensate trough.

3. Water was poured into the aluminum condensate troughs accessible from the finished spaces of the building. The condensate troughs are part of the aluminum mullions which cover the rafters. With the exterior aluminum panel removed, the end of the condensate trough was visible. The engineers observed a large quantity of sealant on the sill at the base of the mullion. Water which flowed down the trough was intended to flow onto the sill which contains weeps, however the water was diverted from its intended path by the sealant at the base of the mullion and spilled onto the L-shaped pan.

4. Water was poured onto the upper piece of the sill which contains weeps. The water was intended to weep out of the upper sill piece onto the lower sill piece below, which has a positive slope, and then to continue down the exterior face of the curtain wall. The water which leaked from the weep holes was trapped behind a sealant joint installed as a remedial repair between the upper and lower sill pieces. The water flowed laterally until it reached a splice between adjacent pieces of lower sill at which point it leaked into the building.

5. Water was poured into the gutters. The water leaked through the connecting pipes of adjacent gutters and flowed onto the L-shaped pan.

6. Water was poured into the L-shaped pan. The L-shaped pan had: anchors for gutter supports penetrating the horizontal surface, which were not sealed; splice joints which were sealed, but in which the sealant had failed adhesively; and no end dams at the north and south ends. Additionally, the channel anchored to the slab edge that supports the sill, aluminum panels, and gutters, was set at an elevation above the L-shaped pan. Water accumulated on the pan to a depth of 1 inch before flowing onto the membrane flashing beneath the granite panels. The accumulated water penetrated the L-shaped pans and leaked onto the floor slab, and off the edge of the floor slab onto the ceiling of the space below.

Accumulated water also flowed off the north and south ends of the L-shaped pans due to the absence of end dams. The water was deposited onto the ceiling below.

The membrane flashing beneath the granite panels, onto which the water was deposited, was not continuous and therefore the water flowed off the end of the membrane flashing and onto the sloped metal decking below. The water flowed down the metal decking and was deposited onto the ceiling below at the window head.

7. Davit sockets existed at the north and south ends of the sloped curtain wall. The davit socket locations were such that the davit sockets penetrated gutters and the L-shaped pans. Water which was deposited in the gutter or L-shaped pan leaked through the pan around the davit sockets which were not adequately sealed.

Repairs

Since this building had been experiencing water leakage into finished spaces from the first day of occupancy, the objective of the repairs was to eliminate water leakage through the sloped curtain wall. Faced with the high cost and the logistics of repairing an area of the building facade that was difficult to access while the building remained occupied, it was agreed that aesthetic changes to the exterior of the sloped curtain wall as well as performing all of the repair work from the exterior were conditions of the repair program. The following repairs were developed to prevent water leakage through the sloped curtain wall and into the building at the 40th through the 43rd floors:

1.   The existing gutters were removed and the resulting openings were covered with new aluminum panels. A new gutter equipped with an ice stop was installed at the edge of the sawtooth in each bay to prevent water from cascading onto the plaza below. These gutters are one-piece welded units, with drains and leaders connected to existing internal downspouts.

2.   Sealant at the base of mullions was removed to allow water to drain from the condensate troughs onto the sill as originally intended.

3.   Sealant between the upper and lower sill pieces was removed to allow water which weeps out of the upper sill piece to drain onto the exterior face of the curtain wall. Sealant was installed at the splices between adjacent sill pieces.

4.   Joints and penetrations in the L-shaped pan were cleaned and resealed. End dams were installed at the ends of the pans and at each mullion to restrict the lateral flow of water within the pans.

5.   All sealant joints and gaskets were replaced with new materials.

6.   Since the granite panels could not easily be removed to repair the membrane flashing below the panels, a new composite stainless steel and membrane flashing was installed over the granite panels, as shown in Fig. 4. A new formed aluminum panel with weeps, finished to match the existing aluminum, was installed over the new flashing. Joints between adjacent aluminum panels were sealed with urethane sealant.

7.   New stainless steel flashing was installed at davit sockets to direct water onto the exterior surface of the curtain wall. Additionally, weathersealed aluminum access doors were installed over the davit sockets to keep rain, snow and ice from reaching the davit sockets when the sockets are not in use.

Since the above repairs were performed, no water leakage into the building has been reported.

CASE STUDY NO. 2

Background

The following describes the results of an investigation of water leakage that occurred at the sloped glazing area, called the "bustle", on a 57-story high-rise building located in a large Midwestern city. The building was constructed in the early 1980's with a reinforced concrete-framed structure clad with granite veneer constructed in the early 1980's. Also described is the remedial repair work performed on the bustle to prevent water leakage.

The bustle on the building is a sloped curtain wall system at the northeast corner of the building that extends from the fourth floor up to the seventh floor between stone clad walls. As shown in Fig. 5 the shape of the bustle is trapezoid in plan, and the width of the bustle is greatest at the seventh floor of the building. At each floor the bustle consists of an aluminum and glass sloped skylight, vertical aluminum and glass curtain wall, and a continuous horizontal aluminum gutter at the base of the vertical wall which is integral with a horizontal strip of aluminum panels. Two windows at each floor are operable at the vertical section of bustle. A partial section through the bustle is shown in Figs. 6A and 6B. Because the shape of the bustle is trapezoid in plan, the sloping skylight and the horizontal strip of aluminum

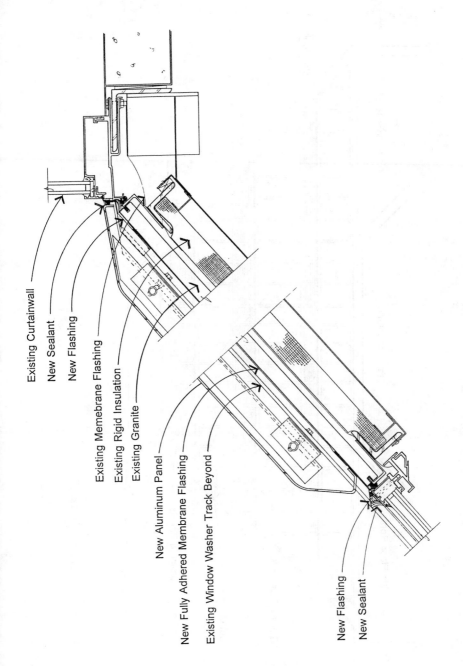

Existing Curtainwall

New Sealant

New Flashing

Existing Memebrane Flashing

Existing Rigid Insulation

Existing Granite

New Aluminum Panel

New Fully Adhered Membrane Flashing

Existing Window Washer Track Beyond

New Flashing

New Sealant

Fig. 4 Section Through Modified Curtainwall

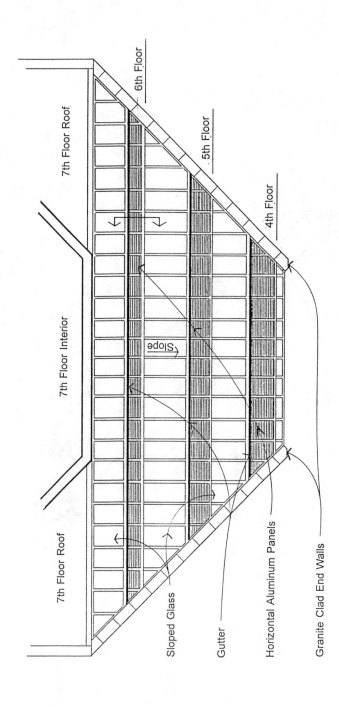

Fig. 5 Plan View of "Bustle"

panels at the sides of the bustle are triangular-shaped in plan.

The portion of the bustle at the fourth, fifth and sixth floors typically consists of a sloped glass skylight, vertical windows, and a horizontal strip of aluminum panels covered with steel grating. Between the windows and the horizontal strip of aluminum panels at each floor, there is a continuous gutter with drains that collects and diverts rainwater from the bustle.

The mullions of the sloped skylight, the windows and the horizontal strip of aluminum panels are supported on structural steel tubular members. The mullions were fabricated with integral, interconnecting, internal drains that collect and drain some of the water from the bustle to the gutters. The mullions were connected together, and the joints between mullions were to be sealed with sealant. Water that entered the sloped portion of the wall was to weep internally between sloped, horizontal, and vertical mullions down to the gutter.

Investigation and Testing

Water leakage, into the building occurred during rains since the time the bustle was constructed. Leakage was observed to occur along the entire length of the gutters. The amount of water leakage was greater at the sides of the bustle than at the middle portions of the bustle. The water leakage inconvenienced building occupants and caused significant damage to interior finishes.

A review of available shop drawings of the bustle showed only typical details of construction. Complex areas of construction were apparently not completely developed by the designer prior to construction. Review of the shop drawings did not indicate that there were obvious locations for water to enter the sloped wall.

Water penetration testing for this investigation was conducted in a two-phased approach. Phase one was to identify obvious deficiencies in the gutter and drainage system, and Phase two consisted of additional testing to identify more difficult-to-locate leaks after deficiencies observed in Phase one were corrected. A phased approach was necessary because the gutter system used to drain water from the sloped glazing was leaking. To prevent extensive water damage to interior finishes during testing the drainage system leaks had to be identified and repaired prior to testing.

Phase 1 Investigation and Testing

Shortly after the building was completed water penetration tests were performed on the bustle. First, the horizontal strip of aluminum panels and the gutters of the bustle were tested. The tests consisted of spraying water using a calibrated nozzle on selected areas of the horizontal strip of aluminum panels and mullions; damming and filling the gutters with water, and inspecting the interior of the building below the test areas for water leaks.

During the tests, water penetrated the building at the following typical locations, as schematically shown in Fig. 6A:

1.   Joints between the gutter and the edge mullions of the horizontal strip of aluminum panels

2.   Joints between mullions of the horizontal strip of aluminum panels

3.   Joints between the sides of the horizontal strip of aluminum panels and the stone wall at the sides of the bustle

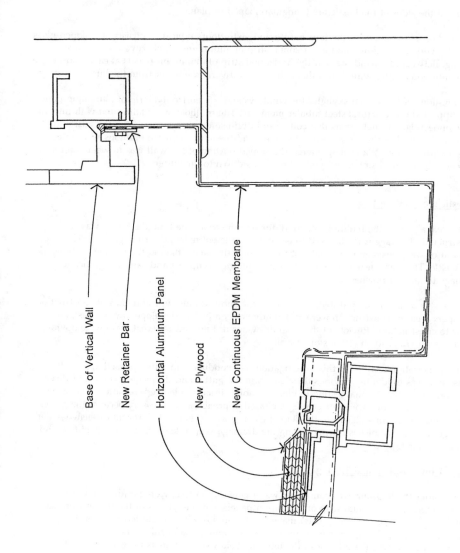

Base of Vertical Wall

New Retainer Bar

Horizontal Aluminum Panel

New Plywood

New Continuous EPDM Membrane

Fig. 6A Section through Gutter and Base of Vertical Wall

4.   Gutter seams covered with a membrane between gutter sections.

The pattern and location of the water leakage into the building produced by the water penetration tests matched the pattern and location of the water leakage that occurred during rains. The primary reason water leaked through the joints listed above is that they were not sealed with sealant as specified. Water leaked through the membrane at gutter splices because the gutters typically retained water continuously thereby causing loss of membrane adhesion to the gutters surface.

Phase 1 Repairs

Based upon the results of the water penetration test, the horizontal strips of aluminum panels and the gutters at the fourth, fifth and sixth floors of the bustle were completely covered with a new continuous EPDM waterproofing membrane in lieu of dismantling the gutter and horizontal aluminum panel system. The latter approach was determined to be unfeasible considering cost and inconvenience to building occupants. Figs. 6A and 6B show partial schematic views of the gutter area of the bustle showing the repair work performed.

The repair work performed on the horizontal strips of aluminum panels and on the gutters resulted in the elimination of water leakage into the building at the middle portions of the bustle, and in a slight reduction of the water leakage at the sides of the bustle.

Phase 2 Investigation and Testing

After Phase 1 repairs were implemented, water leakage continued to occur at the sides of the bustle. Water penetration tests were performed on the sloping skylight and on the windows adjacent to the sides of the bustle. Water penetration testing included use of a calibrated nozzle and hose, and selectively pouring small amounts of water into water drainage areas of mullions.

During the tests, water penetrated the building at the following locations:

1.   Joints between mullions of the triangular portions of the sloping skylight at the sides of the bustle at the stone wall.

2.   Joint between the end mullion of the sloping skylight and the end mullion of the windows at the sides of the bustle.

3.   At operable windows at the fifth floor.

The pattern and location of the water leakage into the building produced by the water penetration tests matched the pattern and location of the water leakage that occurred during rains. The primary reason water leakage occurred at the joints listed above is that joints between mullion sections were not precisely fitted together because of the complex geometry and angles of the bustle. Because mullion sections were not fitted together tightly and because gaps between mullion section were not properly sealed, water that was intended to weep between vertical, horizontal, and sloped mullions easily penetrated these gaps and entered the building.

Phase 2 Repairs

Based upon the results of the water penetration tests, of the internal drainage system in the mullions, the portion of the sloping skylight adjacent to the sides of the bustle was completely filled with sealant and the gaskets in the operable windows at the fifth floor were replaced.

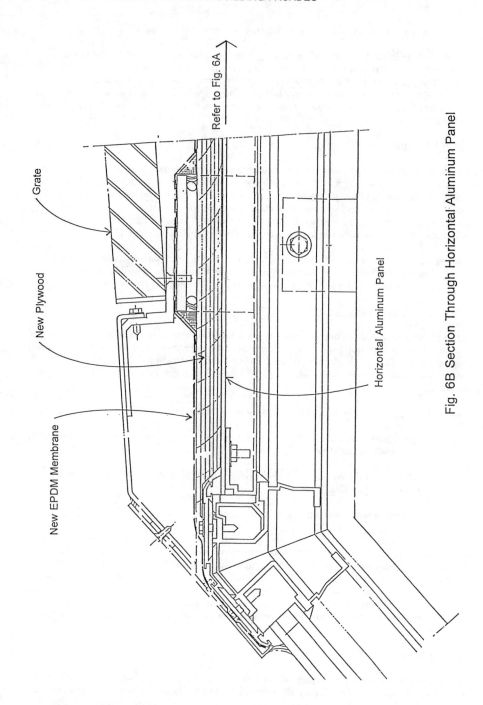

Grate

New Plywood

New EPDM Membrane

Refer to Fig. 6A

Horizontal Aluminum Panel

Fig. 6B Section Through Horizontal Aluminum Panel

The internal mullion drainage system at the ends of the fourth, fifth and sixth floors of the bustle were filled with sealant in lieu of dismantling the system and installing new properly cut and fitted mullions. The latter approach was determined to be unfeasible considering cost and inconvenience to building occupants. The mullion repair is schematically shown in Figs. 7 and 8 as described below.

At the glass rabbet joint:

1.   Old sealant material at mullion joinery was completely removed; surfaces were cleaned; and the entire joint and voids were filled with sealant.

2.   Weep holes were enlarged.

3.   A 6 inch long weep tube with flared ends, set in sealant, was installed through weep holes into the vertical tube drainage channel.

4.   Joinery at bottom of vertical mullion was cleaned and re-sealed, as described in item 1 above.

5.   The weep hole at the glass rabbet into the vertical drainage channel was enlarged. The bottom of vertical drainage channel was cleared of debris.

6.   Sloped glass was cleaned of all previous sealants and contaminants.

7.   The exterior pressure bar seal was reglazed with new one-piece factory-vulcanized gaskets.

8.   The exterior sloped glazing snap-on caps were resealed with sealant.

At the metal edge closure rabbet:

9.   Voids at sloped and vertical elements were filled with sealant.

10.   Aluminum flashing was installed over the closure knee joint, fastened to the sloped metal closure piece, and set in a bed of sealant.

11.   At the corner of the gutter, a piece of fully-adhered membrane was installed at the corner onto vertical metal corner closure piece.

12.   Sealant was installed between the snap-on cover and the granite side wall, at both the vertical corner and the sloped wall.

After the portions of the sloping skylight at the sides of the bustle were repaired as outlined above and the operable window gaskets at the each floor were replaced, no incidence of water leakage into the building at the bustle were reported.

CONCLUSION

Based upon information gained from the above investigations of water leakage at sloped curtain walls and skylights it has been shown that sloped wall systems present special problems for the designer and particularly the installer to construct sloped wall systems that are water tight. Sloped wall systems like those examined above have complex geometries and complex internal water drainage paths. Tolerances become more critical in sloped curtain wall applications because gaps between horizontal, vertical and sloped mullions allow internally

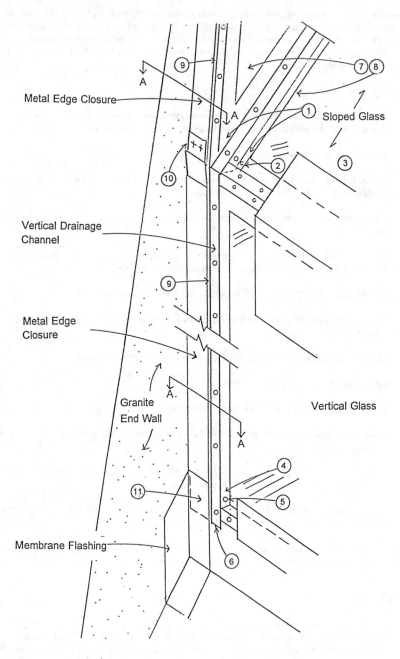

Metal Edge Closure

Sloped Glass

Vertical Drainage Channel

Metal Edge Closure

Granite End Wall

Vertical Glass

Membrane Flashing

Fig. 7 Bustle Corner

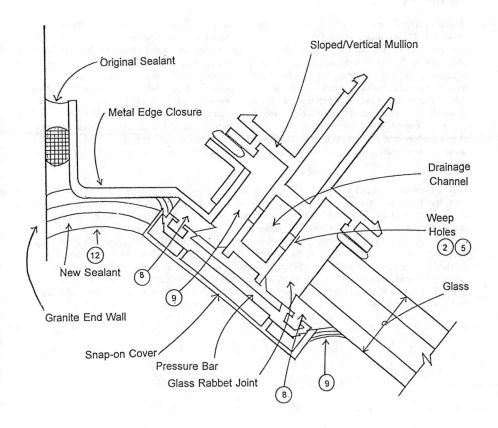

Fig. 8 Section A-A

weeped water to exit the system as a leak. Conversely, in vertical curtain walls water that may leak through gaps between components usually continues to remain within the curtain wall system.

Sloped systems are extremely difficult to diagram and detail and are even more difficult to construct. Often, many aspects of the design are not adequately detailed prior to construction and the most difficult to construct components are dependent on the ability of the installer to improvise or "design" in the field. For these systems, special effort should be given by the designer to fully develop all details prior to construction, and to understand possible limitations in achieving a successful design. Components should have positive slope to drain water and water protection systems, particularly secondary systems, should not be sealant dependent. Water testing components during construction, particularly specialized tests of water drainage systems periodically during construction would likely help in avoiding some of the problems documented in these case studies. A standardized test method specifically for water control testing of sloped curtain wall and skylight systems could greatly improve how these systems perform.

Trying to rectify deficiencies in sloped wall systems is very difficult after construction is completed, particularly because of access limitations for both exposing concealed components and getting men and materials to the sloped area. Also, after the sloped wall is constructed it is usually not feasible to dismantle the system or gain access to concealed components and often the only cost effective repair solution is to modify the original design of the system by covering over elements or altering the way internal components work. These repairs often require extensive use of sealant in difficult to install applications. Frequently performed inspections and maintenance is often required to maintain a repaired system's integrity, and it is likely that, for systems that have been repaired in such a manner, their overall performance and component longevity may not be as good as that expected for the original system.

Testing and Quality Control

Kurt R. Hoigard[1] and Robert J. Kudder,[1]

THE FACTS ABOUT HOSE TESTING

REFERENCE: Hoigard, K. R. and Kudder, R. J., "**The Facts About Hose Testing,**" Water Leakage Through Building Facades, ASTM STP 1314, R. J. Kudder and J. L. Erdly, Eds., American Society for Testing and Materials, 1998.

ABSTRACT: The authors performed laboratory testing to evaluate the behavior of the Monarch nozzle specified by the AAMA 501.2 leakage test method, and localized pressures generated by the water spray impact under various circumstances. Findings include: 1) The Monarch nozzle spray pattern is distinctly non-uniform. 2) The maximum pressures generated by the water spray are not at the center of the spray pattern, but in a concentric ring around the center. Under standard conditions, maximum pressures of 0.34 kPa (7 psf) were measured. 3) As the nozzle/target distance decreases, generated pressures increase significantly. At nozzle/target distances of 102 mm (4 in.), maximum pressures approached 2.15 kPa (45 psf). 4) Multi planar test areas like curtain wall and window systems with protruding mullions require special test techniques to assure similar test pressures are applied to the various exposed components.

KEY WORDS: curtain wall, window, testing, water leakage, water testing

---

Many project specifications written today include provisions for window and curtain wall leakage tests, the two most common being the "chamber" and "hose" tests. Chamber tests use a uniform water spray in conjunction with differential pressure to simulate wind-driven rain. Racks of calibrated nozzles, and sealed test chambers with centrifugal blowers are used to provide the water spray and a measurable pressure differential.

---

[1] Principals, Raths, Raths & Johnson, Inc., 835 Midway Drive, Willowbrook, Illinois 60521

Hose tests, on the other hand, use much simpler equipment. In order to perform a hose test, one only needs a length of 19 mm (3/4 in.) garden hose, a special nozzle, a valve to control the water flow, a water pressure gauge, and an observer stationed on the interior side of the test area to look for leaks. This paper discusses the test method, the physics behind the hose test, testing performed by the authors to evaluate the method, and practical considerations for hose testing.

TEST METHOD

The AAMA Field Check of Metal Storefronts, Curtain Walls and Sloped Glazing Systems for Water Leakage (501.2) test method requires only a 19 mm (3/4 in.) diameter hose, a control valve, a pressure gage and a Type B-25, #6.030 brass nozzle manufactured by the Monarch Manufacturing Works of Philadelphia, Pennsylvania (henceforth referred to as the Monarch nozzle). The procedure involves spraying 1.52 lineal meters (5 ft.) of exterior window or curtain wall jointery for a period of 5 minutes while slowly moving the nozzle back and forth along the test joint. During the test the nozzle is oriented perpendicular to the face of the test wall or window at a distance of 305 mm (12 in.) from the most exterior surface, with the water flow adjusted to produce 207 to 241 kPa (30 to 35 psi) water pressure at the inlet side of the nozzle. An observer on the indoor side of the test area visually inspects for leaks. If no leakage is detected, the

Figure 1 -- Technician performing a hose Test according to AAMA 501.2 requirements.

next 1.52 m (5 ft.) of jointery is sprayed, and so on, until the prescribed area has been tested. Figure 1 shows a technician spraying a test area according to the AAMA 501.2 requirements.

The simplicity of the hose test makes it an attractive quality control and diagnostic procedure. There is no need to erect, seal and pressurize a chamber in the test area, or to operate blowers and spray racks. Hose testing has been considered for masonry as well as window and curtain wall testing [1], but AAMA 501.2 cautions that the method is intended for permanent non-operable jointery and seals unless the procedures and performance requirements are modified accordingly. It must also be recognized that while the hose test most closely simulates a chamber test for water infiltration through an orifice or by capillary action, it does not accurately simulate conditions for water infiltration caused by overflowing storage troughs or air percolation. It also does not reproduce the effects of pressure on concealed compartments, drainage system performance, or component deflection. Since the hose test cannot simulate all aspects of wall behavior represented in a chamber test, or in a natural rain occurrence, the user must determine if the wall property of interest can be properly evaluated by the test method.

PHYSICS

The science of fluid mechanics tells us that a stream of liquid impacting a surface at a given velocity will create a force on that surface. The force is caused by the change in momentum of the liquid as it stops moving forward and splatters toward the sides as shown in Figure 2. The impact force generated can be calculated if the velocity, density and cross-sectional area of the liquid stream are known. In the case of a nozzle spraying water on a test area, the force calculation is simplified if the flow of water as it leaves the nozzle is considered. The thrust from water as it leaves the nozzle is equal and opposite to the impact force generated on the test area if the water droplets are large and the energy imparted to the surrounding air is neglected [2].

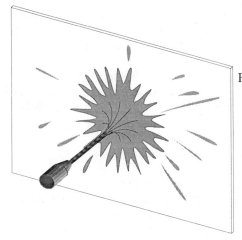

Figure 2--Water stream changing direction as it splatters on a flat surface.

The Monarch nozzle has an exit orifice diameter of approximately 4.95 mm (0.195 in.), and flows approximately 22.3 l/min (5.9 gal/min) at a gauge pressure of 241 kPa (35 psi). Using this data the water stream velocity at the nozzle is calculated as 19.3 m/sec (63.3 ft/sec), and the thrust from the water leaving the nozzle is calculated as 7.16 N (1.61 lbf). The Monarch nozzles owned by the authors have observed spray patterns forming a filled cone with an apex angle of approximately 45 degrees. This means that at a distance of 305 mm (12 in.) the water spray from the Monarch nozzle will be distributed over a circular area with a diameter of approximately 254 mm (10 in.). If the spray pattern is uniform, a water impact pressure of 0.14 kPa (2.95 psf) will be generated on the test area.

NOZZLE PERFORMANCE TESTING

As discussed above, the physics behind the hose test suggest that differential pressures are generated over limited areas as the water spray impacts the test window or curtain wall. Several assumptions were made to arrive at the calculated 0.14 kPa (2.95 psf) pressure previously discussed, including: 1) the Monarch nozzle spray pattern is uniform; 2) the nozzle is always kept at a distance of exactly 305 mm (12 in.) from the test area; 3) the water spray is applied to a flat single plane surface; and 4) the nozzle is always oriented perpendicular to the face of the test area.

In order to test the validity of these assumptions, a series of tests were devised to measure the pressures generated by Monarch nozzles owned by the authors. Each test series used targets made from acrylic plastic to simulate window and curtain wall components. Water spray impact pressures were read with an inclined fluid manometer attached to brass manometer ports mounted flush with the test surfaces. The tests were performed using both 5.33 and 8.76 mm (0.210 and 0.345 in.) inside diameter manometer ports and the results averaged. Feed water line pressures were maintained at 241 kPa (35 psi) during all tests.

Spray Pattern Determination

To check the assumption that the Monarch nozzle spray pattern is uniform, water was sprayed on a flat piece of acrylic plastic using three different Monarch nozzles. The nozzles were kept at the AAMA 501.2 specified distance of 305 mm (12 in.) from the target in a perpendicular orientation. Pressure measurements were made with the nozzles directly aligned with the manometer port, and at lateral offsets of up to 254 mm (10 in.). Figure 3 shows the general arrangement for this series of tests. The measured pressures associated with each of the three test nozzles are shown graphically in Figure 4. The principal findings from this series of tests were:

- The Monarch nozzle spray pattern is not uniform.

- Two of the nozzles tested performed essentially the same. The performance of Nozzle #3 was substantially different in both the magnitude and location of the peak pressure generated.

- The maximum pressures generated were not at the center of the spray pattern, but in concentric rings around the center. Nozzles #1 and #2 generated peak pressures of approximately 0.34 kPa (7 psf), located 50.8 mm (2 in.) outboard of the nozzle centerline. Nozzle #3 generated its peak pressure of approximately 0.45 kPa (9.5 psf) in a ring 25.4 mm (1 in.) out from the nozzle center.

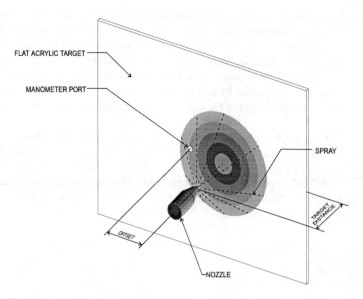

Figure 3--General test arrangement to determine impact pressures generated
under standard hose test conditions.

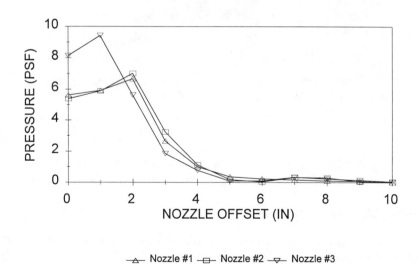

Figure 4--Impact pressures measured on a flat target at a distance of 12 inches.

- Examination of the construction of the three test nozzles revealed a manufacturing difference the authors believe is directly related to the observed performance differences between Nozzle #3 and Nozzles #1 and #2. The 8.1 mm (0.320 in.) long straight bore connecting the mixing chamber to the exit orifice of Nozzle #3 (see Figure 5) was significantly longer than the same bore in Nozzles #1 and #2 which measured 4.3 mm (0.170 in.) long. Increasing the length of the exit bore tightens the spray pattern.

- The impact force imparted by the water to the target can be determined by finding the volume of the solid formed by rotating the pressure/offset graphs shown in Figure 4 about the Y-axis (force = pressure x area) [3]. The calculated impact forces for Nozzles #1, #2 and #3 respectively are 7.60, 8.18, and 7.52 N (1.71, 1.84, and 1.69 lbf). These values compare favorably with the nozzle thrust of 7.16 N (1.61 lbf) calculated earlier.

Figure 5--Cross-sectional view of a Monarch nozzle. Arrow indicates
straight bore connecting the mixing chamber to the exit orifice.

Distance Effects on Impact Pressures

The AAMA 501.2 test method requires the nozzle to be kept at a distance of 305 mm (12 in.) from the test area. To determine the sensitivity of the test to variations in the nozzle/target distance, water was sprayed on a flat target using Nozzle #2 positioned at distances ranging from 102 to 356 mm (4 to 14 in.). These tests used the same general arrangement as for the spray pattern determination discussed above and shown in Figure 3, with lateral offsets ranging from 0 to 254 mm (0 to 10 in.) for each target distance. The pressures measured for each test position are shown graphically in Figure 6. The principal findings from this series of tests were:

- The Monarch nozzle spray pattern continues to be distinctly non-uniform over widely varying target distances.

- Nozzle/target distance significantly affects impact pressure. At target distances of 102 mm (4 in.), maximum measured pressures approached 2.15 kPa (45 psf).

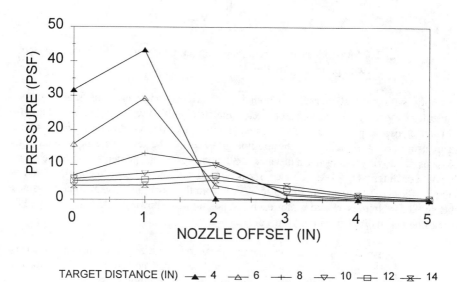

Figure 6--Impact pressures measured on flat targets at varying distances.

Effects of Multi-Planar Test Surfaces

Most window and curtain wall systems are constructed with a series of flat surfaces in different planes. Frequently, the vision or spandrel glass is recessed relative to the frame members as shown in Figure 7. In this type of configuration, the mullion/glass seal is further inboard than the mullion stack joint. The question arises how to position the Monarch nozzle

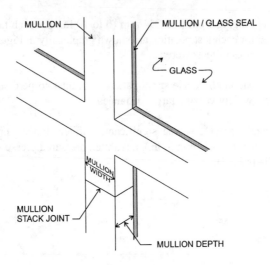

Figure 7--Multi planar test area found on curtain wall and window systems with protruding mullions.

to apply the same test pressure to both joints. To explore this problem the authors constructed mock-up acrylic wall sections to simulate a mullion with a width of 102 mm (4 in.) and exposed depths of 25.4 and 50.8 mm (1 and 2 in.). Manometer ports were installed to measure pressures acting on the mullion/glass seal. The tests were performed with Nozzles #1 and #2 positioned at a distance of 305 mm (12 in.) and perpendicular to the glass. Pressure readings were taken with the nozzles aligned with the edges of the mullions and at lateral offsets of -76 to +178 mm (-3 to +7 in.) from this position. The average pressures measured for Nozzles #1 and #2 for each test position are shown graphically in Figure 8. The principal findings from this series of tests were:

- Positioning the nozzle to spray the outermost surface of the mullion produces negligible pressure at the mullion/glass seal. The geometry of the mullion protrusion deflects the water spray from the mullion/glass seal.

- In order to effectively test the mullion/glass seal, the Monarch nozzle must be positioned at a lateral offset of approximately 50.8 mm (2 in.) from the mullion edge. This position produces pressures of 0.31 to 0.38 kPa (6.5 to 8.0 psf) for 25.4 and 50.8 mm (1 and 2 in.) mullion depths, respectively.

- The 50.5 mm (2 in.) mullion protrusion resulted in a higher peak pressure at the mullion/glass seal than the 25.4 mm (1 in.) configuration. The 50.8 mm (2 in.) configuration appeared to cause more of the spray pattern to be redirected into the corner formed by the mullion/glass interface.

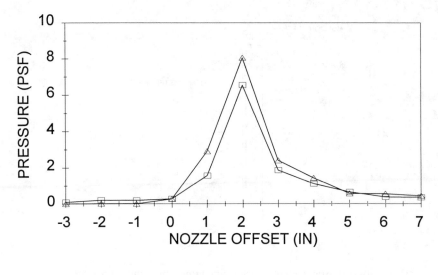

Figure 8--Impact pressures measured on simulated mullion/glass seals at a
distance of 12 inches with the nozzle oriented perpendicular to
the glass.

As an alternate to using a perpendicular spray at an offset as discussed above, the
authors explored the possibility of testing the mullion/glass seal by orienting the nozzle at
a 45 degree angle to the mullion/glass interface and at a distance of 305 mm (12 in.) as
shown in Figure 9. The previously used 50.8 mm (2 in.) deep acrylic mullion target was
reused, and Nozzles #1 and #2 were tested at vertical offsets ranging from 0 to 152 mm (0
to 6 in.) below the manometer port. The average pressures measured for Nozzles #1 and #2
for each test position are shown graphically in Figure 10. The principal findings from this
series of tests were:

- Angling the Monarch nozzle to test the mullion/glass seal produces
  significantly higher pressures than using a perpendicular spray at an offset.
  Maximum pressures of approximately 0.96 kPa (20 psf) were measured.

- The pressure increase appears to be due to substantial redirection of the spray
  pattern by both the mullion and the glass.

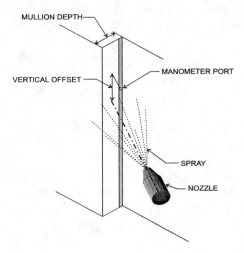

Figure 9--Test arrangement to determine impact pressures generated
with nozzle oriented at 45 degrees into a mullion/glass
intersection.

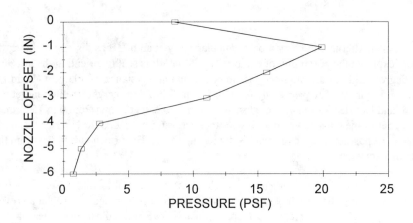

Figure 10--Impact pressures measured on a simulated 2 inch mullion/glass
seal at a distance of 12 inches with the nozzle oriented at 45
degrees into the corner.

CONCLUSIONS

There were unexpected manufacturing variations in the three nozzles used in this study, resulting in variations in measured impact pressures. Two more nozzles purchased by the authors subsequent to completion of the test program (Nozzles #4 and #5) have internal dimensions very similar to Nozzles #1 and #2. Due to its significantly different internal dimensions and performance, Nozzle #3 has been retired from service. Although the variation in exit bore length on Nozzle #3 may have been a unique manufacturing deviation, the authors recommend anyone using Monarch nozzles for AAMA 501.2 hose tests should verify the construction of their nozzles before relying on the test data presented in this study.

The authors find hose testing with the Monarch nozzle produces predictable impact pressures, in general agreement with theoretical calculations, once the distribution of the spray pattern is understood. Although not uniform, the properties of the spray pattern are acceptable for quality control and diagnostic testing if used in appropriate circumstances. Care must be taken in the positioning of the nozzle, however, if the intention of the test is to apply approximately equal impact pressures to all parts of the test area. The specifier and user of the hose test must always remain cognizant that the impact pressures generated by the nozzle extend over a very small area at any given time, and therefore do not fully simulate all aspects of a chamber test or natural wind-driven rain.

REFERENCES

[1]   Monk, C. B., Jr., "Adaptations and Additions to ASTM Test Method E514 (Water Permeance of Masonry) for Field Conditions," Masonry: Materials, Properties and Performance, ASTM STP 778, J. G. Borchelt, Ed., American Society for Testing and Materials, Philadelphia, 1982, pp. 237-244.

[2]   Shames, E. H., Mechanics of Fluids, McGraw-Hill Book Company, New York, 1982, pp. 121-144.

[3]   Beer, F. P. And Johnston E. R., Vector Mechanics for Engineers, Statics and Dynamics, McGraw-Hill Book Company, New York, 1977, pp. 166-212.

Bruce S. Kaskel, Michael J. Scheffler, and Ian R. Chin[1]

CRITICAL REVIEW OF CURTAIN WALL MOCKUP TESTING
FOR WATER PENETRATION

REFERENCE: Kaskel, B. S., Scheffler, M. J., and Chin, I. R., "**Critical Review of Curtain Wall Mockup Testing for Water Penetration**," Water Leakage Through Building Facades, ASTM STP 1314, R. J. Kudder and J. L. Erdly, Eds., American Society for Testing and Materials, 1998.

ABSTRACT: Current industry standard procedures exist for testing of curtain wall mockups for new construction. This paper will critically review how the standard procedures can provide an assessment of the capabilities of the curtain wall to control water and prevent leakage. The review is based on numerous mockup tests that the authors have prescribed and have reviewed during the course of their investigations of water leakage in many types of curtain walls, and during their peer review of the design of the curtain wall on new buildings. This review has revealed that additional test procedures and modifications to the standard test procedures for mockup testing will greatly aid in the value of the mockup towards assuring a leak-free curtain wall.

KEYWORDS: curtain wall, preconstruction mockup testing, water penetration, water leakage

---

Full-scale preconstruction curtain wall mockup testing is today normally considered standard practice for buildings where the curtain wall is a custom application, for high-rise buildings, and for buildings where a high confidence level is desired in the performance of the curtain wall [1]. Curtain wall mockup tests subject a full size representative portion of the proposed exterior wall system to simulated environmental conditions, such as wind, rain, temperature extremes, and seismic exposure. These tests when performed in aggregate, provide a measure of the performance of the proposed curtain wall system. This paper discusses the aspects of mockup testing which relate to water penetration and to water leakage.

Consultant, Consultant and Principal respectively, Wiss, Janney, Elstner Associates, Inc., 120 N. LaSalle Street, 20th Floor, Chicago, IL 60602

Most of the tests that make up the overall mockup test program conform to industry standard test methods. The standard test methods by themselves, however, may not be sufficient to specify all the requirements for the mockup test program for some buildings, especially in regards to water resistance. For example, there are no standard tests for resistance of the overall curtain wall to leakage caused by uncontrolled condensation inside the building, nor are there tests to assess the long-term performance of sealant joints. Tests to establish these important criteria would benefit the value of preconstruction mockup testing to assess the ability of the proposed wall to resist water penetration.

This paper provides guidance on additional mockup test requirements or modifications to the standard tests which should be considered for the overall mockup test program, to gain a measure of the performance of the curtain wall to resist water leakage. Included in the paper is an evaluation and critique of the standard tests used to evaluate mockup water leakage and a review of the impact of other standard and specialized mockup tests, such those used to determine air leakage, and for structural, seismic and thermal performance, and the impact these tests may have on water leakage testing.

BACKGROUND ON MOCKUP TESTS

Full scale preconstruction mockup testing is a relatively standardized procedure, currently available at only a few testing laboratories in the USA. In some cases, full-scale mockup testing may not be required by project conditions, size, or design. In these cases, mockup tests performed by the curtain wall manufacturer in smaller, less adaptable, chambers may provide assurance of curtain wall performance.

For custom applications, high-rise buildings, and for buildings where a high confidence level is desired in the performance of the curtain wall, full-scale mock-up testing should be performed. For these projects, one must consider the process necessary to establish the curtain wall design, coordinate the test program, procure and erect the mockup, and incorporate the lessons learned from the mock-up. Although there are several logical sequences for these critical steps, one common sequence is as follows:

1. Conceptual design of curtain wall by the design architect.
2. Establishment of performance-based curtain wall design parameters by the design architect or by the curtain wall consultant retained by the design team.
3. Based on the specified performance based parameters, schematic design of typical curtain wall areas by the curtain wall designer/builder, after award of construction contract.
4. Design of mockup test wall simultaneously with design of entire curtain wall by the curtain wall designer/builder.
5. Testing of curtain wall mockup prior to curtain wall fabrication.
6. Modification of curtain wall design if required by mockup tests.
7. Finalization of curtain wall design.
8. Fabrication and construction of curtain wall.

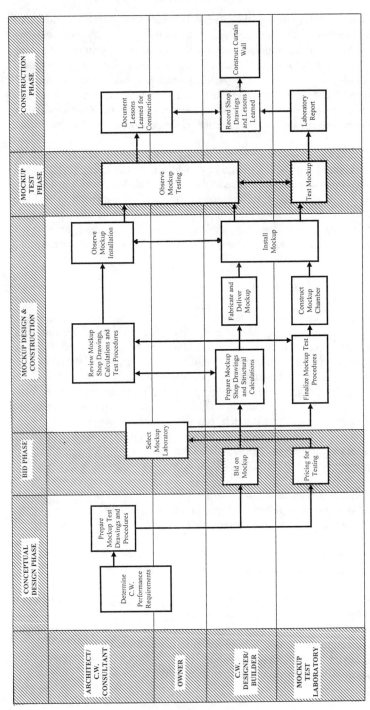

Table 1 -
Flow Diagram of
Curtain Wall
Mockup
Test Process

Successful mockup testing requires considerable planning throughout this entire process, to design the mockup wall and to determine the appropriate tests. Successful mockup testing also requires considerable follow-up after the testing is completed so that the lessons learned from the testing are implemented in the final design of the curtain wall. Table 1 provides a flow sheet which diagrams the process for curtain wall mockup testing.

The design architect and/or the curtain wall consultant initially stipulate the requirements for mockup testing on the project drawings and in the specifications. Complete information is necessary when the documents are released for bid to assure accurate pricing of the mockup. The bid set specifications should include a conceptual mockup test program outlining the tests to perform and the desired levels of performance.

Many of the specified tests are standards either of the American Society for Testing and Materials (ASTM) or the Architectural Aluminum Manufacturer's Association (AAMA). The standard tests for water leakage performance include:

Water Penetration Tests

1.   <u>ASTM E331</u>, "Standard Test Method for Water Penetration of Exterior Windows, Curtain Walls and Doors by Uniform Static Air Pressure Difference" [2]. Figure 1 shows a photograph of the ASTM static pressure test (E331) underway on a mockup.

Figure 1 -
Curtain Wall
Mockup Undergoing
ASTM Water
Penetration Test
Using Static
Air Pressure

2.   ASTM E547, "Standard Test Method for Water Penetration of Exterior Windows, Curtain Walls and Doors by Cyclic Static Air Pressure Difference" [3]

Both ASTM E331 and E547, water penetration tests are similar in that they create a lower air pressure inside the test chamber than outside, which tend to draw water through the wall, as would occur during a windy rainstorm.

3.   AAMA 501.1, "Standard Test Method for Metal Curtain Walls for Water Penetration Using Dynamic Pressure"[4]

The AAMA water penetration test is conducted with a large exterior blower, often an airplane engine, to create the dynamic effect of the wind. Figure 2 shows a mockup undergoing this test. The force of the air pressure must be calibrated against the ASTM static test methods. In the authors' opinion, this test usually does not create as large a pressure differential between the interior and exterior of the mockup curtain wall, as does the ASTM static tests, nor is the pressure differential maintained for as long a time. Especially for designs which anticipate that a static head of water can build up within a drained gutter, this test is not as severe as the ASTM static test E331 or E547.

Figure 2 - Curtain Wall Mockup Undergoing AAMA Water Penetration Using Dynamic Pressure (Supplied by Airplane Engine)

Pressure-equalized rain screen design curtain walls should be tested with the AAMA dynamic test. The ASTM static tests will not adequately assess these walls, since the air barrier is separated from the rain screen. Therefore, imposing a pressure differential on the wall will not aid in drawing water through the rain screen. Furthermore, the ASTM static test projects a horizontal stream of water at the test wall.

A properly designed rain screen will largely prevent this water from bypassing the rain screen. However, rain can move upward due to air currents and capillary forces. This upward water stream is possible to create in the dynamic test. In this instance, the AAMA dynamic test is more critical than the ASTM static test. An exterior applied test chamber to perform the ASTM static test may also be considered for rain screen designs.

Other Tests Useful for Assessing Water Penetration

Tests to evaluate air infiltration, structural, thermal and other performance include both standardized and non-standardized tests. These tests also reveal critical information that relates to the ability of the proposed curtain wall to resists water penetration. These tests are as follows:

4.   ASTM E283, "Standard Test Method for Rate of Air Leakage Through Exterior Windows, Curtain Walls and Doors by Uniform Static Air Pressure Difference" [5]
        This test is similar to the ASTM static water test in that it utilizes a lower air pressure inside the test chamber than outside. The rate of air leakage through the mockup area is measured and compared with the project requirements. This test can reveal significant information that relates to water leakage. A wall with a high air leakage rate may be more likely to also have water penetration. Should high air leakage be a concern, the air leakage test can be used to identify locations where air passes through the curtain wall by application of liquid soap to locations where air leakage is suspected. Soap bubbles formed by the air pressure will allow visual confirmation of leakage paths. The test can also allow for trial solutions to reducing air leakage, such as baffling drainage holes or sealing open joints.

5.   ASTM E330, "Standard Test Method for Structural Performance of Exterior Windows, Curtain Walls and Doors by Uniform Static Air Pressure", [6] and

6.   ASTM E1233, "Standard Test Method for Structural Performance of Exterior Windows, Curtain Walls and Doors by Cyclic Static Air Pressure" [7]
        Structural load testing is an important part of the test program to determine that the wall behaves within project specified limits under design loads intended to simulate wind forces on the curtain wall. These tests are also critical for assessing the water resistance of the curtain wall after it has undergone deflections due to design loads. Typically, after the structural test is complete the air and water tests are repeated to observe whether the mockup remains air and water tight. Later in the test program, structural tests can be repeated with factors of safety, up to the theoretical ultimate capacity of the curtain wall. After factor of safety tests, air and water tests are usually not repeated, since the curtain wall on the building is not intended to be subjected to this level of loading.

7.   Thermal Test
      Thermal tests are performed with equipment available at most of the test laboratories. AAMA has test methods for thermal testing of discrete sized window mockups [8], however, there is currently no ASTM nor AAMA standard procedure applicable to most curtain wall mockups. Thermal testing of curtain wall mockups is performed, commonly for curtain walls proposed for northern climates, to assess the performance of the curtain wall under temperature extremes. These tests heat the exterior of the curtain wall with radiant heating elements and cool the wall with air conditioning.   Figure 3 is a photograph which shows the additional enclosure applied over the mockup during this testing. The wall is typically insulated and vapor sealed for this test, and then these materials are removed for completion of the test program.

      Similar to structural testing, thermal tests are useful for assessing the water resistance of the curtain wall after it has undergone movements due to extreme temperatures. To assess this, the air and water tests are repeated after the thermal test.

Figure 3 - Mockup Enclosed from Exterior with
Thermal Test Chamber (on left)

      Thermal testing is also a critical test procedure for assessing water leakage due to uncontrolled condensation. During the cold cycle, the conditions on the inside of the mockup can provide an indication of condensation in actual conditions. Observation of the quality of the installed vapor retarder seals is especially useful during the mockup to identify problems which can be resolved prior to construction.

The testing agency may not be able to control the inside of the mockup chamber to the specified relative humidity ranges. In such cases, it is important to install thermocouples on the mockup surfaces to assess the surface temperatures and to determine whether condensation would occur based on dew point calculations. The authors recommend that thermocouples be installed both on visible interior wall surfaces and on surfaces enclosed within the curtain wall cavity. This will provide valuable information on temperature conditions within the wall and help in the assessment of condensation conditions.

8.   Seismic Racking Tests

These tests displace the top of the mockup laterally relative to the base of the mockup. These tests can afford the same possibility to assess for water leakage after testing, as previously described.

Other Factors

Other factors which can have a significant impact on the performance of mockup testing for water leakage are:

1.   Mockup design
2.   Mockup construction
3.   Interpretation of mockup test results
4.   Testing for long-term performance
5.   Implementation of results into final curtain wall design and construction

The remainder of this paper will explore the impact that these issues can have on water leakage.

MOCKUP DESIGN

The design architect's drawings should identify the representative mockup area to be tested. For a simple building, the size and features of the mockup may be indicated on the building elevations. In the case of complicated curtain walls, a specific mockup drawing should be developed, so that all the key portions of the curtain wall to be tested are represented. Shop drawings of the mockup prepared by the curtain wall designer/builder are equally important. The mockup shop drawing and structural calculation submittal is the first review of the proposed curtain wall system in detail, and should be carefully reviewed to verify that it meets the design intent. The mockup testing laboratory will use the shop drawings to construct the test chamber.

The question often arises as to how big to make the curtain wall mockup. Since mockups are built with full size elements, they are as big as the portion of the curtain wall they represent. There are upper bounds to the size of laboratory test chambers, although most laboratories can accommodate sizes greater than 30 ft. wide by 40 ft. high with a custom chamber.

The authors believe that to assess water leakage, the curtain wall mockup should be large enough to include all typical conditions of the curtain wall, such as flat wall areas, corners, sloped areas, transitions, setbacks, horizontal interruptions and terminations. For curtain walls made of more than one system, each system should be included and terminations between adjoining systems should be included. Alternately, multiple mockups may be built for one project to cover all variations in geometry, detailing and integration of different cladding systems.

Many curtain walls use a two story structural module, in which case at least a two story high wall section is necessary for structural testing. Structural connections need to replicate proposed structural behavior and in some instances this may mean that the mockup is constructed differently than the actual wall.

The mockup should incorporate the key features of the water collection, control and drainage system to allow for observation of the total system performance. For instance an internal water collection gutter which is designed to collect water from above, and then to direct water into a lower internal drainage system (such as a drained window frame), should not be installed at the bottom of the mockup. If it is, the water collection from above would be reasonably modeled, but the water egress path would not be.

Many contemporary curtain walls are designed with increasing complexity in the exterior wall system. These curtain walls, should have a mockup of adequately large size to model all of the principal design elements of the curtain wall. The authors are familiar with one contemporary high-rise, where a common design feature was a sloped section of curtain wall. However, the mockup did not include the sloped curtain wall. Leakage occurred at the building in these sloped areas, which may have been diagnosed, if the mockup had included these areas in the test.

As a follow up to the preconstruction laboratory mockup and prior to installation of the cladding on the project, in-site field mockups can be performed. In-situ water penetration tests can also be performed during actual curtain wall construction, especially of the transition and edge conditions [9]. It is often these portions of the curtain wall that are the most susceptible to design and construction deficiencies and which often lead to building water leakage.

MOCKUP CONSTRUCTION

Once the mockup is designed, the shop drawings and structural calculations are reviewed and approved, then mockup construction can begin. The mockup components are fabricated and shipped to the testing laboratory. Figure 4 shows a mockup under construction at a testing laboratory. Erection of the mockup should be performed by the same installer who will construct the curtain wall on the building. This is an important opportunity for the curtain wall designer/builder, the design architect and the curtain wall consultant to learn how to efficiently construct the wall system. Even if the curtain wall system is a standard wall system, there may be subtle variations in the particular application that need attention. Resolution of any problems at the mockup is likely to be less expensive, troublesome and disruptive than resolving the problem at the building site during construction.

Figure 4 - Mockup Under
Construction by Curtain
Wall Installer

Prior to implementing the formal mockup test procedure, the mockup often is pre-tested. Pre-testing is usually desired by the installer of the mockup, since workmanship errors will reflect poorly on the system once the formal testing commences. The laboratory also desires to pretest to check for and correct any leakage through the mockup chamber walls.

Should pre-tests reveal workmanship problems, the installer of the mockup may perform "touch-up" repairs without recording what was done. These "touch-up" repairs may be critical to the success of the curtain wall both, at the mockup test, and later at the building. It is therefore important that the mockup installer be required to provide written results of all "touch-up" repairs. It is also important to understanding the side effects of such repairs on the design and whether they are actually installable on the building. It is best to have the complete design team on site during installation and pre-testing to observe and document the entire process. The testing laboratory will not perform this observation function as a matter of course.

INTERPRETATION OF TEST RESULTS

A disturbing trend in the industry is to re-interpret the meaning of a "water leak". The two ASTM standards which pertain to water leakage (E331, E547) now have the following definition of water penetration:

"water penetration - penetration of water beyond the vertical plane intersecting the innermost projection of the test specimen, not including interior trim and hardware, under the specified conditions of air pressure difference across the specimen."

Later this definition is used in the standards as follows:

"Unless otherwise specified, failure criteria of this test method shall be defined as water penetration . . . Failure also occurs whenever water penetrates through the perimeter frame of the test specimen. Water contained within drained flashings, gutters, and sills is not considered failure.

Therefore, the visible presence of water in any quantity on the interior side of the curtain wall is not necessarily a failed condition according to the ASTM standards. Standing water on an interior window sill would not be considered a failure as long as it is "controlled" and does not run off the sill.

The authors have seen several examples where "controlled" water, once inside the curtain wall, saturates insulation and other materials not intended to become wet, and causes a significant problem. These interior materials may not even be present as part of the mockup test. Therefore, the authors caution that for mockup tests where water does enter the wall, the potential damage that water can cause should be carefully assessed. Reliance on the ASTM standard language may not be critical enough to accurately assess the risks of water leakage. For face sealed barrier design claddings, no water leakage should be accepted inboard of the exterior face of the wall.

TESTING FOR LONG-TERM PERFORMANCE

The mockup tests provide an indication of the performance of the curtain wall only at the time it is brand-new. Workmanship quality of the mockup is usually very good because every element is constructed under a scrutiny that is not expected during construction of the curtain wall on the building. Especially in an all face sealed curtain wall design, water infiltration in the mockup is therefore unlikely.

In service, curtain walls rarely have all the joints completely sealed. Whether through aging or because of sealant related problems, most curtain wall systems let some water enter the exterior seals. It is the manner in which this water is directed out of the curtain wall that ultimately will dictate the performance of the wall. Careful evaluation of how the curtain wall will perform over time as it ages and how maintenance repairs can be made will play a large role in the effectiveness of the curtain wall to stop water leakage.

In face sealed and internally drained curtain wall mockup tests, the authors have sought to simulate the long-term condition that not all sealed joints will remain water tight. This has been accomplished by cutting the sealed joints in the mockup with a knife blade at random intervals over about ten percent of the overall joint length. Figure 5 illustrates this procedure. After the sealant joints are cut, standard water penetration tests are performed. Through the openings in the sealant joints, water will reach the internal water collection and control system, or the "second line of defense" and the performance of these backup systems can then be observed and evaluated.

Figure 5 - Cutting Sealant Joints in
Preparation to Test for Long-Term Performance

Other tests useful to determine how the internal collection and control system will handle water can be performed simply by spraying water on the inside of the curtain wall in locations where water may originate due to a seal failure or due to condensation. Observation of how the internal drainage system works under these conditions will also provide an indication of the long term performance of this system.

IMPLEMENTING RESULTS RECOMMENDED FROM MOCKUP TESTING

Problems can occur in curtain walls if information learned by the observers of the mockup tests are not shared with those responsible for designing and constructing the curtain wall. The authors have investigated several buildings where modifications in the mockup testing were not carried through to the construction phase of the curtain wall.

The mockup test report is critical as a learning tool. Records should be kept of each change made to the mockup and its impact on the curtain wall performance.

Modifications to the design should be recorded on as-built mockup drawings, so that there is no question about these changes. The curtain wall installer should understand the critical impact of the changes made in the mockup.

CONCLUSIONS

The process of mock-up testing can play an important role towards the achievement of a leak-free curtain wall. However, the concept of mockup testing is viewed by some project team members as a hurdle to by-pass during the construction process instead of as a means of understanding the curtain wall performance and a way to learn how to properly construct the curtain wall. When information gained from curtain wall mockup testing is not incorporated into final curtain wall design, or when tests are conducted on mockup walls that are not truly representative of the final design, it becomes more likely that the building curtain wall could experience water leakage.

The standard procedures for mockup testing are based on sound physical principles and usually result in curtain walls that are leak free. The authors have suggested modifications to standard procedures in the mockup design and construction procedure; in the interpretation of mockup test results; in additional tests to verify long-term performance; and in the implementation of results into the final curtain wall design and construction. These modifications if incorporated into the standards developed by ASTM Committee E6, will provide better and more comprehensive results from preconstruction curtain wall mockup testing.

BIBLIOGRAPHY

[1]   Sakhnovsky, A.A., "Full-Scale Performance Testing of Curtain Walls", Exterior Wall System: Glass and Concrete Technology, Design and Construction, ASTM STP 1034, B Donaldson, Ed., ASTM, Philadelphia, 1991, pp. 47-58.

[2]   ASTM E331 - 93, "Standard Test Method for Water Penetration of Exterior Windows, Curtain Walls and Doors by Uniform Static Air Pressure Difference", Vol. 4.07, ASTM, Philadelphia, 1996.

[3]   ASTM E547 - 93, "Standard Test Method for Water Penetration of Exterior Windows, Curtain Walls and Doors by Cyclic Static Air Pressure Difference", Vol. 4.07, ASTM, Philadelphia, 1996

[4]   AAMA 501.1-94, "Standard Test Method for Metal Curtain Walls for Water Penetration Using Dynamic Pressure", American Architectural Manufacturers Association, Schaumburg, 1994.

[5]   ASTM E283 - 91, "Standard Test Method for Rate of Air Leakage Through Exterior Windows, Curtain Walls and Doors by Uniform Static Air Pressure Difference", Vol. 4.07, ASTM, Philadelphia, 1996.

[6]   ASTM E330 - 96, "Standard Test Method for Structural Performance of Exterior Windows, Curtain Walls and Doors by Uniform Static Air Pressure", Vol. 4.07, ASTM, Philadelphia, 1996.

[7]   ASTM E1233 - 96, "Standard Test Method for Structural Performance of Exterior Windows, Curtain Walls and Doors by Cyclic Static Air Pressure", Vol. 4.07, ASTM, Philadelphia, 1996.

[8]   AAMA 1503.1-88, "Voluntary Test Method for Thermal Transmittance and Condensation Resistance of Windows, Doors, and Glazed Wall Sections", American Architectural Manufacturers Association. Schaumburg, 1988.

[9]   Johnson D.K., Weber A.S., "Field Versus Laboratory Performance Testing", Progressive Architecture, Aug. 1991.

Paul E. Beers[1] and William D. Smith[2]

QUALITY CONTROL PROCEDURES TO PREVENT WATER LEAKAGE THROUGH WINDOWS

REFERENCE: Beers, P. E. and Smith, W. D., **"Quality Control Procedures to Prevent Water Leakage Through Windows,"** Water Leakage Through Building Facades, ASTM STP 1314, R. J. Kudder and J. L. Erdly, Eds., American Society for Testing and Materials, 1998.

ABSTRACT: Most water leakage problems through windows and doors are the result of installation errors. Even the best system designs cannot overcome poor installation techniques. Simple mistakes such as the omission of an internal seal can result in major water leakage that damages building interiors, upsets building occupants and often results in costly repairs.

By establishing a quality control procedure that specifically addresses windows and doors, common installation mistakes can be prevented. This paper will present a series of steps to follow before and during the construction process to insure proper installation of windows and other glazing products.

KEYWORDS: windows, sliding glass doors, water leakage, window installation, field water test

[1] President, Glazing Consultants, Inc., 8895 North Military Trail, Suite 306-C, Palm Beach Gardens, FL 33410
[2] Vice President, Glazing Consultants, Inc., 8895 North Military Trail, Suite 306-C, Palm Beach Gardens, FL 33410

Many windows are designed, engineered and tested for a particular project or application. Others are deemed appropriate for use because of compliance with industry standards and voluntary specifications such as the ANSI/AAMA 101 certification program [1] . These programs require products to be tested in a laboratory using established standards for items such as air and water infiltration, structural adequacy and forced entry requirements. In spite of all this, a window or door still is dependent on proper installation for adequate performance.

Often installers are not informed as to how the window was designed or tested. Accordingly, they do not know how it should be installed. Rather, they must rely on past experience, if any, and guess as to how the window was detailed for the project. This dilemma can be avoided by following certain quality control steps to ensure the proper flow of information. Then field water tests and third party inspections can be used to verify performance and quality.

BEFORE INSTALLATION

Determine the Project Requirements

Before installation, the project performance requirements must be established. This information may be based on architectural plans and specifications, building code requirements, or an independent certification program such as ANSI/AAMA 101 [1]. Basic performance requirements include structural adequacy, air infiltration and water infiltration [2]. Each window type to be used should have published performance data based upon laboratory testing or engineering and testing for the project.

It is important to verify that each window type complies with the project performance requirements. This can be determined by reviewing the manufacturer's published test data or copies of the laboratory test reports. The product should have been tested exactly as it is being proposed for use at the project.

Review of Shop Drawings and Submittals

Large projects require a detailed set of shop drawings for the window installation. The shop drawings can be used to confirm that the windows properly interface with surrounding surfaces. They can also be used by the installer to reference the requirements for proper window installation.

Shop drawings must contain elevation drawings of all window types and configurations. They should contain full-sized details of each section of the window. Surrounding surfaces and how they interface with the window must be carefully detailed.

Nothing can be left to interpretation or guessing. The shop drawings must include all anchors and fasteners, sealant locations and all other materials, even if they are not being furnished by the window manufacturer. In addition, the drawing notes should clearly specify each material by product name, type and manufacturer.

In addition to shop drawings, manufacturers' literature for the windows, and all accessories and components should be submitted and reviewed. The literature includes published installation instructions and product limitations.

These documents can be reviewed and approved by the project owner, architect, consultant, general contractor, subcontractors affected by the work, and the installer. Often, the workmen who install the windows have not reviewed or even seen the shop drawings and submittals. They cannot possibly understand the project requirements and installation details without carefully reviewing these documents.

Installation Conference

Prior to window installation, it is a good idea for all parties to meet at the building site and review the details and requirements of the installation. The parties may include, but are not limited to, the architect, general contractor, consultant, installer and other subcontractors affected by the work.

A site inspection may be conducted to check the rough openings and make sure they are ready. In addition, the shop drawings should be reviewed and compared to field conditions. Any unanticipated problems can be worked out before installation begins.

DURING INSTALLATION

Field Water Tests

The installed window must replicate the product as it was tested in a laboratory for certification. Unfortunately, field conditions often make this difficult to achieve. Therefore, it is important to construct a field mockup of the installation and test it as early as possible during the project. The mockup should include windows from the production run for the project and all surrounding finishes, such as perimeter caulking, and the exterior wall surface.

It is critical to use the proper test method. A field variation of the test performed in the laboratory with an air pressure difference across the assembly and a uniform water spray is appropriate. A primary example is ASTM Standard Test Method for Field Determination of Water Penetration of Installed Exterior Windows, Curtain Walls and Doors by Uniform or Cyclic Static Air Pressure Difference (E 1105). The American Architectural Manufacturers Association (AAMA) publishes variations of ASTM E 1105 which may also be used [2].

Other test methods do not adequately represent the anticipated in-service conditions and may provide unreliable results [3]. Water spray tests from a hose or spray rack without an air pressure difference across the specimen do not represent conditions present during a wind driven rain storm. Hence, there is a risk the specimen may pass an inferior field test and then leak during an actual storm.

Each different window type and configuration should be tested. Once each specimen is successfully tested using a method such as ASTM E 1105, they will establish the standard of quality for the remainder of the installation. For large projects, it is appropriate to conduct follow-up tests at various stages of the project to assure installation procedures are being followed and quality is being maintained. Reports should be prepared upon completion of each test to document the results.

Third Party Inspections

Inspections by someone other than the installer are helpful to make sure nothing has been overlooked. This can be done by a consultant, representative of the owner or general contractor, architect, or other qualified party. Inspections must be done often enough to review each phase of the work. For instance, inspections can be timed appropriately to check internal seals before they are covered up.

Each inspection should examine each element of the work to ensure the installation is being done as required by the shop drawings. Workmanship, particularly sealant application, should be carefully reviewed. Also, the installation must comply with the standard of quality established during the field water tests.

It is good practice to prepare a written report of each inspection and submit it to all interested parties. The installer can use the report to correct any observed deficiencies. Also, it can be used as a reference for subsequent inspections. For large projects that require multiple inspections, it is good practice to prepare and maintain a punch-list and update it with each inspection.

CONCLUSION

Workmanship is a critical aspect of window installation. Attention to detail, field water tests and third party inspection all contribute to the ultimate success of a project. With a commitment to quality from all parties and by following the procedures outlined in this paper, a high quality, leak-free window installation can be achieved.

REFERENCES

[1]   AVoluntary Specifications for Aluminum And Poly (Vinyl Chloride)(PVC) Prime Windows and Glass Doors,@ American Architectural Manufacturers Association, Publication No. ANSI/AAMA 101-93, August 18, 1993.

[2]   Smith, W.D., "Water Management - Designing and Installing Storefronts to Prevent Water Leaks," Glass Digest Magazine, July 15, 1993, pp. 46-49.

[3]   AField Check of Metal Storefronts, Curtain Walls, and Sloped Glazing Systems for Water Leakage,@ Methods of Tests for Exterior Walls, American Architectural Manufacturers Association, Publication No. AAMA 502-90, 1990, p.1.

[4]   Beers, P. E., AField Testing Windows for Water Leakage,@ U.S. Glass Metal and Glazing, August 1990, pp. 52-55.

William D. Smith[1] and Paul E. Beers[2]

EVALUATION OF WATER RESISTANCE TESTING PROBLEMS FOR
INSTALLED FACADE SYSTEMS

REFERENCE: Smith, W. D. and Beers, P. E., "Evaluation of Water Resistance
Testing Problems for Installed Facade Systems," Water Leakage Through
Building Facades, ASTM STP 1314, R. J. Kudder and J. L. Erdly, Eds., American
Society for Testing and Materials, 1998.

ABSTRACT: The use of hose testing as a field check for water penetration of installed
assemblies has gained popularity throughout the construction industry because of its
simplicity. This paper will detail the use of hose testing methods, variations of the
procedure, intended application, and limitations. This information will be compared to
ASTM E 1105 "Standard Test Method for Field Determination of Water Penetration of
Installed Exterior Windows, Curtain Walls, and Doors by Uniform of Cyclic Static Air
Pressure Difference." A comparison of test results will allow the reader to evaluate the
accuracy of hose testing procedures and to determine whether it is a reliable method of
evaluating product performance. This paper will also detail variations in the use of
ASTM E 1105 including application of the test procedure to wall assemblies of masonry,
EIFS, and others.

KEYWORDS: air pressure, curtain walls, doors, EIFS, hose testing, water infiltration,
windows.

---

[1] Vice President, Glazing Consultants, Inc., 8895 No. Military Trail, Suite 306-C,
Palm Beach Gardens, FL 33410-6212

[2] President, Glazing Consultants, Inc., 8895 No. Military Trail, Suite 306-C, Palm
Beach Gardens, FL 33410-6212

The use of hose testing as a field check for water penetration of installed assemblies has gained popularity throughout the construction industry because of its simplicity and low cost. Many variations of the procedure are performed on a variety of wall assemblies, often in deference to the intended purpose, and without consideration for variables in performance needs or material differences. Nevertheless, these "tests" are often relied upon as evidence of water infiltration, or lack thereof, with no consideration given to actual in-service performance requirements. Consequently, it is prudent to evaluate the validity of such test procedures in light of desired performance characteristics.

COMMON FIELD TESTING METHODS

<u>Hose Testing</u>

While many variations are used, hose testing is often referenced to AAMA 501.2, a method published by the American Architectural Manufacturers Association (AAMA). Previously known as the "Field Check of Metal Curtain Walls for Water Leakage," [1] it has since been revised and is now known as "Field Check of Metal Storefronts, Curtain Walls, and Sloped Glazing Systems for Water Leakage" [2]. This procedure subjects a glazing specimen to the application of water on the exterior surfaces using a 19 mm (¾") diameter hose fitted with a Type B-25, #6.030 brass nozzle. The hose is fitted with a control valve and pressure gauge located between the valve and the nozzle, and water pressure is to be 207 to 241 kPa (30 to 35 lbf/in^2) at the nozzle inlet (Figure 1)

FIG. 1:   Type B-25, #6.030 brass nozzle, fitted with control valve and pressure gauge for use in AAMA 501.2 hose testing.

The AAMA procedure has been developed for the specific purpose of determining water resistance of glazing components that are designed as permanently closed elements of the test specimen [2]. These include joints in aluminum frames, gaskets, and sealants. The procedure allows for modification to both the test method and the performance requirements for specimens that contain joints surrounding operable frame elements such as doors or window sash, but definition of the allowable modifications is not provided.

Conducting the AAMA procedure requires wetting of the specimen on the exterior, working from bottom to top. For example, a typical procedure would begin by wetting the sill or other lowest portion of the glazing specimen for a period of 5 minutes by slowly moving the nozzle back and forth across approximately 1.5 m (5 ft.) of sill framing while the nozzle is perpendicular to the face of the wall and spaced approximately 30.4 cm (12 in.) from its most exterior surface. The procedure continues by then wetting the intersection at the lowest horizontal framing member and the adjacent intersecting frame members for 5 minutes, then moving upward on the vertical member for 5 minutes, and so on. The procedure is to continue in a similar manner until the entire specimen is fully wetted.

ASTM Field Testing Procedures

ASTM publishes a test method that has gained wide spread industry acceptance for use on a variety of products. The method is known as ASTM E 1105 Standard Test Method for Field Determination of Water Penetration of Installed Exterior Windows, Curtain Walls, and Doors by Uniform or Cyclic Static Air Pressure Difference (Figure 2). This test method is referenced by AAMA for use in field testing a variety of glazing assemblies [3, 4]. It's use has also gained acceptance by some as a method for testing of installed Exterior Insulation Finish Systems (EIFS) [5]. In addition, the authors have used ASTM E 1105 to test a variety of exterior assemblies and building components including construction joints, sealant joints, glass block walls, and others.

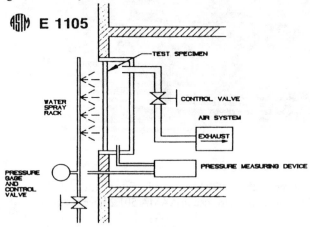

FIG. 2 - General arrangement of water infiltration test apparatus (from ASTM E 1105).

The ASTM E 1105 method attempts to replicate in-service performance requirements by subjecting specimens to water sprayed on the exterior surface while the static air pressure on the interior side of the specimen is lower than that on the exterior side. This is accomplished by attaching a sealed chamber to the specimen, normally mounted on the interior side from which air is evacuated, while applying a uniform volume of water to the exterior. For barrier walls such as an Exterior Insulation Finish System (EIFS) or a pressure equalized wall with an interior air seal, it may be preferable to place the chamber on the exterior side so as to subject the exterior wall surface to the prescribed air pressure.

VARIATIONS OF WATER TESTING METHODS

Many variations of hose testing are attempted, most with inconclusive results. While the AAMA 501.2 method was developed to check permanently closed joints of fixed glazing assemblies, it is often used as a basis for determining water infiltration of glazing assemblies such as operable windows and doors. Observations of such procedures have sometimes resulted in no evidence of water infiltration where it has been experienced in the past, while others result in water infiltration where it has not been observed before. For example, hose testing of an aluminum framed sliding glass door may not reveal water infiltration flowing over the track, while spraying water on the weather-stripping joints at a pressure of be 207 to 241 kPa (30 to 35 psi) is likely to cause water infiltration that may not be representative of in service performance requirements.

Further disregard for the intent of AAMA 501.2 has also been observed in tests of exterior walls and other assemblies. Hose testing of EIFS construction has been observed on several occasions, many times with inconclusive results. EIFS is a composite wall system that by its manner of assembly provides avenues that may allow water to flow downward undetected. For example, the authors witnessed testing of an EIFS assembly using the AAMA 501.2 which revealed no water intrusion until subsequent testing using the ASTM E 1105 method discovered water entered through an exterior joint and then flowed downward between the insulation board and substrate before exiting at the base of the wall. Consequently, what has often been provided as "conclusive evidence" for the lack of water infiltration, has been shown otherwise when testing the specimen with a static air pressure differential similar to ASTM E 1105.

It has also been observed that not only are a variety of materials subjected to AAMA 501.2 testing, but a number of variations to the method have been attempted. These include conducting the procedure with an improperly sized supply hose and/or nozzle, an unknown water pressure, or applying water to the specimen in an inconsistent manner.

Unlike hose testing, ASTM E 1105 provides versatility that allows for considerable flexibility in adapting the test method to a number of field conditions [6]. For example, the test method allows that the procedure may be performed on installed windows, curtain walls, and doors installed up to 15 ° from vertical, on new installations or existing in service conditions, and with uniform or cyclic static air pressure differentials applied with either interior or exterior mounted test chambers.

COMPARISON OF TEST RESULTS

A disparity in test results led to the hypothesis that hose testing may not accurately represent the conclusions derived from that procedure. It was noted that while the AAMA 501.2 procedure revealed obvious failures, other deficiencies were often not discovered until the ASTM E 1105 test method was done.

Interestingly, when testing aluminum curtain wall or storefront glazing assemblies, it was observed that the types of failures discovered when using AAMA 501.2 normally fell into a pattern of failures. Usually, the deficiencies discovered were represented as one of three modes: 1) adhesive failure of perimeter frame sealants, 2) lack of sealant at installation fastener penetrations of the sill flashing pan, or 3) failure of the flashing pan seal at its end points. These failures correlate to the those most commonly found in aluminum framed glazing systems [7].

In one case, the AAMA 501.2 test method revealed a sealant failure that allowed water infiltration around a number of fastener penetrations through the sill flashing pans. Although repairs were subsequently performed, water infiltration into the building continued. Additional testing using the ASTM E 1105 method found that while sealant repairs to the fastener penetrations were successful, the glazing rabbet of the horizontal framing member was not able to adequately drain water to the exterior, resulting in the water overflowing the horizontal on the interior side.

Testing using both the ASTM and the AAMA methods illustrated the potential of variable results. While some specimens revealed similar results regardless of the test method used, others revealed differences in test results as illustrated by Table 1. Therefore, while testing was also performed on specimens that are not shown in Table 1, results of those tests are not relevant to the scope of this paper due to the failure mode observed. The test specimens selected for this study accurately reflect the variable results that can occur in field testing of the products noted.

TABLE 1 – Comparison of field water infiltration testing results.

Building Identification	Specimen Numbers	AAMA 501.2 Results	ASTM E 1105 Results	S.A.P.D.[1]	Failure Mode[2]
A	1, 2	Pass	Fail	575 Pa(12.0 lbf/ft^2)	1
A	3, 4, 5, 6	Pass	Fail	575 Pa(12.0 lbf/ft^2)	2
B	7, 8, 9,	Pass	Fail	517 Pa(10.8 lbf/ft^2)	1
B	10	Pass	Fail	517 Pa(10.8 lbf/ft^2)	3
C	11, 12	Pass	Fail	297 Pa(6.2 lbf/ft^2)	1
D	13, 14	Pass	Fail	575 Pa(12.0 lbf/ft^2)	1
E	15, 16, 17	Pass	Fail	575 Pa(12.0 lbf/ft^2)	1
E	18	Pass	Fail	575 Pa(12.0 lbf/ft^2)	2
E	19	Pass	Fail	575 Pa(12.0 lbf/ft^2)	3

[1] Static Air Pressure Differential used for ASTM E 1105 test method.
[2] Definition of Failure Mode:
1. Water infiltration at joint between horizontal and vertical frame members, exiting at the top of the glazing rabbet of the horizontal member.

2. Water infiltration at corner joint of the horizontal and vertical glazing gaskets.
3. Water infiltration due to perimeter sealant failure, unrelated to glazing assembly. The buildings selected for testing as shown in Table 1 included two governmental complexes (Buildings A and D), one condominium (Building B), one single family residence (Building C) and one commercial office building (Building E). Specimens 8, 9, and 10 are aluminum framed storefront glazing systems while all others are glazed aluminum curtain wall systems. The aluminum framed glazing system in Building A provides a 16 mm (0.625 in.) deep glazing rabbet while all others provide a 25 mm (1.00 in.) deep rabbet. A review of the data provided in Table 1 reveals the following observations:

1. Twelve of the specimens (63 percent) failed ASTM E 1105 testing due to a failure near the top of the seal between the horizontal and vertical members that was not revealed during AAMA 501.2 testing (Failure Mode 1, Table 1).
2. Five of the specimens (26 percent) failed ASTM E 1105 test due to water overflowing the glazing rabbet that exited from the corner joints of the interior glazing gaskets, which was not revealed during AAMA 501.2 testing (Failure Mode 2, Table 1).
3. Two of the specimens (11 percent) failed the ASTM E 1105 test due to the infiltration of water through a faulty frame-to-structure perimeter sealant joint which was not revealed during the AAMA 501.2 test (Failure Mode 2, Table 1)

These observations reveal that discrepancies in test results most commonly occur when the point of failure is located near the top of the water collection area, or is otherwise positioned where the water must rise vertically to reach the point of entry. For example, the glazing rabbet of the horizontal frame members in each specimen represented in Table 1 is intended to provide a collection area for water infiltration. The collected water is then diverted back to the building exterior through a series of weep holes. When testing using the AAMA 501.2 method, water collecting in the rabbet of the horizontal framing member flows to the drainage points unimpeded. However, if water in the collection area must also overcome air pressure as in the ASTM E 1105 test method, the collection area may begin to fill with water. As the water continues to rise, it eventually overflows the horizontal, escaping at the glazing gasket intersections or other open points. Mode of Failure 1 and 2 in Table 1 reflect these failures. It has also been shown that discrepancies in test results can occur because of water infiltration around the perimeter seals of aluminum frames. In Specimens 10 and 19, as reported in Table 1, the point of water infiltration was found to be an adhesive failure of the sealant where it contacts the aluminum framing member. It is suspected that this failure was not revealed during the AAMA 501.2 method because of the location of the adhesive failure and weather conditions at the time of testing. In both specimens, the point of water entry was located below the sill member of the frame which was designed in a manner that partially protected the sealant from direct exposure to the water spray. In addition, testing of both specimens was done on a warm day when the substrate materials had expanded thereby compressing the joint width, whereas the point of entry was clearly obvious when viewed in the coolness of early evening when the substrate materials had contracted resulting in an expanded joint width. Of interest, ASTM E 1105 testing of the same specimens, in weather conditions similar to those present during AAMA 501.2 testing, clearly revealed the point of water infiltration, and the test results were unaffected by either location of the deficiency or the weather conditions.

The AAMA test method subjects specimens only to an intermittent flow of water. The ASTM test method subjects specimens to a continuous spray of water along with a static air pressure differential. Therefore, as revealed by the testing, although a building may exhibit evidence of water infiltration, unless the point of entry is positioned in an especially vulnerable location, hose testing similar to AAMA 501.2 may not be adequate to reveal the deficiency.

CONCLUSIONS

It has been demonstrated that the industry recognized AAMA 501.2 hose testing method, when performed in strict compliance with the published data, may result in findings that are not consistent with the results of testing in accordance with ASTM E 1105 procedures. Further, if hose testing is performed with non-conforming equipment, or if tests are made on assemblies that do not comply with the requirements of those stated by AAMA 501.2, the results may not accurately duplicate in-service observations. Therefore, while hose testing is intended as a check of glazing components and joints that are designed as permanently closed elements of the test specimen, the reader is advised to exercise caution in drawing conclusions from the use of the procedure for assemblies or glazing seals that can be influenced by pressure differential since the test method may not reveal the failure. In addition, given the variables of construction materials and assemblies, and allowing that the recognized method is not intended for materials other than glazing assemblies, the use of hose testing for other types of materials or assemblies may not be appropriate at all.

It is the responsibility of the professional directing the tests to evaluate the appropriateness of the procedure and to report any elements may or may not be influenced by the test method employed. If the objective is to reveal deficiencies observed under variable in-service conditions, the test method employed should attempt to replicate in service performance requirements. Since satisfactory performance relies on the ability of the system to control the basic principles of water infiltration, normally including that of static air pressure differential, this also should be considered as an element of the test procedure. Since static air pressure differentials are not accounted for in the AAMA 501.2 hose test procedure, the testing professional must therefore consider the relevance of hose testing to the desired objectives.

REFERENCES

[1]   "Field Check of Metal Curtain Walls for Water Leakage," AAMA 501.2-83, Methods of Test for Metal Curtain Walls, American Architectural Manufacturers Association, 1983.

[2]   "Field Check of Metal Storefronts, Curtain Walls, and Sloped Glazing Systems for Water Leakage," AAMA 501.2-94, Methods of Tests for Exterior Walls,

American Architectural Manufacturers Association, Publication No. AAMA 501-94, 1994, pp 9-10.

[3]   "Voluntary Specifications for Field Testing of Windows and Sliding Glass Doors," American Architectural Manufacturers Association, Publication No. AAMA 502-90, 1990, p. 1.

[4]   "Voluntary Specifications for Field Testing of Metal Storefronts, Curtain Walls and Sloped Glazing Systems," American Architectural Manufacturers Association, Publication No. AAMA 503-92, 1990, p. 1.

[5]   Williams, M. F. and Williams, B. Lamp, Exterior Insulation and Finish Systems, Current Practices and Future Considerations, ASTM Manual Series MNL 16, American Society for Testing and Materials, 1994.

[6]   Beers, P. E., "Field Testing Windows for Water Leakage" U.S. Glass, Metal & Glazing; August 1990, pp. 52-55.

[7]   Smith, W. D., "Water Management - Designing and Installing Storefronts to Prevent Water Leaks," Glass Digest Magazine, July 15, 1993, pp. 46-49

Paul G. Johnson[1]

BUILDING EXTERIOR WALL WATER INFILTRATION CONTROL USING QUALITY ASSURANCE PROGRAMS

REFERENCE: Johnson, P. G., **"Building Exterior Wall Water Infiltration Control Using Quality Assurance Programs,"** Water Leakage Through Building Facades, ASTM STP 1314, R. J. Kudder and J. L. Erdly, Eds., American Society for Testing and Materials, 1998.

ABSTRACT: Building exterior walls are complex construction systems with criteria which vary according to project, design, and construction delivery systems. They are by nature subject to performance problems which may include water infiltration. A properly implemented Quality Assurance Program which begins during the Design phase of the project and follows through final acceptance of the construction offers an opportunity to reduce or eliminate these problems. These programs should involve all parties of the Design/Construct process since their success is highly dependent upon planning and communication. The successful implementation of a quality assurance program can result in higher performance of the wall system, better conformance to project schedule and budget requirements, and reduced likelihood of conflict including litigation. While there is a cost to implement such a program, the cost to benefit ratio is favorable and they are particularly beneficial for complex or high risk projects.

KEYWORDS: Quality Assurance Program, exterior building walls, water infiltration, communication, leakage, performance

---

Building exterior walls serve several functions; they act to define interior spaces by providing a separation from the surrounding external environment, and they provide

---

[1]   Certified Construction Specifier, Associate and Consulting Architect, Smith, Hinchman & Grylls Associates, Inc., 150 West Jefferson, Suite 100, Detroit, Michigan 48226 USA

barriers to create and protect interior environments, which are normally different from the exterior conditions. Hopefully, they will also provide color texture and form which is pleasing to the eye. Of these functions, the merits of how well the form, color and texture or design considerations are handled will always be open to debate. The task of defining the separation between the exterior and interior is relatively simple. If there is a wall the separation is accomplished.

However, the task of providing barriers which will separate the exterior environment from the desired interior environment can be difficult, and too often is not adequately accomplished. These walls must be designed, fabricated and constructed to resist the penetration of water, limit the transfer of air across or through the walls, and limit heat transfer between the interior spaces and the outside environment. In special cases, walls may also be required to reduce or minimize (from either side) the passage of light, radio waves, radiation, electromagnetic energy, or sound. They must also withstand exposure to the elements of weather, including water in its various forms.

This paper describes practical procedures which may be implemented to control the passage of water in liquid form through exterior building walls. While the specific issue is water infiltration, the broader issue is quality. The procedures identified can and should be used to attain satisfactory results for all of the required performance characteristics of the wall.

THE PROBLEM

Exterior walls sometimes allow leakage of water from the exterior to the building interior and many building problems are related to water leakage through exterior walls. The results of this leakage range from minor inconvenience to the occupants, to cases where the building may be unusable. The consequences of water leakage may include:

- disruption to building occupancy
- physical damage to building or contents
- delays in initial occupancy after construction
- lost business opportunities to occupants/tenants
- safety and health hazards
- loss of income to owner and tenants
- damaged reputations of architects, engineers, owners, suppliers and contractors
- damaged relationships between the owners and the project design and construction team
- legal action (justified or not)
- lost opportunities due to time spent resolving a water leakage problem

barriers to create and protect interior environments, which are normally different from the exterior conditions. Hopefully, they will also provide color texture and form which is pleasing to the eye. Of these functions, the merits of how well the form, color and texture or design considerations are handled will always be open to debate. The task of defining the separation between the exterior and interior is relatively simple. If there is a wall the separation is accomplished.

However, the task of providing barriers which will separate the exterior environment from the desired interior environment can be difficult, and too often is not adequately accomplished. These walls must be designed, fabricated and constructed to resist the penetration of water, limit the transfer of air across or through the walls, and limit heat transfer between the interior spaces and the outside environment. In special cases, walls may also be required to reduce or minimize (from either side) the passage of light, radio waves, radiation, electromagnetic energy, or sound. They must also withstand exposure to the elements of weather, including water in its various forms.

This paper describes practical procedures which may be implemented to control the passage of water in liquid form through exterior building walls. While the specific issue is water infiltration, the broader issue is quality. The procedures identified can and should be used to attain satisfactory results for all of the required performance characteristics of the wall.

THE PROBLEM

Exterior walls sometimes allow leakage of water from the exterior to the building interior and many building problems are related to water leakage through exterior walls. The results of this leakage range from minor inconvenience to the occupants, to cases where the building may be unusable. The consequences of water leakage may include:

- disruption to building occupancy
- physical damage to building or contents
- delays in initial occupancy after construction
- lost business opportunities to occupants/tenants
- safety and health hazards
- loss of income to owner and tenants
- damaged reputations of architects, engineers, owners, suppliers and contractors
- damaged relationships between the owners and the project design and construction team
- legal action (justified or not)
- lost opportunities due to time spent resolving a water leakage problem

It is recognized that resolution of wall problems is most readily and cost effectively resolved in the earliest stages of the project by avoiding the problem. At the concept development phase the cost is nearly zero. As the project proceeds through design, the cost to avoid or resolve potential problems is minimal in the early stages and progressively increases as the design is completed. As the walls become closer to reality (the final engineering through the completion of construction) and occupancy of the building, there will be a dramatic increase in the cost to resolve problems.

A quality assurance program can assist in avoiding or resolving problems at the earliest opportunity, and thereby reduce costs.

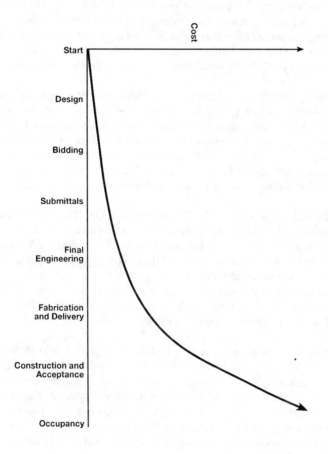

FIG. 1--COST TO TIME RELATIONSHIP OF PROBLEM RESOLUTION IN A PROJECT

plays a critical role in the wall construction process and can greatly influence the quality of the finished product. Each group should be brought into the QAP at the appropriate time to realize the best results of their involvement.

It is also important that all parties be provided with a clear understanding of their role in the process. All should participate willingly, not as an obligation or burden, and everyone should be recognized for their contributions to the process.

- **Develop a plan** -Develop a plan for the program and follow it, however, the plan may have to change as the project develops, so it must be flexible. Without a clearly defined plan it is easy to lose control of the program.

- **Involvement at all phases** -The QAP should be followed through all phases of the design and construction process. It is easy for the process to go astray if progress is not checked as the design and construction proceeds. Scheduled reviews of assumptions, criteria, previous decisions, and progress to date is necessary to help discover problems at the earliest possible point.

- **Budget for quality** - The project budget should be reviewed at each phase of the project as an integral part of the QAP. The portion of the project budget identified for exterior walls must be adequate to support the established performance, appearance and durability criteria. If it is not, there will be natural pressure to design down to a price as the project proceeds. The end product may or may not meet the established criteria, but most likely it will not. Losing control of the project budget is one of the most certain paths to wall failures.

- **Build in time and cost for the program** -A QAP is not free, it can however be a bargain. The project schedule and budget as well as allocations for professional service fees, testing, mock-ups and construction must reflect the time and effort required to adequately implement the program. This is especially true of unique or innovative designs, or those which are highly detailed or have special schedule considerations. These types of projects may require the most effort, they are also the projects most prone to failure and therefore stand to realize the greatest benefit from the implementation of a successful QAP.

- **Consider the project delivery system** -Each project delivery system (general contract, construction management, multiple prime, design build, fast tract/phase construction) has its own set of procedures, working arrangements and protocol. A QAP must be tailored to suit each delivery system while maintaining the basic functions and purpose of the program. If a QAP designed for one project is forced onto a project with a different type of delivery system the chances for success are greatly reduced. If the system does not fit, it will soon be discarded, or reduced to a meaningless formality.

- **Communicate** -Establish a clear process of communication for the project team and encourage and reward participation. Each participant in the program has something to offer and will likely perform better and more productively if they know they are being heard. Communication is also the key to making sure that all parties share a common goal and understanding. Regular meetings and written progress reports can facilitate this process.

PROJECT PHASES

During each phase of the project, the QAP has different objectives, all directed toward the goal of obtaining walls which do not leak. For purposes of explaining a method of developing and implementing a QAP directed to controlling water infiltration, this paper deals with seven basic phases of exterior wall construction projects [1]:

- Design
- Bid and Award
- Final Design and Engineering
- Mock-Up/Performance Testing
- Fabrication and Delivery
- Construction
- Acceptance

While this breakdown may need to be adjusted to accommodate a specific project or delivery system, it provides a basic framework to establish a QAP for any project.

Design

The design phase starts with concept development by the designer and continues through the completion of documents for bidding or negotiating. During this phase the appearance, configuration, basic system selections, terminations, materials, performance criteria and interface conditions with other building systems are established. The majority of the basic decisions regarding the wall have been made by the completion of this phase. Depending upon the wall system, erection/construction procedures may also be determined directly or indirectly by the choices made regarding materials, systems, configuration, and performance requirements.

The objectives of the QAP during the design phase should be directed to insure that the following considerations have been adequately and appropriately addressed:

- wind load
- wind exposure
- precipitation characteristics
- precipitation exposure
- ambient outdoor conditions of temperature and humidity
- solar exposure

- interior pressurization
- interior temperature and humidity conditions
- constructability
- review and approval schedules
- mock-up and testing schedules
- manufacture/fabrication schedules
- construction /erection schedules
- compatibility with adjacent systems
- appearance criteria
- durability (service life conditions)
- initial cost
- life cycle cost
- code/regulatory approvals
- maintenance requirements

Quality assurance efforts during the design phase should include the following basic procedures:

- Evaluate project criteria which establish characteristics of the acceptable end product.

- Review the schedule for completion of the project including consideration for:

  - owner reviews
  - design team checking
  - cost estimating
  - manufacturers/fabricators review and comment
  - consultant reviews
  - review by regulatory or code agencies
  - peer reviews, redesign
  - special testing or analysis such as wind tunnel load analysis (Figure 2)

- Confirm that good communication procedures between the project team have been established including:

  - design team
  - owner/tenant
  - contractor/construction manager
  - consultants/testing agencies
  - cost estimators
  - manufacturers/fabricators/erectors (design/build projects)

- Implement periodic reviews and sign-off of the criteria and design as they are developed. These can be "on-board" reviews which do not stop the project development, or they can be scheduled for a longer length of time with wall development halted until the review is completed and the review comments are received. All review comments should be responded to, and resolved.

- Establish a series of value enhancement workshops to be held at key development points. The purpose is to add value to the completed project, not just reduce cost. Beware of "value engineering" services offered by organizations who are not qualified to properly perform the task, they may do more harm than good by in reality performing "cost cutting".

- Require a final sign-off for the documents before they are released for bidding or negotiations. The documents will often receive a more conscientious review if sign-offs are required.

- Perform periodic estimates of cost as the project is developed. These should be accomplished at regular intervals throughout the project development to insure that costs do not get out of control.

If the QAP has been successful during the Design Phase, there will be an added degree of comfort that many of the causes of water leakage have been avoided. It is important that the continuity of the QAP be preserved into the Bid and Award Phase.

Figure 2--Scale model used for wind tunnel testing of wind loads and snow accumulation patterns.

Bid and Award

This phase may include negotiating or bidding, as a means of selecting a contractor to provide the exterior wall construction. In today's construction market it sometimes seems that there are as many methods of contracting for construction as there are projects. The specific method selected may depend upon a number of factors including [2]:

- size of the project
- cost of the project
- complexity of the design
- local or regional market conditions
- overall project delivery system
- material availability
- schedule requirements
- local or regional practices
- client purchasing preferences or requirements

In any case, there are a number of precautions which can be implemented during this phase to assure that the proper quality is attained, and a reduction in water infiltration problems is realized. These precautions are designed to insure that there is an accurate understanding of the project criteria on the part of the bidders, or in the case of award by negotiation, the parties making proposals, and on the part of the owner. All major issues should be understood by both sides before a contract agreement is reached. To this end, include the following quality assurance efforts during the bid and award phase:

- Allow adequate time for the preparation of bids or proposals.

- Make complete sets of documents available to all bidders. Require certification by bidders that pricing is based on full documents.

- Require pre-bid conferences to allow bidders the opportunity to ask questions regarding the documents. If the project is a retrofit or renovation include on-site walk throughs.

- Where possible, require mandatory attendance at the pre-bid meeting as a condition of bid.

- Require certification by the bidder that their bid is based upon full contract documents including addenda, and that they meet the quality standards of the documents for length and type of prior experience.

- Limit the number of pre-bid addenda to avoid confusion. However, if pertinent and legitimate questions arise during bidding, make sure that they are answered by an addendum communicated to all bidders.

- Do not provide verbal responses to bidders questions. If a response is required, include it in an addendum.

- Document the results of the pre-bid meeting by addendum to all participants. Do not allow dependence upon the spoken word. Require that only the written minutes issued by an addendum be relied upon as the response.

- Upon receipt of bids, allow adequate time for evaluation of each bid. Review each bid individually to ascertain that the bid is responsive; is comprehensive in nature; and that the proper bidder certifications are provided.

- If possible, do not base contract award on price alone. Award of contract based on a combination of quality, price, and schedule can provide a very successful selection process.

- Require proposal drawings for performance based bids. Test reports and calculations should also be submitted for evaluation. Fully evaluate these documents and resolve any concerns before contract award.

- Meet with the bidders for a face to face review of their bids during the bid evaluation process. Perform a detailed review of their bids to confirm compliance with project requirements.

- Allow time for the bidders to consider and respond to any questions which may result from the detailed review. If necessary, allow the bidders to modify their bids in response to these issues.

- For projects with complex phasing, scheduling or other special schedule related concerns, provide this information and require the bidders to confirm their ability to comply with these special needs. In some cases, it may be prudent to require the bidders to submit a detailed response indicating how they would respond to these special conditions.

These procedures may vary from project to project, and may not all be required for, or applicable, to every project. Each project should be evaluated individually to determine which procedures are best suited to the specific conditions. The primary issue is to avoid conditions during the bid and award phase which will lead to problems later. A contract which is issued based on an inadequate understanding of project appearance, performance, schedule and job site criteria, or the contractor's abilities to perform is more likely to result in problems during the final design and engineering phase, and ultimately more performance problems possibly including water infiltration. If the QAP goals have been attained during the Bid and Award phase, it is likely that the next phase will proceed smoothly, or at least with fewer problems.

Final Design and Engineering

Following award of a contract for construction of the walls, the successful contractor is normally responsible to demonstrate their knowledge of the required installation through the process of submittals. During the course of this process, the contractor will submit material finish and color samples, test reports, detailed shop and sometimes fabrication and erection drawings, product literature, test reports, certifications, fabricator or manufacturer's engineering calculations and other pertinent data. This process is necessary to assure all parties that the requirements of the project are understood, and will be met. The contractor, manufacturer or fabricator, will also perform the final engineering of the system during this phase.

This further effort is required to move the wall system forward from the design level of development to the more detailed level of development required to bring together the various components of the exterior wall into an integrated wall construction system. This necessarily includes coordination with other adjacent construction systems which are also moving along a similar and concurrent path of development. Even with the best contract documents, there may be a number of unforeseen conditions to resolve during this phase. It should be remembered that this is often the last opportunity to resolve any problems of design or coordination before fabrication or manufacture of the wall system. This is particularly true of prefabricated systems such as metal and glass curtain walls or precast concrete, which are normally prepared to a high degree of completion off-site and delivered for on-site erection. Generally speaking, the higher the degree of system or component fabrication performed off-site, the more critical the attention to detail and coordination needs to be during this phase. While it is true that these systems normally offer a superior degree of quality and workmanship than site fabricated systems (due to the advantages of assembly in a protected and controlled environment), they are difficult, and sometimes impossible, to successfully alter in the field. Therefore, they must be correct as fabricated.

The critical point regarding quality assurance during this phase is to maintain control of the process through communication and attention to detail. If this control is not maintained, there is an increased risk of loss of quality and performance, which may result in water infiltration in the finished wall. When a project encounters problems during this phase, there is likely to be great pressure to proceed with the construction in spite of the problems, due to financial and/or schedule considerations. Techniques which can be employed to maintain control of the project and insure adequate attention to detail include:

- Require pre-submittal meetings to review submittal requirements and expectations. Review the technical and procedural requirements of the project as well as any revisions which may be required, or which may be found to be helpful as the project develops. Require documentation of these meetings and distribute minutes to those involved.

- Obtain a submittal schedule from the wall contractor as the first issue to be considered. This schedule should provide a comprehensive listing of all expected and required submittals, and should include time for multiple submittals and reviews [3].

- Distribute approved wall system submittals to contractors of adjacent construction for purposes of coordination review. Conversely, provide submittals of critical adjacent construction systems to the wall systems contractor for coordination. It is essential that coordination problems be resolved during this phase, not on the job site.

- Establish means and methods of communications between the project team members. Whatever the details are to be, make sure that communication is facilitated, not hindered. It is important to maintain some control of this communication but it is more important to encourage open lines of communication and to foster valuable exchange of information. One method of accomplishing this goal is to allow ready access between the team members, but require documentation of any decisions made or major information development, by means of written project team communications. This can be facilitated by the use of facsimile transmissions, E-mail and other electronic communication techniques.

- Hold regularly scheduled meetings to review project development. These should be designed to keep the project team in tune with the progress of development, and identify problems which may require resolution. They also serve to notify the team of what level of activity will be required, which will help each team member perform in a timely fashion, by providing advance notice of the type and amount of effort required of them. Do not get bogged down in solving specific technical or coordination issues in these meetings. Address such issues in separate problem specific meetings.

- Require separate problem resolution or working meetings outside of the regular progress meetings. These meetings can often be held with fewer people, will be more focused on specific technical or coordination issues, and are more likely to conclude with solutions to specific problems or concerns.

- Establish adequate review, transmittal and response times for each cycle and each item required by the submittal process. Submittals which are prepared or reviewed in a rush are more likely to contain errors or be inadequately prepared or reviewed. This leads to frustration on the part of the team and too often to unacceptable or inadequate construction.

- Evaluate and resolve problems as they are discovered. This is critical! At this stage of the project there is no time available to push problems downstream. Questions which go unanswered at this point are likely to result in delays or unacceptable "field solutions". Additional costs are often the result of not adequately addressing issues remaining at this time. (Figure 1)

- Require submittal of mock-up, production, fabrication, delivery and erection schedules. These are necessary to ascertain that adequate time will be available to deliver and install the wall system to meet the overall project schedule. These schedules should be provided in a format common to the overall project to allow integration and coordination. Experience shows that projects which encounter schedule difficulties are likely to have a higher degree of wall failures, including water leakage.

- Resolve monetary issues as expeditiously as possible. If requests for additional compensation are submitted due to problems discovered during this phase resolve them. If resolution is not possible, at least document the claim thoroughly for future resolution. Money problems have a way of disrupting good thinking and common sense.

These procedures are suitable to projects of varying size, degree of difficulty and delivery method, with modification to suit the specific project. In all cases, the goals should be to communicate and pay attention to detail. Upon completion of this phase the efforts of the entire project team and the QAP will be tested through the mock-up and performance testing phase of the project.

Mock-Up/Performance Testing

Many exterior wall systems will require mock-up or performance testing to confirm that the wall design will conform to the particular appearance and performance criteria of the project (Figure 3). This process is especially important to those wall systems with appearance, design, or performance criteria which are unusual, or which have not been previously constructed. After exterior walls are in place, repairs can be expensive and difficult. During this phase of the project, the QAP should be continued as a means to verify that the wall will meet the project criteria and schedule.
The major points to address through the QAP during this phase of the project should include the following procedures which should have been established during the previous project phases in preparation for this effort:

- Review submittal review and approval procedures relative to the mock-up or testing. This process should have been completed in the previous phase and confirmed at this point.

- Coordinate location of testing or mock-ups. If on-site (or on the building) ongoing construction activities must be considered.

- Establish the length of time which the mock-up or tested panels are required to be retained. Premature destruction or removal of test panels and/or mock-ups can lead to problems.

- Confirm required levels of performance, and test procedures to be utilized.

- Review configuration of the wall test panels and the sequence of testing. Sequence is particularly important if any of the testing will be destructive.

- Validate conditions to be tested, and the acceptance criteria.

- Confirm conditions under which re-testing will be required and who will be responsible for the cost of re-testing.

Figure 3--Mock-up testing utilizing an airplane engine to simulate driving rain.

- Review procedural requirements for witnessing of the testing.

- Re-evaluate and confirm schedules for production of test panel or mock-up material, erection of the mock-up or wall panels, and use of testing facilities or equipment.

- Update schedule for testing, whether on the building, or at a separate location such as a testing facility.

- For on-site mock-up or testing, confirm the conditions if any, for which the mock-up or test panels will be acceptable for inclusion in the finished wall.

After these QAP efforts have been completed the mock-up construction and/or performance testing can proceed. Additional QAP procedures to be followed for the remainder of the Mock-Up/Performance Testing Phase of the project include:

- Document each step in the mock-up/performance testing procedure. Include photographic as well as video documentation.

- Take special note of any differences between the mock-up/performance testing specimens and the material to be installed.

- Allow adequate time for sealants and other "wet" components to cure before testing.

- After mock-up construction and prior to testing, remove and reglaze sample panels to demonstrate procedures (metal or glass curtain walls).

- Monitor testing procedures and results to confirm compliance with project criteria.

- In the event of failure, modify system details and retest.

- After completion of testing, resubmit shop and erection drawings revised to indicate required changes.

- Require a final written report of test results from the testing agency or consultant.

Keeping the mock-up and performance testing on the proper schedule track can be a critical link in avoiding water infiltration problems in the completed wall. As in many other areas of construction, if the mock-up or performance testing does not keep pace with the overall project schedule, there is likely to be pressure to short cut the process. If this pressure is successful, a valuable tool in discovering potential sources of water infiltration will be lost. Again, it is particularly important to complete this phase of the project for wall systems which are new or unique. If this is not accomplished in this phase of the project, then the building can become the test facility, which is not acceptable. In many cases, fabrication of the project material has been waiting for the successful completion of the mock-up and performance testing. The wall systems are now ready for production. With the assurance that the QAP has steadily helped to identify and resolve or avoid potential problems, the project proceeds.

Fabrication and Delivery

During the fabrication and delivery phase of the project there is often a tendency for the project team to push the wall systems out of their minds. Instead, they pay attention to other pressing, and also valid, problems relating to other aspects of the project. It is easy to forget that the wall system is proceeding through fabrication for delivery to the project site. However, it must be remembered that there are still opportunities for errors to occur and problems to develop which can dramatically affect the ability of the installed wall system to resist water infiltration.

As indicated earlier, shop fabricated material is normally preferable to field fabricated material, but is often very difficult to revise on-site. Therefore it must be correct when received. Generally speaking, the higher the degree of off-site fabrication, the greater the need for continuation of the QAP during this phase of the project. Fabrication or material errors, as well as late delivery dates of material, or delivery of damaged or incorrect materials can lead to an increased probability of water infiltration problems. A QAP can and should be continued at the fabrication facility or facilities to reduce the probability of thoccurring.

By following the proper QAP procedure, during fabrication and delivery, water infiltration problems related to this phase can be minimized or avoided entirely. Action items during this phase should include:

- Periodic inspections of fabricated materials to insure that the required quality is being attained (Figure 4).

- Checking of fabricated material to confirm that it conforms to the project requirements, and the wall system as approved by testing and mock-ups. This will include any revisions made as a result of mock-ups and /or testing.

- Review of erection drawings and installation instructions to confirm that any revisions required as a result of the mock-ups and/or testing have been included.

- Monitoring of the procurement of components to be delivered directly to the job site from separate suppliers. Confirm that it will be the correct material, and will fit with products being fabricated. Delivery dates and locations should also be confirmed.

- Confirmation that the on-site construction schedule has been considered and accommodated by the fabrication and delivery schedule. The order of on-site erection and/or assembly can be critical.

- Review of delivery requirements to confirm that the phasing of materials delivery will accommodate the amount of available, adequate on-site storage. Materials and fabricated systems which are not properly stored are more subject to problems in the finished construction.

- Review of the method of delivery as related to on-site materials handling capability. Fabricated assemblies which are improperly handled on site may be subject to damage which can be avoided by planning ahead.

- Monitoring of packaging practices and procedures. Improperly packaged materials can be damaged to the point of being unusable upon receipt at the job site. This can result in schedule problems and the attendant risk of errors in fabrication as pressure builds for the damaged material to be replaced or worse, incorporated into the wall.

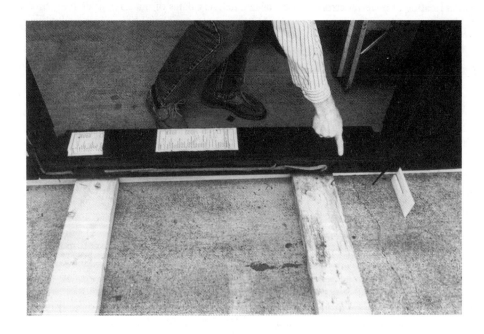

Figure 4--Quality assurance during the fabrication and delivery phase. Note the quality assurance label attached to the prefabricated curtain wall frame.

- Review of the packing lists and manifests to confirm that all of the required components are delivered to the correct location, and on time. Missing items may be replaced with the incorrect material or left out completely in the rush to keep the project moving. This can result in water leakage.

- Verification that assemblies are packaged and shipped in a manner which will prevent damage. This is especially true of large metal windows or frames which can move during handling or transport thus possibly opening corner joints. Confirm that needed bracing and/or packaging material is provided, and that these assemblies will be correctly placed and secured in the shipping vehicles.

- Require the erecting or installing contractor to check or "shake-out" the delivered material for completeness and condition as it arrives. Erection or installation should not be started before this process is completed. It is critical to get the process for replacement of damaged or otherwise unacceptable material, or the delivery of missing material started as soon as possible. In this way, problems can be resolved before they become schedule critical.

By following the established procedures for good communication and attention to detail, the goals of the QAP will be facilitated and the required fabricated materials should arrive on site complete, correct and in acceptable condition. By avoiding or limiting problems during the fabrication and delivery phase of the project, the Construction Phase should proceed more smoothly. This is likely to result in fewer problems and better conformance with the project requirements for performance, including the avoidance of water leakage.

Construction

During the construction phase of the project, the previous efforts of the Owner, designers, consultants, fabricators, material suppliers and contractors are brought together for the true test. Will it work, will it fit, will it look right and can the work be completed on time? If the project team has performed their jobs correctly, and if they have communicated properly, and paid attention to the details the answer will be yes. However, since this is an imperfect world and within this world is the very complex and even more imperfect world of construction, there is still a need for the continuation of the QAP through the construction phase of the project. The efforts required of the QAP during this phase may vary by the complexity of the wall system, however some general guidelines should be followed for any project:

- Require a pre-construction meeting prior to arrival of wall material on the job site. Issues to be addressed should include [4]:

    - Phasing and schedule of wall construction.
    - Wall material storage locations, conditions and facilities.

- Review of previously constructed wall mock-ups where appropriate.
- Review of erection drawings and system and interface details.
- Communications between designer, consultants, owners and contractors.
- Review of problem resolution techniques and procedures to be followed.
- Lift schedules where common use cranes or material hoists are provided.
- Site access for cranes where common use cranes or material hoists are not provided.
- Weather limitations for exterior wall work.
- Meeting schedule for coordination with other work.
- Review of acceptance criteria for substrates to which wall systems will be attached, and corrective procedure requirements and procedures.
- Acceptable tolerances of the finished wall work.
- Cleaning procedures.
- Inspection and acceptance procedures and criteria for work in progress.

• Require a pre-installation meeting between the designer, consultants reviewing construction, the general contractor or construction manager, the wall system contractor, and the tradesmen. During this meeting review the wall system design, critical details, acceptable and unacceptable practices, and inspection procedures. This meeting helps to establish a strong working relationship which can provide great benefits, especially for wall systems which are labor intensive on-site, such as masonry or cast in place concrete.

• Schedule and hold regular progress meetings to review the status of exterior wall work as it proceeds.

• Review storage conditions periodically to identify and correct problems.

• Review in-place work regularly to assure conformance to project requirements, and protection as necessary. Notify contractors of required remedial work.

• Review typical detail conditions with contractors and tradesmen as the work is started. This is often the last opportunity to be sure that the work will be performed correctly.

• Identify examples of acceptable work for each wall condition and review with contractors and tradesmen. Where possible the on-site mock-up should be used as the acceptable level of quality.

• Resolve problems as they are identified, do not procrastinate. Once on-site wall system work is started delays are not acceptable and may lead to unacceptable construction if not resolved quickly.

• Require a complete set of project documents be available on site at all times, including submittals and samples. Refer to these documents regularly.

- Check materials which are being incorporated in the wall. Read labels, check manufacturer's precautions and compare to approved submittals and project usage.

- Establish clear lines of communications between the designer, consultants, contractor/construction manager and installing or erection contractors. This is necessary to facilitate identification and resolution of problems with a limited amount of conflict and delay.

- Establish and foster working relationships on individual as well as organizational levels. Individual working relationships have the potential to provide a very successful quality assurance tool.

- Arrange access for inspection of the work, even and especially at hard to reach locations. If these locations are difficult to access, they may well be difficult to work on also, and are a likely source of problems.

- Establish schedule and requirements for in-situ progress testing and reporting. Involve all parties and distribute the results of meetings and testing.

- Require cleaning test areas to establish acceptable methods, tools, cleaning materials and end results. Document the results and identify an acceptable example area. Manufacturers of chemicals to be used and finished wall materials should be represented at these meetings and test cleanings.

- Where possible, perform acceptance review of work as the work is completed by area. This will allow corrections to be completed while there is still ready access and help to discover unacceptable conditions which may have been missed. This will facilitate correction of the problems in the ongoing work.

- Keep records of job site weather and progress. These can be valuable in identifying the sources of problems, or likely problem areas.

- Require daily reports of work in progress, problems encountered, crew sizes and individuals, and planned areas of work for all exterior wall work. These records may also prove valuable in problem resolution and can help the exterior wall contractor in planning his work.

When implementing quality assurance procedures during the construction phase it may be necessary to make additional efforts to explain the intent and process of the QAP. Many site representatives and tradesmen may not be familiar with the process and may not understand the goals and objectives. However, if you can successfully explain the program and gain their active support and participation, the results can be impressive.

Acceptance

Upon completion of the wall construction, final acceptance and payment is normally requested by the wall contractor. In order to assure that the owner has received a wall which is in conformance with the requirements of the contract documents, the design team and contractor or construction manager are required to review and comment on the completed product. In some cases, this process may also include in-situ testing for compliance with the specified performance criteria including water infiltration. This testing is normally performed under the guidance of, or directly by specialized consultants with experience and expertise in this area.

In order to obtain valid results from the acceptance process the following quality assurance procedures can be implemented:

- Require submission of "as-built" records indicating the final construction of the walls. The project documents will often contain detailed requirements for submission of these documents.

- Review the qualifications of the specialized consultant or testing agency to insure that they posses the proper knowledge and experience to perform and evaluate the results of the required in-situ testing procedures.

- Hold a pre-acceptance meeting with the project team to review and confirm the acceptance process and schedule. Document and distribute the results of this meeting to all parties.

- Require that installing contractors, general contractor/construction manager, design team and manufacturer or fabricator of the wall system be represented at testing and/or acceptance reviews. This will facilitate understanding of written review comments and test reports.

- Require written comments documenting the results of review and inspections. Depending upon the nature of the project, comments or a legend, and elevation drawings and details may also be required. Beware of tagging or marking comments directly on completed construction. Tags tend to blow away or wash off, and markings may damage finishes. If tagging or marking are to be used, review proposed methods with contractors and obtain their permission.

- Review the results of reviews, inspections and testing with contractors before corrections are implemented. All corrective procedures should be agreed upon by the project team before they are started.

- If required, perform in-situ testing on examples of proposed corrective procedures before they are implemented through the wall construction. This should be limited to critical conditions where there is a serious flaw and doubts regarding the ability of the proposed corrective procedures to perform. (Figure 5)

- Require final sign-off of the work by the designer, consultant, wall contractor, owner's representative and general contractor or construction manager.

The process is complete, the wall is constructed and the owner has a nice, new and dry building. The QAP has contributed to the finished quality of the walls and helped to avoid problems which would lead to water leakage. Hopefully the process has also helped to keep the project on schedule and on budget, and avoided potentially damaging conflict and litigation.

Figure 5--In-situ water spray testing of installed window assembly.

CONCLUSION

It is important to remember that the owner as well as the team members in the design/manufacture/fabrication and construction business have everything to gain and nothing to lose by the production of a quality project. There is no progress or benefit in doing otherwise, especially in the long term. Many of the quality assurance procedures suggested will be a matter of common practice for some team members. For others it will offer a new experience. Hopefully, it will be a good experience for all and an educational experience for those not familiar with the process.

More importantly if each team member walks away from the project believing that the process works, they will be likely to become supporters of the process for the next project. The process does have the ability to avoid the problems which lead to water infiltration and should be considered for your next project.

REFERENCES

[1]   FF/010, The Construction Specifications Institute Manual of Practice, Alexandria, VA 1992.

[2]   FF/040, The Construction Specifications Institute Manual of Practice, Alexandria, VA 1992.

[3]   CA/030, The Construction Specifications Institute Manual of Practice, Alexandria, VA.

[4]   CA/020, The Construction Specifications Institute Manual of Practice, Alexandria, VA.

[5]   "Cladding", Council on Tall Buildings and Urban Habitat, pp. 84-101, McGraw Hill, Inc., New York, 1992.

Norbet V. Krogstad,[1] Dennis K. Johnson,[2] and Richard A. Weber[3]

USING MODIFIED ASTM E 1105 TO IDENTIFY LEAKAGE SOURCES IN BUILDING WALL SYSTEMS

REFERENCE: Krogstad, N. V., Johnson, D. K., and Weber, R. A. **''Using Modified ASTM E 1105 to Identify Leakage Sources in Building Wall Systems,''** Water Leakage Through Building Facades, ASTM STP 1314, R. J. Kudder and J. L. Erdly, Eds., American Society for Testing and Materials, 1998.

ABSTRACT: The paper reviews an evaluation procedure for addressing water leakage problems. The procedure includes water leakage testing along with interviewing the building occupants, reviewing drawings and specifications, surveying the building components, and performing exploratory openings. The water leakage testing uses a modified version of ASTM E1105. This test utilizes a spray grid to apply water to the exterior surface of the wall. The primary modification from the ASTM specification is the longer time durations used on absorptive surfaces such as masonry. The test can be used on virtually any building material, including masonry, precast concrete, EIFS, metal panels and aluminum and glass curtain walls. Areas can be isolated by systematic positioning of the spray rack or by careful masking of the wall components or both. These procedures can be effective in identifying sources of water leakage problems. After repairs are performed, the test can be used to evaluate the effectiveness of such repairs. The test can also be included in a preconstruction testing program to locate potential leakage sources in a mock-up assembly. The paper outlines critical steps in using the procedure to reliably isolate the sources for water entry into buildings.

KEYWORDS: water leakage, masonry walls, curtain walls, leakage survey, water testing, air pressure, water penetration

---

Water leakage can sometimes be a problem in new and existing construction. Leakage problems, however, are often very difficult to identify because they often involve multiple sources or long exposure to wetting to develop as noticeable leakage. Most modern wall systems incorporate many different materials with many different interface conditions. Leakage problems can also be difficult to identify because the leaks are not well documented. Building occupants often do not know what to look for and do not notice subtle leakage problems. The

---

[1]Consultant, Wiss, Janney, Elstner Associates, Inc., 330 Pfingsten Road, Northbrook, IL 60062

[2]Consultant, Wiss, Janney, Elstner Associates, Inc., 330 Pfingsten Road, Northbrook, IL 60062

[3]Architect/Engineer II, Wiss, Janney, Elstner Associates, Inc., 330 Pfingsten Road, Northbrook, IL 60062

frequency of the water leakage problems and the weather conditions
associated with the water leakage are not often recorded. Many times,
the most reported leaks are not necessarily the most frequent or largest
volume leaks. The worst leaks may go unnoticed. For a water leakage
investigation to be effective, the problems must be accurately
identified. The investigation should be sufficiently comprehensive to
develop effective repairs.

On certain projects it is necessary to perform preconstruction
testing on a mock-up of the wall systems to locate potential problems.
The test is performed as a preconstruction evaluation procedure.
Potential problems must be identified as timely as possible to allow
revisions, as necessary, to the design without delays to the project
schedule. The investigative approach subsequently described is directed
towards water leakage in existing buildings. For preconstruction
testing, the approach may be even simpler because more information
regarding the design and construction would be available.

APPROACH FOR INVESTIGATING WATER LEAKAGE

The water leakage investigation program typically begins by
surveying the problem and determining if a pattern exists in the
location of leakage and the direction of the rain storm. The best way
to do this is to survey all the areas where water leakage has been
reported and to interview the occupants as to the nature of the water
leakage problems. The information gathered in the initial survey should
be carefully reviewed to identify potential patterns such as leakage
problems associated with a particular elevation or with particular
elements within a facade.

It is also important to review the original architectural drawings
and specifications, component shop drawings, available manufacturer's
data as well as all available construction data. It is equally
important to review past repairs to determine if they have been
effective and to understand how repairs may have modified the wall
system. The review of these documents provides helpful insights as to
why the pattern of observed leakage is occurring.

After gathering the initial information, a more comprehensive
investigation is undertaken. The investigation includes identifying
particular areas that represent typical leakage problems. These areas
should be well distributed across the building, both vertically and
horizontally. Whenever possible, they should be located on different
exposures and elevations. In the selected areas, a detailed visual
investigation of the interior and exterior wall surfaces is initially
performed. The purpose of this investigation is to identify potential
sources of water leakage problems. A close-up examination of the
exterior/interior surfaces allows the investigator to examine large
areas of the walls and to begin to formulate ideas based on past
experience as to why and how leakage problems are occurring. Many areas
can be surveyed in a relatively small amount of time. This is essential
in identifying the type and amount of water testing that is desirable to
confirm the leakage paths.

Water leakage testing is an important tool to be used in
conjunction with a detailed exterior and interior survey. Although the
surveys alone can identify potential sources, they do not confirm
sources nor do they allow the investigator to observe the severity of
the leakage from each source. There is a tendency to identify defects
as major leakage sources that, in fact, may be only minor contributors
to the leakage problem.

Inspection openings or the disassembly of components is essential
in understanding the as-built conditions in order to evaluate how water
moves through the wall system. Merely examining the exterior and
interior or performing tests without dismantling the wall system may not
clearly identify the leakage path if the wall system is built
differently than that which is shown on the drawings and specifications.

USING ASTM E1105 IN A WATER LEAKAGE INVESTIGATION

There are many test methods available for testing wall systems. ASTM E1105 "Test Method for Field Determination of Water Penetration of Installed Exterior Windows, Curtain Walls and Doors by Uniform or Cyclic Static Air Pressure Difference", [1], however, provides one methodology that can be used on most different wall components. By subjecting each component to the same test procedure, it is possible to compare the relative contribution of these elements to the leakage problem. ASTM E1105 can often be used in conjunction with many other water tests to further pinpoint leakage sources. These include American Architectural Manufacturing Association (AAMA) 501.2 [2], AAMA 502 [3], wall drainage tests [4] and flood testing of horizontal surfaces.

ASTM E1105 allows the user to test relatively large areas of wall systems in each test by positioning a spray rack near the top of a large section of wall system. A sheet of water develops on the face of the wall which can test multiple floors of the building as the water flows downward. The spray rack used in ASTM E1105 can easily be adapted to many variations in wall system configurations. This test also does not disturb the wall surface prior to and during testing. If combined with systematic masking, the test can be used to test individual wall components.

The three main parameters in the ASTM E1105 test are the duration of the test, the applied rate of water to the wall surface and the air pressure, if any, across the wall surface. Currently, two of these parameters are set in the ASTM E1105 Standard. The time duration is 15 minutes and the applied rate is at least five gallons per hour per square foot ($3.4 L/m^2.Min.$) of wall surface.

Test Duration

The Standard states that the test should be performed for a duration of 15 minutes. On absorptive surfaces such as masonry, a duration of 15 minutes is not sufficient or appropriate. If the masonry surfaces are dry, it may take well over one-half hour before the surfaces absorb enough water to reproduce the water leakage problem. Even for curtain-wall systems, 15 minutes is sometimes not sufficient to develop the observed leakage patterns. Windows that leak into wall systems and saturate other components of the wall may need to go for well over one-half hour before the leaks become apparent on the interior.

There are many factors that are used to determine the duration of the test. Water leakage reported by the building occupants is an important consideration. If leaks are reported occurring immediately after the start of a rain storm, tests as short as 15 minutes may be appropriate. For absorptive surfaces or wall assemblies that contain absorptive materials, where the occupants report leaks well after a rain has started, test durations of an hour or greater are appropriate. Also, where the interior is not fully accessible, the test should be run for a longer period of time so that water has time to flow to the locations of observed leakage. We have found, however, that with most wall systems, leaks observed after three hours of testing may not be representative of recurring leakage problems and are identifying minor sources of leakage that are normally not exposed to this quantity of water.

Water Application Rate

The second variable is the rate of water application to the surface of the wall. ASTM E1105 uses a minimum rate of five gallons per hour per square foot ($3.4 L/m^2.Min.$) of wall surface area. It is difficult to correlate this with a rainfall intensity. There are many factors that must be considered. The first of these is that the amount of rain hitting a horizontal surface does not typically translate to the

amount of rain hitting a vertical surface. Wind blown rain would have
to travel at a 45° angle before the rain hitting a vertical surface is
equal to that of a horizontal surface. Typically, the angle of
incidence is less than this. Rundown from upper surfaces will
significantly affect the amount of water contacting the wall surface.
In multi-story buildings, water hitting upper levels will run down and
add to the water at the lower levels. In this way, the water hitting
the lower level may be many times greater than water hitting the upper
level. Studies on masonry wall systems have indicated that once an
uninterrupted sheet of water develops over the surface of the wall,
increasing the thickness of the sheet has very little impact on the
water penetration. [5] For these reasons, once water is flowing across
small voids and other openings in the wall surface, increasing the
thickness of the sheet of water over the face has virtually no impact on
increasing the penetration through the void. In most cases, the current
application rate in ASTM E1105 is appropriate. By using this flow rate,
leaks can be successfully recreated within the wall system. The leakage
observed during testing mimics not only the location of the actual leaks
but often the pattern of leakage that is being experienced during
rainstorms. In cases where more or less water is expected, the spray
grid can be modified to increase or reduce the rate of water applied to
the wall surface. This could be based on reoccurrence intervals for
rains in a region of the country where the building is located. [6] If
modifications to application rates are made, rundown factors should be
considered.

Air Pressure

     The current Standard states that the air pressure is to be as
specified by the investigator. It has been our experience that repeated
leakage problems can be duplicated without applying any air pressure
difference across the wall system. Even when the occupants of the
building report leakage only when the wind is coming from a certain
direction, this may merely mean that the wind is forcing the rain to
strike this surface of the wall. However, in some cases, it may be
appropriate to apply a pressure difference. Some window systems with
short sill heights may only leak when air pressure is applied to the
wall system, because the air pressure will allow water to overflow the
sills. Each individual test area must be reviewed to determine if
applying a pressure difference across the system is required.

Test Set Up

     Leakage sources can be identified by employing two different
procedures while using the E1105 test. One approach is systematic
positioning of the spray rack. Generally, the spray rack is positioned
beginning at the lowest portion of the wall and selectively moving the
rack up the wall. In these cases, lower components within the wall
system can be ruled out prior to testing at higher levels of the wall.
It is important, however, to use care when examining the interface
between wall systems with this method to determine if leakage is
occurring due to overspray of the adjacent element. Some overspray of
water will likely occur. By using water-indicating paper or other
careful examination, it is possible to determine the source of water
penetration at these interfaces. The spray rack can also be positioned
at several points across the wall horizontally in order to pinpoint
leakage.
     The second approach is to selectively mask the wall. This will
allow testing of entire wall elements including interface conditions.
Plastic sheeting or other barriers are constructed to avoid overspray on
other elements. Often tape is used to attach the masking to the surface
of the wall. In many cases, water can bypass the tape especially on
porous surfaces. One way to reduce the potential for this is to use a
small bead of sealant on the edge of the tape to limit water

penetration. It must be recognized that some water may still bypass the barrier and, therefore, care must be taken when examining the source of leakage to make sure that this has not been a factor. Even with masking, it is still important to systematically position the rack in order to test different components or simplify the amount of masking required. In general, when openings through the interior finishes are not possible to check for leakage or when the interface condition between materials is to be tested, the masking method is recommended.

CASE STUDIES

High-Rise Building With Alternating Vertical Bands of Masonry and Curtain Walls

The curtain wall was constructed with windows alternating with precast concrete panels. The masonry is face brick with concrete masonry backup. The water leakage was occurring on the interior plaster-covered surface of the concrete masonry near the window jambs and at or below the window sill. In order to isolate the leakage between the masonry and the window system, masking was installed for 12 stories of the building. The masking was attached to the jambs of the masonry and extended perpendicular from the surface of the wall to the cables spanning between the outrigger beams at the top of the wall and weights at the base of the wall, as shown in Fig. 1. The edges of the tape were sealed with silicone to prevent water from migrating across the masking.

Fig. 1 - Modified ASTM E1105 test on masonry wall
with masking in Case Study 1

The water rack was positioned at the top floor of the building to create a sheet that would run down the full height of the building. The postition of the spray rack tested a large portion of the masonry wall at one time. During the test, inspections were made of all but one of the units included in the test. We were unable to gain access to this unit. When the masonry was tested, no overspray was hitting the windows on either side. In other words, the masking was effective in preventing the water from reaching any other portion of the wall system. A sheet of water was effectively developed for the full height of the masonry even though the spray rack only applied water directly against the upper six feet of the top floor of the building, as shown in Fig. 2.

Fig. 2 - Water flowing down face of masonry
during the water test in Case Study 1

Water leaks developed in the masonry wall near the jambs of the windows at 4 of the 6 locations where staining and interior damage was observed, as shown in Fig. 3. The two units that did not leak in this test did leak during tests of the curtain-wall system. One unit that did not have visible damage prior to our test developed a leak at the head of the window. Because of the location of this leak, it may have

Fig. 3 - Interior leakage at window jamb during
test of masonry wall in Case Study 1

occurred in the past without leaving a stain. The leakage closely
resembled the pattern of staining as well as what was reported by the
building occupants.

        After the masonry was tested, the walls were allowed to dry and
the spray rack was positioned at the windows which were also masked on
both jambs. The masking was positioned to include the interface between
the vertical sealant joint and the windows along the edge of the
masonry. The water ran down the face of the windows and the face of the
precast concrete and developed a sheet of water over both that covered
approximately 75 percent of the surface. It was not possible to develop
an uninterrupted sheet because of the many changes in the plane of this
wall. Four of the six windows developed leaks on the interior in
locations where they had been reported to leak previously. The two
units that did not develop leaks in this window test had previously
developed leaks in the masonry test. Two units that did not have
visible damage prior to our test, developed leaks during our test.
Because of the location of these leaks, it may have occurred in the past
without causing damage.

The testing showed that some of the moisture damage near the jambs of the windows was caused by water penetration through the masonry, through the window system and in some areas through both. It should be noted that previous investigators attributed all of the leakage to the window system alone. Masonry openings at the locations where leakage was observed during testing determined that water was able to bridge from the brick outer wythe to the concrete block and saturate the interior plaster surface.

Following the test, openings were made to confirm the conditions. Based on the results of the testing and openings, repairs were made to the windows and masonry. The area was then retested to confirm the effectiveness of the repairs.

Low-rise Building with Alternating Horizontal Bands of Masonry and Window Walls

The curtain wall construction on this three-story office building consisted of alternating horizontal bands of brick masonry and aluminum framed fixed windows. The brick masonry veneer is supported by a steel framework and is tied to metal studs covered with exterior gypsum sheathing. The masonry flashing is a copper fabric. The horizontal band of windows is thermally a broken, two-sided structural sealant framing system. Gaskets are used for glazing at the head and sill. A sill cover is installed beneath the windows.

Water leakage was occurring on the interior drop ceiling, dripping from the window head and at window sills. In order to recreate the leakage, a water rack was used to spray various portions of the exterior building wall. By selective positioning of the rack at different elevations and removal of interior components, the water leakage was effectively traced.

When the water rack was positioned to spray only the masonry, water leakage developed, as shown in Figs. 4 and 5. Water leakage was

Fig. 4 - Spray rack positioned on masonry at
masonry at head of window at Case Study 2

Fig. 5 - Water leakage at head of window in Case Study 2

observed at seven different locations when testing with the water spray
rack at six different locations. Water leakage appeared at the interior
of the building within 15 minutes of testing at three of the seven
locations and after one hour at the remaining four locations. All seven
leakage locations occurred immediately adjacent to splice joints in the
steel window lintel. Six of the seven leakage locations occurred
immediately adjacent to splice joints at the aluminum window head
receptor. All leakage locations had water stains prior to testing.
Water within the cavity space of the exterior brick masonry wall
construction above the window system was bypassing the flashing at the
window lintel and entering the building interior at the lintel splice
joints.

By lowering the water rack to spray only the windows, water
penetration to the building interior was also occurring through
unadhered and torn exterior sealant profiles at window sill splice
joints, sill cover splice joints and between the window sill extrusion
and sill cover at numerous locations. The sealant at these locations
was brittle, and the existing configuration of the sealant profiles was
inadequate to resist thermal movements of the aluminum members. These
areas also coincided with water stains. These areas were identified by
removing some interior finishes.

Masonry openings at the leakage locations revealed poorly bonded
flashing joints, mortar droppings within the cavity, and poor sealant
adhesion of the flashing to the supporting steel and window head
receptor. Visual examination of windows revealed brittle sealant,
poorly configured sealant joints, and lack of attention to alignment of
splice joints of the window sill with the sill cover.

Based on the results of the testing, repairs were made to the
flashing and to the sealant. The area was then retested to confirm the
effectiveness of the repairs.

CONCLUSIONS

The test illustrated in ASTM E1105 has been effective in recreating leakage in wall systems. The procedure can be used both with masking and/or selective positioning of the spray rack. The time durations of testing must be set based on information of the project such as the delay between the occurrences of leakage and the beginning of rainstorms, and the materials involved in the projects. Absorptive materials and absorptive interior finishes may require longer test durations than would systems such as metal and glass. The current ASTM E1105 rate of application on the wall system appears reasonable in most cases. In some cases the rates may be modified in order to mimic actual rainstorms expected at a selected reoccurrence interval for the region of the country where the building is located. It is important, however, to consider the impact of rundown and the importance of developing a sheet of water over the wall surfaces if these rates are varied. Based on our experience, developing a pressure difference across the wall system is generally not important. We have been able to successfully redevelop the leaks without any air pressure difference. Developing a pressure difference is very difficult and time consuming and the plane of pressure drop is often difficult to recreate. However, each project must be evaluated independantly to determine appropriate diagnostic methods.

ASTM E1105 is an important diagnostic tool when used in combination with observations, interviews of occupants, review of drawings and specifications, and inspection openings and disassembly of units. The information used from this approach is often essential in order to develop effective repairs. The effectiveness of repairs can be evaluated by performing the tests before and after repairs are made.

The test can also be effective when performing preconstruction testing of mockup walls. Using similar approaches, the vulnerability of new construction to water leakage can be evaluated.

REFERENCES

[1]   1995 Annual Book of ASTM Standards, Volume 04.07, "Standard Test Method for Field Determination of Water Penetration of Installed Exterior Windows, Curtain Walls, and Doors by Uniform or Cyclic Static Air Pressure Difference".

[2]   Architectural Aluminum Manufacturers Association, AAMA 501.2 Methods of Test for Metal Curtain Walls.

[3]   Technical Information Center, "Voluntary Specification for Field Testing of Windows and Sliding Glass Doors", Publication No. AAMA 502-90.

[4]   Krogstad, N.V., "Masonry Wall Drainage Test - A Proposed Method for Field Evaluation of Masonry Cavity Walls for Resistance to Water Leakage," Masonry: Components to Assemblages, ASTM STP 1063, John H. Matthys, Editor, American Society for Testing and Materials, Philadelphia, 1990.

[5]   Krogstad, Norbert V., Weber, Richard A. "Using Modified ASTM E1105 to Evaluate the Resistance of Masonry Barrier, Mass and Skin Walls to Rain" Masonry: Design and Construction, Problems and Repair, ASTM STP 1180, John M. Melander and Lynn R. Lauersdorf, Eds., American Society for Testing and Materials, Philadelphia, 1993.

[6]   Hershfield, D. M., National Technical Information Service, Technical Paper No. 40, Rainfall Frequency Atlas of the United States for Durations from 30 Minutes to 24 Hours and Return Periods from 1 to 100 Years.

Mark F. Williams[1] and Barbara Lamp Williams[2]

AN OVERVIEW OF WATER LEAKAGE PROBLEMS IN SINGLE-FAMILY RESIDENCES CLAD WITH EXTERIOR INSULATION AND FINISH SYSTEMS (EIFS)

REFERENCE: Williams, M. F. and Williams, B. L., **"An Overview of Water Leakage Problems in Single-Family Residences Clad with Exterior Insulation and Finish Systems (EIFS),"** Water Leakage Through Building Facades, ASTM STP 1314, R. J. Kudder and J. L. Erdly, Eds., American Society for Testing and Materials, 1998.

ABSTRACT: Water leakage has occurred in numerous EIFS-clad residences in the U.S. Field investigations of North Carolina homes indicate that deficiencies within and between various building components are allowing water leakage. Moisture behind EIFS claddings has jeopardized the in-service durability of the EIFS as well as other building components. A brief history of EIFS provides a framework for understanding the water leakage problems in residential construction. A classification of leakage sources identified to date in the North Carolina investigations is provided. Window-related leaks are discussed, and a remedial detailing for the typical interface between EIFS and windows is provided.

KEYWORDS: EIFS, exterior insulation and finish systems, moistureproofing, North Carolina, residential construction, synthetic stucco, water leakage

---

High levels of moisture have been detected at circumscribed areas of EIFS claddings installed on numerous single-family residences in North Carolina. Exterior wall investigations of the residences have been initiated. On some residences, symptoms of active and persistent water leakage are visible, including wet or deteriorated exterior sheathing board, degraded wood framing elements, and damaged interior finishes. On other residences, manifest symptoms are minimal, but investigative data indicate that moisture is present behind the installed EIFS claddings. Concerns about the possibility of similar problems on a national level have been raised.

Preliminary findings from North Carolina suggest that water leakage is typically occurring within and between various exterior wall components. Residential building systems including windows, doors, roof terminations, and through-wall penetrations are

---

[1] President and [2] Vice President, Williams Building Diagnostics Inc., 945 Tennis Avenue, Maple Glen, PA 19002.

allowing the initial entry of moisture into the wall assembly. Based on field data, it is clear that the EIFS is not capable of redirecting incidental moisture that intrudes from building envelope systems and typical residential building features. Instead, EIFS claddings are trapping moisture behind their face-sealed barrier, contributing to the deterioration of underlying sheathing and framing members.

In the authors' opinion, moistureproofing requirements for typical EIFS-clad residential construction are not sufficiently developed from a technical standpoint. Adding to the problem is the fact that the existing details, methods, and procedures have not been clearly thought out and articulated by the EIFS industry or other manufacturers of common building envelope systems and components. A brief history of EIFS provides insight into how the current situation in the EIFS residential market developed.

History of EIFS

Originating in Europe, EIFS were initially conceived as seamless claddings that relied on a "barrier wall" concept to resist water penetration. "Hydraulic renderings" consisting of trowel-applied or sprayed-on coatings over an exterior insulation component were reportedly used to clad sugar beet silos and other storage structures that had minimal through-wall features or openings.

Soon lightweight claddings composed of thin-renderings over exterior insulation were being installed throughout Europe on residential buildings and other structures designed for human occupancy. Typical installations involved the retrofit of existing masonry buildings. In the decades that followed the initial use of these systems, the use of EIFS on various building types increased substantially. By the mid-1980s, 40 percent of all exterior walls in Germany and Switzerland were clad in some type of EIFS assembly; 80 percent of these claddings were found on retrofit installations [1].

Mechanisms for handling cladding transitions, interfaces, and interruptions were developed to accommodate door and window openings, mechanical systems, and other building features. These mechanisms consisted chiefly of system accessories with specialty profiles. In addition, the masonry facades common to European constructions provided a durable barrier if water infiltrated behind the claddings, since masonry substrates are, for the most part, unaffected by the presence of incidental moisture. Thus, the European structures possessed a built-in redundancy with respect to water intrusion.

EIFS claddings were introduced in this country during the late 1960s. The systems were initially called "synthetic stucco." The expansion to the North American construction market necessitated some modifications to the standard European system due to market differences in situational use. The U.S. market relied on sheathing and stud assemblies as opposed to masonry substrates. Moreover, new construction, not retrofit, was the predominant building application for these systems.

Early use of these systems in the U.S. typically involved commercial construction projects. From the late 1960s to the mid-1980s, EIFS were used almost exclusively on low- and mid-rise commercial buildings such as offices and shopping malls. EIFS was promoted as a less expensive alternative to insulating and finishing exterior walls. It provided a masonry-like appearance, similar to traditional materials, with a range of design flexibility due to its color, texture, and detailing choices.

As North American use grew, the panelized segment of the market developed. The design features of commercial buildings, often configured in regular and repetitive patterns, allowed EIFS panels to be pre-fabricated and cost savings to be realized. Panel fabrication also allowed system details to be modified. The tedious task of backwrapping that is required for EIFS field installations was replaced with edge-wrapping. During panel fabrication, the EIFS components as well as the substrate edges are covered with a moisture-resistant lamina—an integral layer formed by base coat, embedded mesh, and finish coat—to create a full seal over the substrate and framing. In addition, quality assurance issues can be more closely monitored.

By the 1990s, EIFS was widely used for commercial buildings in the North American market. Use on single-family residences that began in the mid-1980s was growing rapidly, especially in the southern U.S. In the mid-1990s, industry analysts anticipated a continued growth of the residential segment in the EIFS market [2].

EIFS Use for Single-Family Residential Construction

New single-family residential construction in the U.S. has several typical and distinguishing characteristics. Residential structures traditionally consist of wood framing covered with wood-based sheathing materials. Typical materials include exterior grade plywood, oriented strand board, oriented wafer board, asphalt-impregnated fiberboard, and various types of exterior grade gypsum sheathing. Many of these sheathing materials are susceptible to moisture damage if exposed to water for extended periods of time.

In residential construction, a traditional solution for protecting sheathing and wood framing components from moisture has been the use of a weather barrier. For instance, asphalt-saturated building felt in compliance with building code requirements is installed over the sheathing and the exposed framing surfaces at rough openings. Other moisture-protective materials widely used in residential construction include synthetic water-resistant membranes. These materials provide moisture protection around the rough openings and behind the exterior wall finish, thereby protecting the sheathing and framing from exposure to incidental moisture.

The weather barrier approach is well suited to residential structures with conventional exterior wall treatments such as brick masonry, wood siding, and stucco. Inclusion of a weather barrier is possible because these conventional finish assemblies are attached using fasteners, anchors, or other mechanical means. Procedurally, the weather barrier membrane is installed on the outer face of the sheathing/stud framework, followed by the mechanical attachment of brick units, siding boards, or stucco components.

Weather barriers do not provide a suitable surface for EIFS adhesive bonding. Most of the EIFS claddings installed to date on residential construction rely solely on adhesive attachment. With this method, the integrity of the cladding's attachment to the face of the wall depends on the strength of the adhesive bond between the sheathing substrate and the system's exterior insulation component. The use of a traditional weather barrier is therefore precluded in adhesively attached systems.

These same adhesively applied systems can be installed, however, with other residential construction components designed to facilitate drainage and drying. Spacers (metal or plastic lath or preformed drainage mat) are installed on the face of the sheathing to create a drainage/drying space behind the EIFS cladding. Some types of lath accommodate adhesive use as the means of EIFS attachment. To date, however, these additional moisture-protective methods have seldom been used on residential construction, apparently due to a lack of perceived need and the added cost associated with these methods. The recent introduction of drainable EIFS products by many manufacturers is in part a response to the moisture intrusion problems encountered with standard assemblies. These new systems typically include a drainage medium, mechanical fastening, and flashing.

Residences clad in standard EIFS assemblies rely on the continuity of the EIFS lamina for moisture protection. Because lamina continuity is interrupted by building features on most types of construction, EIFS manufacturers' detailing must address terminations of the lamina to ensure moistureproofing of the exterior wall. Moistureproof terminations can be obtained using the lamina materials, flashings, or an alternative weather barrier product at critical system interfaces. Without satisfactory system termination details, EIFS-clad residences are compromised with respect to handling moisture intrusion.

Residential construction tends to incorporate diverse design features. Design features often vary according to geographic location. One of the widely recognized benefits of EIFS use is its capacity to create projected and recessed details on building facades. These details are frequently designed for placement around window and door penetrations, building corners, and other areas. The type and number of windows on residences can be extensive, an observation easily confirmed by reviewing the windows on typical two-story homes. Single as well as ganged units are frequently incorporated in the design. To meet special design needs, custom "one-off" units as well as mass-produced assemblies may be used.

The water-resistance performance requirements for windows commonly used in residential construction are relatively low. Many residential windows have published water penetration resistance values of 137 Pa (2.86 lbf/ft^2) in accordance with the Standard Test Method for Water Penetration of Exterior Windows, Curtain Walls, and Doors by Uniform Static Air Pressure Difference (ASTM E 331). Converting this static pressure value to wind velocity reveals that these windows are designed to resist a wind-driven rain of approximately 56 km/h (35 mph). Sustained winds in excess of this velocity occur in many regions of the country. Due to their relatively low water-resistance rating, these windows are more susceptible than higher rated units to the entry of wind-driven rain and other moisture. Many wood windows have factory-installed perimeter trim; however, few are tested by the manufacturers with the trim in place. The trim decreases the already low water resistance of these window units by providing additional avenues for water penetration.

Regardless of shape, type, manufacturing process, or performance rating, each window installed on an EIFS-clad building represents a through-wall penetration, necessitating integration of the EIFS cladding with fenestration elements. Strip window systems commonly used on commercial construction often possess continuous head and sill features configured in a regular and uniform manner. The strip configuration of these windows usually lends itself to the successful use of drainage features (flashings and weeps) for the collection/discharge of incidental moisture, eliminating the need to solve challenging end conditions that are formed by the termination of the flashings with the EIFS. Moreover, the windows specified for larger-scale buildings tend to have comparatively higher performance ratings, including a higher resistance to water penetration.

Residential work relies exclusively on EIFS field application to resolve the complicated configurations created by the many and diverse penetrations and terminations of the cladding. EIFS terminations in field-applied installations address only the outside face and edge condition of the insulation board. These terminations do not provide a covering for the sheathing/structural frame plane. The treatment of system edges during backwrapping is labor-intensive. Even when backwrapping is perfectly executed, gaps or breaches between the exterior insulation and the sheathing plane can occur. In general, the industry literature for adhesively applied EIFS does not take into account the construction means and methods typically used on residential buildings at window and door openings. Furthermore, the literature does not consider the impact of the typical residential construction sequence on EIFS installations.

Another characteristic of single-family residences is the typical construction sequence. In field-applied EIFS, the building structure is framed and sheathed, and the through-wall penetrations are completed prior to EIFS application. Roofs, windows, doors, and other elements are typically installed; ledgers for wood decks and side wall chimneys are in place on the building structure. This means that EIFS field applicators must work around various components and systems, making it difficult or impossible to obtain a continuous watertight lamina across building facades, the moistureproofing principle inherent in the original concept of the system.

By contrast, on certain types of non-residential construction, the continuity of the EIFS lamina is established first. The pre-fabrication practices mentioned earlier serve as an example. On panelized EIFS jobs, edge wrapping over the sheathing and framing components helps to protect the sheathing and inner wall assembly from incidental moisture due to leaks at system interruptions or within adjacent wall components (e.g., windows or doors).

These common characteristics and features of residential construction underscore the current "misfit" between typical residential construction practices and the unique needs of EIFS barrier claddings. These needs center largely on system termination issues, which have been brought to the fore by the situation in North Carolina.

The North Carolina Situation

Investigations of single-family residences in different parts of North Carolina have established that (1) on uninterrupted expanses of the system, EIFS water-resistance performance is generally adequate but (2) at certain common EIFS termination conditions, water leakage into residential wall construction is occurring.

These barrier systems are primarily designed to keep moisture out; however, they can also trap unwanted moisture within. Once water has infiltrated behind the EIFS barrier, these cladding constructions can cause moisture entrapment. This is especially true in North Carolina where the vapor drive can be in either direction, depending on the season and prevailing temperature/humidity conditions.

Moisture at the sheathing plane or within the stud cavity is moved downward by the force of gravity until it encounters construction conditions or adhesive patterns conducive to moisture accumulation. This process represents a challenge for EIFS field investigations undertaken to identify the path(s) and point(s) of moisture accumulation. Moisture typically creates circumscribed and irregular patterns within concealed areas of the exterior wall. Obtaining spot readings with a resistance meter can miss moist areas at the substrate level of the wall.

The authors have been involved in hundreds of residential investigations in North Carolina where moisture surveys were initially performed using destructive as well as non-destructive metering techniques. Many of these houses were surveyed a second time after their EIFS claddings had been removed, allowing the location of damaged materials as well as leakage source(s) to be recorded. A summary of the most common sources of leakage found in the survey is presented in Table 1.

Table 1 underscores the contribution of EIFS terminations and interfaces in the leakage problems occurring on residential construction in North Carolina. Leaks are originating in various building systems and components, including windows, doors, and the EIFS itself. The EIFS terminations at windows, doors, roofs, and decks are allowing infiltrating water to travel behind the cladding. The presence of moisture has been documented behind EIFS assemblies at the sheathing and framing planes.

Windows constructed of wood, aluminum, vinyl, or a combination of these materials have been examined in the North Carolina investigations. High moisture readings have been obtained most often below the sills of specific window types. On aluminum and vinyl-clad windows, common sources of moisture infiltration are (1) openings at the jamb/sill corners and (2) openings at the meeting mullion conditions. Specifically, leakage originating at sill-to-jamb frame corners, a common source of moisture, migrates behind the EIFS termination. This corner leakage from window frames is thus allowed to migrate into the underlying layers of the wall assembly because of the inadequate closure (Figure 1).

Many vinyl- and aluminum-clad residential windows contain self-flashing flanges. The flange performs several functions. While facilitating window installation, it also prevents water from migrating into the wall framing. Self-flashing window units have proven to be effective in construction that incorporates different types of traditional wall claddings. With adhesively applied EIFS, however, the flange is installed at the interior face of the exterior insulation. Given their placement, the flanges serve to encourage the migration of incidental moisture behind the EIFS in the proximity of window terminations. Case study investigations in North Carolina have shown that water is channeled into the EIFS from these self-flashing flanges. These findings suggest that self-flashing windows should be modified when used with EIFS.

EIFS system details to date have focused on excluding moisture entry at the outer plane of the wall. While better performance will no doubt be obtained by improving face-sealed details, this approach misses the mark. It fails to address moisture entrapment problems. Backwrapping as currently shown by the manufacturers and executed by EIFS applicators is not effective in controlling moisture migration or in protecting the underlying components (sheathing and framing) from moisture once it has entered the wall. This is because backwrapping addresses closure only at the edge of the insulation, not at the juncture of the insulation and sheathing. If water is present, moisture penetrates the inside edge of the EIFS, resulting in sheathing and/or framing damage.

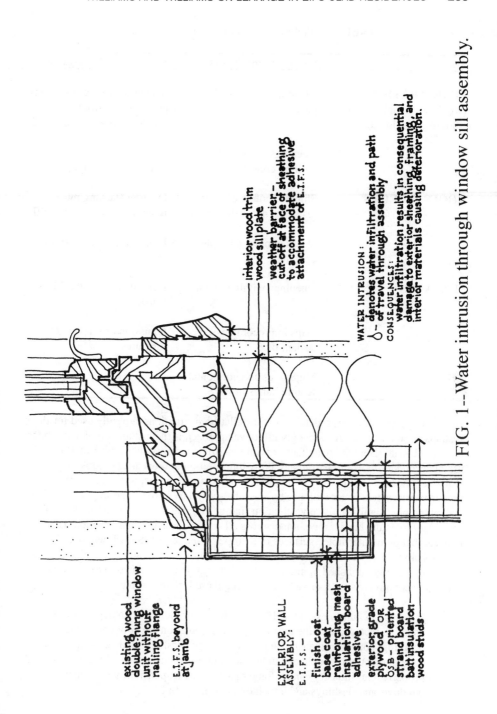

FIG. 1--Water intrusion through window sill assembly.

TABLE 1—Preliminary list of water leakage sources

System	Source within System	System-to-EIFS System
FENESTRATION (windows, doors, sliding glass doors)	Openings at jamb/sill junctures	Standard EIFS terminations permit water from fenestration to intrude behind EIFS
	Openings at joining mullion conditions	Improper integration of self-flashing flanges
ROOFS & DECKS	Shingle roofs are water resistant (not waterproof)	Diverter flashing must integrate perfectly with EIFS
	Decks contain multiple openings	Breaches in EIFS terminations
SEALANTS	Openings within sealant	Delamination of the EIFS finish coat
	Gaps in precompressed sealant tape	Omission of sealant at junctures
EIFS	V-grooves and horizontal feature bands in EIFS	---

The closure features, details, and installation instructions currently used for these systems are inadequate. A seemingly effective approach is the installation of a secondary moisture barrier. Both the manufacturers and building code officials have sanctioned the use of secondary moisture barriers as a possible solution to the leakage problems. However, these secondary barrier membranes also require proper termination. If not properly terminated, water will also by-pass the secondary barrier, and migrate within the wall assembly. Significantly, investigation findings to date do not support the need for a secondary moisture barrier membrane across all wall planes. The investigation data indicate that on uninterrupted surfaces of a properly applied EIFS wall, without V-grooves or projected EIFS features, moisture infiltration is generally not a problem.

A recently published opinion about the current industry situation expresses the need for a comprehensive approach to resolving these leakage problems:

"Leakage in buildings with EIFS has painted our industry in a negative light, when, in fact, some of the reasons for water intrusion are poor design and detailing, poor workmanship and lack of proper flashings and caulking. This development will not change unless we address all the scopes of the exterior wall properly. Our industry can no longer pass on the responsibility for sealants, windows and flashings and how they interface with EIFS." [3]

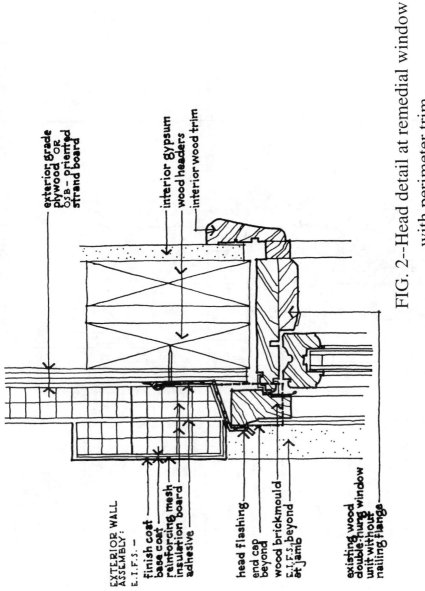

FIG. 2.--Head detail at remedial window with perimeter trim.

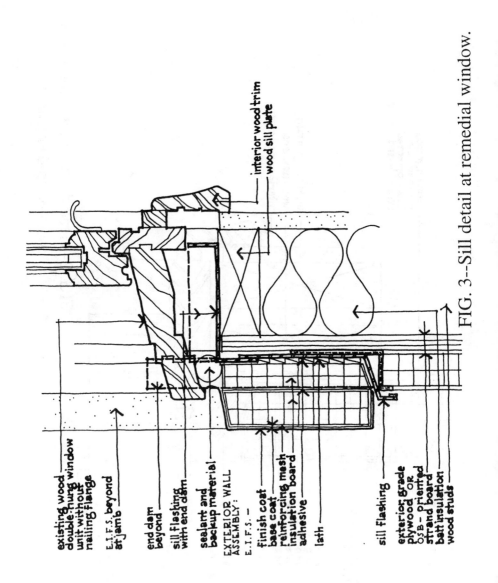

FIG. 3--Sill detail at remedial window.

interior wood trim
wood sill plate

existing wood
double-hung window
unit without
nailing flange

E.I.F.S. beyond
at jamb

end dam
beyond

sill flashing
with end dam

sealant and
backup material

EXTERIOR WALL
ASSEMBLY:
E.I.F.S. –

finish coat
base coat
reinforcing mesh
insulation board
adhesive

lath

sill flashing

exterior grade
plywood OR
OSB - oriented
strand board
batt insulation
wood studs

Published construction details on how to terminate residential-grade doors, windows, roof junctures, joints, and abutments with other exterior wall materials are inadequate with respect to leakage from adjoining assemblies. New details are required. Figures 2 and 3 illustrate a proposed remedial design for an existing window with a brick mold trim commonly used on residential construction. In the repair method shown, portions of the existing cladding material are removed, and new EIFS termination materials are installed. This remedial design protects the wall assembly by improving the system's capacity to control, direct, and discharge incidental moisture.

Conclusion

Due partially to an historically strong emphasis on commercial construction in the U.S. EIFS market, standard design details and practices for residential EIFS use do not adequately address the in-service needs of typical residential construction. The water leakage problems in the single-family residential market are attributable to inadequate standard industry details as well as misunderstandings about the specific needs of EIFS in residential installations.

Initiatives are needed to develop appropriate details for residential use of EIFS and to educate designers, contractors, and homeowners about the limitations of these systems. The EIFS industry and other interested parties can no longer "pass" on the situation. Intensified efforts on the part of the EIFS industry and other manufacturers are needed to ensure that the design and installation of claddings incorporate satisfactory moisture protection measures and achieve long-term serviceability.

References

[*1*]   Tamburrini, V., "The History and Development of EIFS—From the Original Concept to Present Day Activities," *Development, Use, and Performance of Exterior Insulation and Finish Systems (EIFS), ASTM 1187*, Mark F. Williams and Richard G. Lampo, Eds., American Society for Testing and Materials, 1995, p. 8.

[2]   Ellis, S. A., "Future Growth for EIFS is in Residential Market," EIMA Outside/In, March 1995.

[*3*]   Drury, R., "Vancouver Action Holds Lesson For Industry," Walls & Ceilings, February 1996, pp. 36-38.

Mark F. Williams,[1] Barbara Lamp Williams,[2] and Lucas J. Hamilton

IN SITU ASSESSMENT OF MOISTURE LEVELS IN EXTERIOR WALLS OF SINGLE-FAMILY RESIDENCES CLAD WITH EXTERIOR INSULATION AND FINISH SYSTEMS (EIFS)

REFERENCE: Williams, M. F., Williams, B. L., and Hamilton, L. J., **"In Situ Assessment of Moisture Levels in Exterior Walls of Single-Family Residences Clad with Exterior Insulation and Finish Systems (EIFS),"** Water Leakage Through Building Facades, ASTM STP 1314, R. J. Kudder and J. L. Erdly, Eds., American Society for Testing and Materials, 1998.

ABSTRACT: This paper discusses comparative test results obtained using different kinds of moisture meters on mockup walls clad in an exterior insulation and finish system (EIFS). The accuracy and efficacy of intrusive and non-intrusive meters as moisture screening tools was evaluated. Specifically, a mockup of the most commonly used EIFS wall assembly was constructed and a known quantity of water was introduced into the various layers of the assembly. Moisture meters were then used to determine their effectiveness in locating moisture within the mockup wall. Comparison of the moisture meter data found that non-intrusive meters appear to be a practical, effective, and accurate means of moisture detection when supplemented with intrusive meter use. This finding is important since the need to screen EIFS-clad residences for moisture has increased due to recent findings of moisture behind EIFS claddings installed on some houses.

KEYWORDS: barrier wall, exterior insulation and finish system (EIFS), intrusive moisture meter, moisture testing, non-intrusive moisture meter

---

Exterior building walls are designed and constructed to modify or exclude environmental forces from the building interior. These forces include heat, light, wind, sound, and moisture in its different forms—vapor, rain, and ice. This paper focuses exclusively on the moisture testing of EIFS barrier walls. As a barrier construction, this face-sealed system is expected to exclude all moisture at the outer face.

In many EIFS-clad residences investigated by the authors, moisture has intruded behind the face-sealed cladding. Because EIFS barrier walls do not typically include secondary moisture protection or sufficient means for collecting and redirecting incidental

---

[1] President, [2] Vice President, and [3] Manager of Technical Services, Williams Building Diagnostics Inc., 945 Tennis Avenue, Maple Glen, PA 19002.

moisture, water can become trapped within or behind the wall assembly, causing deterioration of the substrate and framing. For this reason, the assessment of in situ moisture levels on EIFS claddings is useful. Depending on the type of meter employed, moisture assessment can strategically identify wet areas of the wall in need of repair. Moreover, in situ assessment has proven a useful means of monitoring the performance of remedial cladding installations.

The study described herein included different kinds of moisture meters. Other types of screening tools such as infrared thermography can also be a valuable means of detecting moisture; however, these were not included in the study.

Resistance Meters

The most common devices for determining moisture levels within or behind exterior EIFS walls are intrusive-type resistance meters. These instruments are calibrated for the material being tested and employ a set of probes which are inserted into the wall system. An electrical current is then sent between the probes and analyzed by the attached meter. Because the resistance of a material is changed by the presence of water, the change in current flow between the two probes can be expressed as a percentage of moisture present. While this type of "direct" reading may seem to be the most accurate, there are several limitations to such a method.

One of the most limiting aspects of resistance meter use is the small area of wall assessed. The two probes on this type of meter are positioned at either a fixed or variable distance. Regardless of probe positioning, resistance meters are only capable of detecting the presence of moisture between the two probes. This means that many intrusive tests must be performed to create a database which is representative of exterior wall conditions as a whole. Because repeated probing of the wall assembly is required to obtain an accurate assessment, this type of meter can harm a cladding's barrier function.

Another drawback to intrusive "pinpoint" testing is testing depth. These meters are most effective when readings are obtained at each level of the wall construction. Multiple probes of the wall assembly are required in order to take readings at each component layer. Obtaining these measurements ultimately entails penetrating the entire cross-section of the multi-component EIFS cladding. An undesirable maintenance situation is thereby created because probed areas must be repaired. Repairs are commonly achieved using sealant material. These repairs must be performed in a manner that is itself non-destructive. For instance, solvent release type sealants damage EIFS claddings and cannot be used. Test areas that have been repaired become a building maintenance item. If not properly maintained, these test areas can become avenues for water intrusion and related deterioration. Due to these and other shortcomings of intrusive moisture testing, the authors developed an interest in non-intrusive methods of moisture detection for EIFS-clad residences.

Moisture detection equipment can be an excellent tool for "mapping" a wall's condition. To create such maps, many meaningful data points must be collected and the data compiled to generate an overall picture of moisture conditions. Because both types of meters used in the study, intrusive and non-intrusive, are capable of producing a range of numeric values, the information generated represents the amount of water present at the test location. Gradations of test values can be "mapped" to predict where moisture is most likely entering the assembly as well as how far it has migrated within the system. As mentioned above, a sufficient number of data points is required to create a truly representative map. From a practical standpoint, this volume of data points cannot be gathered by an intrusive meter due to its destructive effect on the assembly.

Capacitance Meters

The non-intrusive devices currently on the market employ an electromagnetic field to measure the capacitance of the area within the field generated by the instrument. A capacitance meter operates on the principle of dielectric constants. The meter sends out an alternating electrical field and then measures the wall assembly's ability to store and dissipate the transmitted energy. When moisture is present within the material assembly, the capacitance of the system is altered. By calibrating the meter on a dry area of the cladding system, the natural properties of the cladding system are "zeroed" out. All gains experienced by the meter field are then due to additional materials with a greater capacitance than the cladding construction itself. A knowledge of the exact cladding construction being tested is required to accurately interpret the data generated by capacitance meters. Given such knowledge, non-intrusive capacitance meters can be used with sufficient accuracy to identify dry, transitional, and wet areas of the cladding system or wall assembly.

The advantages of non-intrusive meters are many. The field generated by a capacitance meter depends on the size of its sensor and its power output. Capacitance meters typically have field areas ranging from 6 cm x 10 cm to 30 cm x 70 cm, with corresponding depths of up to 13 cm. Larger areas of the cladding system can be evaluated with a single measurement compared to resistance meter use. This results in more efficient data collection.

Because the readings generated by non-intrusive meters are relative to system construction and meter calibration, select intrusive measurements should also be taken. These complementary readings should be taken to confirm the accuracy of the non-intrusive tool, the wall system's construction, and the condition of the substrate. Intrusive readings should be kept to a minimum, however, for the reasons explained above.

Study of Meter Effectiveness

To perform a comparative and simultaneous evaluation of both intrusive and non-intrusive equipment and methods, a typical residential wall section clad in removable sheathing and EIFS panels was constructed. The mockup construction consisted of a base assembly and removable panels made of the following materials:

Base assembly
— 1.27 cm interior gypsum sheathing
— 6 mil polyethylene vapor retarder
— 5.08 cm x 10.16 cm wood studs
— 8.89 cm batt insulation

Removable panel
— 1.27 cm plywood sheathing or 1.27 cm oriented-strand board (OSB) sheathing
— non-cementitious adhesive
— 2.54 cm expanded polystyrene (EPS) insulation board
— standard polymer-based (PB) EIFS lamina

The mockup was constructed on a box platform measuring 1.2 m long x 1.2 m wide. Testing was performed with each type of removable panel, situated on the base assembly. On one half of the mockup, a known quantity of water was introduced at different material layers, while dry conditions were maintained on the other half to serve as a control. Four meters were employed to measure the relative moisture content of the wall construction:

1) Non-intrusive meter A (capacitance)
2) Non-intrusive meter B (capacitance)
3) Intrusive meter C (resistance)
4) Prototype non-intrusive meter D (capacitance)

Non-intrusive meters A and B and intrusive meter C are commercially available; the prototype non-intrusive meter D was developed by the authors based on the perceived need for a diagnostic tool specifically for use on typical EIFS claddings (Figures 1 and 2).
Adapted from the existing capacitance technologies described above, the components of the prototype meter include a measuring circuit with a transmitter to send a signal to the cladding, a receiver to measure the reflected signal energy, and instrumentation to display the signal measurements [1]. The meter was adapted for use on typical residential EIFS claddings by optimizing the gain and impedance of the circuit and minimizing the distortion of the wave form.
The non-intrusive meters were calibrated on the dry half of the assembly. For both intrusive and non-intrusive meters, readings were obtained at two locations on the wet half of the mockup.
The values reported herein are derived from the specific meter scales referenced and have been rounded to the nearest numerical reading. Both non-intrusive meters A and B have relative scales from 0-100. Non-intrusive meter A has a color-coded scale with values from 0-35 in the green area of the scale, 35-60 in the yellow area, and 60-100 in the red area. Non-intrusive meter B has a relative scale with color-coded ranges. Intrusive meter C reports a percentage of moisture in wood ranging from 0%-50%. Its color-coded scale identifies "Wood Moisture Equivalence" with percentages from 0%-15% (the green area of the scale) representing safe conditions for wood, 15%-17% (the yellow area of the scale) representing conditions that should be monitored, and greater than 17% (the red zone of the scale) indicative of moisture levels which may adversely affect wood materials. The prototype non-intrusive meter D has different color-coded scales. It reports relative values ranging from 0-300 depending on the scale used; the green scale with values ranging from 0-100 was used for the study.

Fig. 1—Non-intrusive meter D in use.

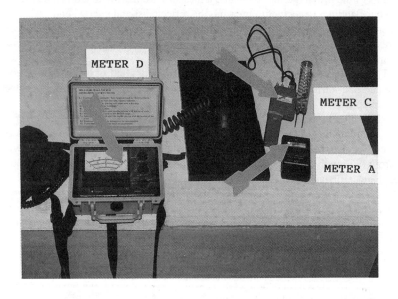

Fig. 2—Moisture meters A, C, and D; meter B is not shown.

TABLE 1—Moisture readings using different types of meters at various test locations

Test Location Point of Water Introduction	Meter A Non-intrusive	Meter B Non-intrusive	Meter C Intrusive	Meter D Prototype Non-intrusive
Batt insulation behind plywood	0, 0	0, 0	30, 30	20, 20
Batt insulation behind OSB	0, 0	0, 0	30, 50	40, 30
Saturated plywood	10, 10	0, 0	35, 50	65, 65
Saturated OSB	10, 5	0, 0	20, 40	65, 65
Face of plywood	100, 100	100, 100	45, 45	100, 100
Face of OSB	100, 100	100, 100	45, 50	100, 100
In EPS board	100, 100	100, 100	50, 50	100, 100

Testing performed on the wall mockup generated the data displayed in Table 1. As the table shows, when water was introduced within the EPS board, all meters detected its presence with a high degree of reproducibility. When water was introduced at the "face of sheathing" level, all meters once again detected its presence. Intrusive meter C gave varying readings depending on the positioning of its probes.

When water was introduced farther back into the system (within the sheathing plane), two of the non-intrusive meters became ineffective. When soaked sheathing was placed within the mockup assembly, non-intrusive meters A and B did not detect this critical condition. By contrast, both intrusive meter C and prototype non-intrusive meter D gave clear and highly reproducible responses to this condition. When the batt insulation behind the sheathing was wetted, non-intrusive meters A and B were again unable to produce the field or power output required to detect the presence of moisture. Intrusive meter C and prototype non-intrusive meter D detected and expressed the presence of moisture at this level. Because water was introduced at only one level of the construction at a time, the cumulative effect of several wet layers was not a factor in the test results.

Field investigations have found many instances where the outer layers of EIFS walls are dry, but the underlying substrate and other materials are wet. In this type of situation, the study results indicate that meters C and D would be an effective means of moisture detection.

The mockup study results are similar to those obtained from numerous EIFS field investigations conducted by the authors. To date, the prototype non-intrusive meter D has been used to evaluate more than 300 EIFS-clad, single-family residences in conjunction with the use of intrusive meter C and selective removal of the installed EIFS claddings. These supplemental measures have confirmed the accuracy and reliability of the prototype non-intrusive meter. In situ assessments of EIFS-clad residences continue to be conducted to further establish the value of this method of moisture detection.

Conclusions

On the basis of the study findings, the following conclusions are offered:

1) The use of a non-intrusive meter results in less damage to the existing construction.
2) Two of the four meters used in the study (meters C and D) were effective in detecting moisture throughout the mockup wall assembly.
3) Prototype non-intrusive meter D is a practical and effective means of moisture detection on EIFS-clad wall assemblies when used in conjunction with intrusive meter C.

References

[1]   "Bridges and Impedance Measurements," *Reference Data for Radio Engineers*, Howard W. Sams & Company, Inc., 1975, pp. 12-1 to 12-7.

Mikael H. Salonvaara[1] and Achilles N. Karagiozis[2]

THE INFLUENCE OF WATERPROOF COATING ON THE HYGROTHERMAL PERFORMANCE OF A BRICK FACADE WALL SYSTEM

REFERENCE: Salonvaara, M. H. and Karagiozis A. N. **"The Influence of Waterproof Coating on the Hygrothermal Performance of a Brick Facade Wall System,"** Water Leakage Through Building Facades, ASTM STP 1314, R. J. Kudder and J. L. Erdly, Eds., American Society for Testing and Materials, 1998.

ABSTRACT: The effect of a waterproof coating on the long-term hygrothermal performance of a high-rise wall was investigated by combining experimental and numerical approaches. The water vapor permeances (WVP) of the waterproof coating on the brick and mortar masonry were experimentally determined as a function of relative humidity. These performance characteristics for the (WVP) of the waterproof coatings applied on the brick and mortar surface layers were included in the LATENITE version 1.2 hygrothermal model. A series of 1-D and 2-D simulations were performed studying the effects of waterproof coatings on a selected wall system. Additional simulations studied the effect of the existence of cracks.   Results indicate that brick-mortar interaction as a system must be included in analysis of the hygrothermal performance of the waterproof coating. Simplifications to 1-D can lead to erroneous results.   Rain penetration can be far more important than ambient surface diffusion fluxes and must be included in all hygrothermal analysis. The waterproof coating reduced the yearly average heat flux by 3 % for the city of Vancouver by reducing the latent heat effects of absorbed moisture from wind-driven rain.

[1] Research Scientist, VTT Building Technology, Technical Research Centre of Finland, P.O.BOX 1804, 02044 VTT, Finland

[2] Research Officer, Institute for Research in Construction, National Research Council Canada, Bldg M-24, Montreal Rd., Ottawa, ON, K1A 0R6, Canada

KEYWORDS: Moisture Transport, Heat Transport, High-Rise Walls, Thermal Transport, Sorption, Water Vapor Permeance, Moisture Diffusivity

---

Hygrothermal (combined heat-air and moisture) performance in building envelopes dictates to a large extent the durability and service life of the building envelope. The dominant role of hygrothermal performance on the resistance to deterioration (durability) is mainly because hygrothermal processes can occur in all three states namely vapor , liquid and ice. Each of these three states contribute differently to the deterioration mechanisms created by the response of the building envelope system to both interior and exterior environment excitations. Deterioration can exist in various forms, i.e., surface damage (discolourization by efflorescence), aging processes (chemical damages) (moisture induced salt migration) structural cracking (due to thermal and moisture gradients), corrosion of steel, and mould or bacteria growth. The exact description of these deterioration processes is still not well understood; however, as the amount of available moisture increases, so does the severity of degradation of the construction materials.

The hygrothermal performance of a building envelope depends on the integral performance of the building envelope system under consideration and its sub-systems. A building envelope system consists of all 1-D, 2-D and 3-D components such as the material layer systems, and includes all unintentional cracks and intentional openings.   Sub-systems are defined by the close formation-interaction of two material systems such as the brick-mortar masonry interface, gluing two material together forming a substrate (EIFS board) and the various waterproofing membranes and coatings. To date, a very limited number of analyses of have been performed on building envelope systems with their associated subsystems. Indeed, a comprehensive experimental or even field study on the hygrothermal performance may not yet be available. The analysis, design and long-term prediction of the hygrothermal performance of building envelope systems must be carried out employing as many as possible of the more dominant systems and sub-systems characterizing the structure. Indeed, hygrothermal performance prediction can only be accomplished by integrating sophisticated analytical models with material properties and system as well as sub-system information via laboratory and field measurements. To date, only a limited number of such research models exist allowing multidimensional 1-D, 2-D and 3-D treatment of the building envelope system with coupled heat and moisture transport via diffusion and natural and forced convection transport, capillary and gravity flow transport. Models that permit the "capturing" of the systems and associated sub-systems of building envelopes can be employed in hygrothermal waterproof coating performance studies.

Wind-driven rain has been documented as the single most important source of moisture for certain brick-veneer exterior facade walls [1]. Indeed the amount of available water striking the surface of a wall can exceed the precipitation rate by a factor of 40 times. As an example, an east-facing wall in Vancouver can receive up to 400 kg / m^2. The authors' results in a recent paper [2] showed that a brick cavity wall in Vancouver retained 36 times more moisture with wind-driven rain (liquid water) than did the same wall with only vapor transfer. Waterproof coatings could then become attractive remedies to reduce water penetration and thus enhance the service life and durability of certain wall structures. The substances that are used for this purpose are sprayed or painted onto the exterior wall, creating a layer that has a high resistance to liquid flow. At the same time, most manufacturers of these coatings claim that these thin layers have insignificant resistance to vapor flow, thus allowing the building envelope to naturally "breathe." Previous work carried out by the authors of this paper [2] parametrically investigated the effect of the waterproof coatings on the hygrothermal performance of a brick cavity wall for two different climates: Vancouver (moderately cold) and Ottawa (cold). Literature information was not readily available on the vapor resistance of waterproof coatings and the authors developed a sensitivity analysis employing coatings that were assumed to have vapor resistances equivalent to a multiplication factor of 10, 1 and 0.1 times the resistance of the exterior brick (2.5 perms or 1.5 10^{-10} kg/m^2·s·Pa) and that were totally impermeable to liquid flow. Results showed that, for ideal conditions, i.e. without the existence of any coating cracks, the walls performed well when applied on initially dry walls. However, as cracks developed, yearly moisture accumulation in walls in climates such as Vancouver were found when low vapor permeance coatings were employed. Furthermore, walls without waterproofing displayed higher yearly heat fluxes than those with coating (2% in Ottawa and 9 % in Vancouver) due to evaporation latent heat component.

In this paper, a waterproof coating (elastomeric coating) from a well-known manufacturer was selected and measurements were performed to determine the hygrothermal material properties of the exterior facade. The sorption isotherm of brick, mortar and water vapor permeance of the waterproof coating were measured at the NRC/IRC laboratories. These measurements were then incorporated into the LATENITE material property database [3] and simulations were performed to investigate the hygrothermal performance of a high-rise wall structure. Two sets of simulations were performed, both deterministic: one employing a 1-D formulation and another a 2-D formulation. The 1-D formulation did not account for the effect of mortar and represented the exterior material as one layer of solid brick (this being the approach followed by 1-D models such as MOIST (Burch and Thomas, 1993), MATCH (Pedersen, 1988) and WUFIZ (Kunzel, 1994) [4]. The 2-D simulations accounted for the presence of mortar, and two conditions were investigated: one a perfect crack-free wall and the other permitting a crack between the mortar and the brick horizontal surface. All simulations were performed employing the weather location of Vancouver. The long-term performance of the waterproof coating on the hygrothermal behavior of the wall system is presented.

MATERIAL PROPERTY DETERMINATION

Hygrothermal material properties for the exterior facade of a wall system were measured. These were the sorption isotherms (hygroscopic regime) for the brick and mortar layers, the water vapor permeances for brick, mortar and the waterproof coatings on both the brick and mortar. Examining both brick and mortar vapor permeances preceded investigating the importance of the waterproof coating on the surface morphology. If differences were present, these would be incorporated in the simulations. The water vapor permeance of the brick, mortar and the combined effect of the coating on both of these materials were measured at different relative humidities. The properties were then included in the LATENITE Database [3] and used in the model.

Water Vapor Permeance

The water vapor transmission characteristics of mortar, brick and waterproof coating were determined according to the the ASTM E 96 Test Method for Water Vapor Transmission of Materials. Four different sets of relative humidities were used as boundary conditions in order to determine the dependence of vapor transmission characteristics as a function of relative humidity. The tests were performed on brick and mortar samples of dimensions 75 mm x 150 mm x 25 mm (thickness). Three samples for each material were employed. The water vapor permeance for the waterproofing coating was measured by applying this compound on three samples of brick and mortar. The relative humidity in the climatic chamber was varied from 32 to 82 % and only two interior cup conditions were employed, one corresponding to 100 % vapor saturation and the other at 0 % relative humidity (dry conditions). The relative humidity fluctuations were controlled to within 2% and the temperature to within 0.5 °C. This approach allowed higher accuracy in the water vapor permeances by eliminating the uncertainty associated with salt solutions.

Experimental Results for Brick, Mortar and Waterproof Coating

The permeance of waterproof coating was extracted by comparing the permeances of plain and coated material layers (brick, mortar). The waterproof coatings were applied to the specimens using the same method for both brick and mortar layers in order to obtain the same coating thickness on different specimens.

Table 1 summarizes the results for water vapor permeability of brick and mortar and water vapor permeance of the waterproof coatings, applied to the mortar and brick specimens. The results show that indeed the coatings are not totally permeable as claimed by the manufacturer. Differences of more than twice the permeability can exist at low relative humidities. These results also reveal that the waterproof coating produces different permeances depending on the material it coats. Both the brick and mortar coated samples show that the permeances increase as a function of relative humidity. In fact, at a relative humidity of 91%, the coating has hardly any resistance when applied to mortar surface. This makes it an attractive feature since it allows drying by vapor transfer. This sub-system behavior was incorporated in the simulations, and the combined experimental and numerical method allowed the capturing of the physical phenomena.

TABLE 1--Vapor transfer properties of brick, mortar and waterproof coating.

Sample	Brick	Brick with Coating[3]	Mortar	Mortar with Coating[3]	Coating on Brick	Coating on Mortar
Average RH, %	Vapor ng/s·m·Pa			Permeability,	Vapor ng/s·m²·Pa	Permeance,
16	2.35	1.31	17.9	6.78	98.33	630
27	2.29	1.31	16.5	7.03	113.33	663.33
77	2.86	1.94	17.9	10.8	223.33	1566.67
91	4.49	3.75	22.0	21.1	≈520	≈6000

DESCRIPTION OF THE MODEL

A detailed model description of the LATENITE version 1.0 hygrothermal model is given by Hens and Janssens (1993) [4], Karagiozis (1993) [5], Salonvaara and Karagiozis (1994) [6] and only a brief overview is presented here with regard to the additional features imbedded in version 1.2. The moisture transport potentials used in the model are moisture content and vapor pressure; for energy transport, temperature is used. The equations are developed on a Cartesian rectangular co-ordinate system, contain explicit and implicit time discretizations, and are spatially discretized using the control

---

[3] Permeability in this case is not a property of the material but instead represents the system property of a combination of two materials of certain thickness. Shown for comparison purposes only.

volume formulation. Approximate factorization and full solution procedures are incorporated into the model to solve the differential equation in delta form.

The LATENITE 1.2 model has been recently upgraded to include the porous air flow through insulation and cracks by solving a subset of the Navier Stokes equations: Darcy's equations. In addition, the solution domain has been extended to 3-dimensions, allowing real practical problems to be solved. The model recently included the capability for handling internal heat and moisture sources, gravity driven liquid moisture, and surface drainage   capabilities. An important feature of the upgraded LATENITE 1.2 model is its extension from providing   deterministic   solutions   to   stochastic-statistically   based   ones. LATENITE employs non-linear hygrothermal properties as found in nature. The porous media transport of moisture (vapor and liquid) through each material layer is considered strongly coupled to the material properties (i.e., the sorption-suction curves). The corresponding moisture fluxes are decomposed for each phase and are treated separately. The set of the governing partial differential equation are thus highly non-linear. The Newton-Raphson method for linearizing the coefficient/equations is used to provide a more direct, stronger coupling. The strong coupling between the moisture and energy transport primarily exists due to the presence of phase changes. This mechanism is dependent on material properties.

The moisture transfer equation, including liquid and vapor transfer, is

$$q_M = -\rho_0 D_w(u,T)\nabla u - \delta_p(u,T)\nabla P_v + v_a \rho_v + K(u)\rho_w \vec{g} \tag{1}$$

where

q_M = mass flux, kg/m^2·s
ρ_0 = dry density of porous material, kg/m^3
D_w = liquid moisture diffusivity, m^2/s
u = moisture content, kg$_w$/kg$_d$
T = temperature, °C
δ_p = vapor permeability, kg/s·m·Pa
P_v = vapor pressure, Pa
v_a = velocity of air, m/s
ρ_v = density of vapor in the air, kg/m^3
K = moisture permeability, s
ρ_w = density of liquid water, kg/m^3
g = gravity, m/s^2.

Wind driven rain is modelled as a source term on the exterior wall surface. However, the amount of water that can penetrate into the porous material is limited by the maximum allowable moisture content in the exterior material.

PROBLEM DESCRIPTION

The hygrothermal performance of a high-rise wall depicted in Figure 1 was analyzed with and without the application of the exterior waterproofing. A comparison of the one and two-dimensional simulation results were carried out to determine the importance of properly including the building envelope system and sub-systems on the hygrothermal performance of the wall shown in Figure 1. The 1-D simulations did not include mortar in the analysis and assumed that only brick was present. For one set of the 2-D simulations, the wall was assumed to be ideal (no cracks or holes). This was used to compare with the 1-D simulations. The measured water vapor permeabilities for the brick, mortar and coatings on both brick and mortar were employed in all simulations (Table 1). Material properties for all other layers were employed from the LATENITE property database [3]. The mortar employed in this study did not include any air-entraining agents allowing high liquid diffusivities.

The high-rise wall structure selected for the numerical analysis is shown in Figure 1. The wall that is centrally located in the middle of a 10-floor building (5th floor) is composed of the following layers starting from the exterior to interior: a 1mm waterproof coating, a 90 mm clay fired brick, a 25 mm air space, 0.2 mm paper sheathing, a 100 mm glass fiber insulation, a 0.15 mm vapor retarder and a 9.5 mm gypsum board. In two-dimensional calculations, the height of the simulated wall section is 0.067 m. The inside surface of the gypsum board was coated with a vapor tight paint (permeance approximately $3 \cdot 10^{-11}$ kg/m^{2}sPa or 0.5 perms). This also produced a similar effect as a vapor retarder. A vapor retarder is normally required in cold climates like Canada.

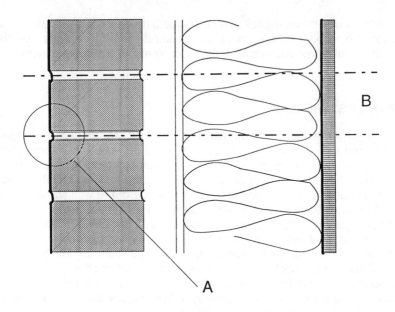

FIG. 1--The analyzed wall structure in detail: 90 mm brick, 25 mm air gap, 0.2 mm building paper,100 mm glassfibre insulation, 0.15 mm polyethylene vapor retarder and 9.5 mm gypsum board. Mortar layers between bricks are16 mm thick. A= Location of the crack. B= Simulated section.

In two-dimensional simulations with and without the presence of the crack, a mortar layer of 16 mm thick was employed (8mm on each side of the brick) with 50 mm thick brick. In the cases examining the effect of the crack, a crack layer thickness of 0.5 mm was employed, allowing the wind driven rain water to come in contact with the crack opening. This surface was then exposed to the amount of rain that typically hits a vertical wall. This amount depends on the intensity of precipitation, wind speed and wind direction as well as the location on the wall surface. Driving rain was used in the analysis as calculated by employing a commercially developed model [7]. An equation for wind-driven rain used in the hygrothermal model was created and was based on a numerical study [1] that presents the results generated by the wind-driven rain droplet simulations.

The wall was exposed to outside air temperature and the relative humidity that varied according to the weather data from the selected location (Vancouver). The simulations were carried out for a two-year exposure starting on the 1st of July. The solar radiation and long wave radiation from the outer surfaces of the wall were included in the analysis. In this study, no air infiltrating or exfiltrating was considered; therefore the primary mode of water transmission is due to diffusion processes, both vapor and liquid transport. The LATENITE 1.2 hygrothermal model was employed, and the deterministic method was invoked for all simulations.

BOUNDARY AND INITIAL CONDITIONS

Internal conditions were kept constant at a temperature 21 °C and relative humidity 40 % RH (Pv = 997 Pa) throughout the year. The BMY (Best Meteorological Year) weather file of the Canadian city of Vancouver [8] was used in the simulations. This one-year weather file was repeated during the two-year simulations, i.e., the second year had the same exterior boundary conditions as the first year. The monthly average temperatures and vapor pressures for Vancouver are shown in Figure 2. The yearly average temperature and vapor pressure in Vancouver is 9.1 °C, and 958 Pa, respectively. The total amount of driving rain when temperatures are above freezing (T>0 °C) on a vertical east facing wall (5th floor, center of the wall) is 332 mm in Vancouver. The total amount of precipitation is 1124 mm in Vancouver, and the long term (1950-1980) average yearly precipitation is 1329 mm in Vancouver [9], i.e., the weather file used in the simulations had less precipitation than the average year in the location.

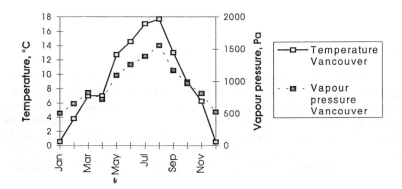

FIG 2.--The monthly average temperatures and vapor pressures in Vancouver weather file.

The modeled wall on the 5th floor of the building was facing east, i.e., the azimuth angle of the wall was 90 degrees. Dry initial conditions were investigated in this study. The exterior brick and the insulation were assigned initial relative humidities[4] of 50%. An initial condition RH of 50% corresponds to moisture content 0.0004 kg_w/kg_d in the brick and the maximum capillary moisture content of the brick is 0.111 kg_w/kg_d.

The heat transfer coefficients for external and internal surfaces were kept constant at 25 and 10 W/m^2K, respectively. The mass transfer coefficients for the exterior coating were assigned values from the measurements, and varied from hour to hour depending on the exterior weather temperature and vapor pressure conditions. The complete information on the interior and exterior conditions are shown in Table 2.

TABLE 2--Heat transfer properties for the external and internal surfaces.

Property	External surface	Internal surface
Heat transfer coefficient, W/m^2K	25	8
Short wave absorptivity, -	0.6	-
Long wave emissivity, -	0.9	-

SIMULATION RESULTS

Hygric Behavior

1-D and 2-D Comparisons--The effect of including the mortar layer in the long-term hygrothermal analysis was shown to be important. The inclusion of the mortar layer in the 2-D simulation increased the amount of moisture present in the exterior layers. The exterior brick was found to display higher maximum amounts of total moisture, increasing from 0.35 kg (per 50 mm high and 90 mm thick brick) for the 1-D simulations to 0.67 kg for the 2-D simulations. This behavior is depicted in Figure 3. In both the 1-D and 2-D simulations, the

---

[4] Relative humidity in pores of a material is related to moisture content via sorption isotherm.

moisture contents stay slightly below the maximum capillary moisture content throughout the two-year simulation period.

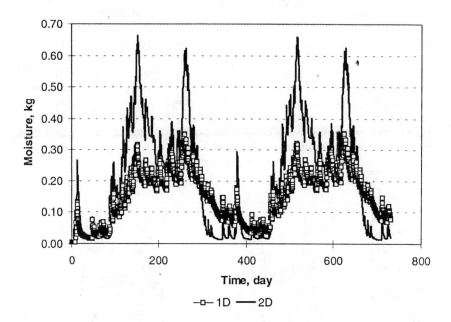

FIG 3.--Moisture content in the exterior brick as a function of time for the comparison of the 1-D and 2-D results (uncoated). The starting date is 1 July. Dimensions of the brick are: height/depth(/length)= 50mm/90mm (/1000mm). The full saturation of the brick amounts to 0.84 kg of water.

2-D Simulations: Comparison of walls with and without the presence of waterproofing coating--Three 2-D simulation cases were numerically investigated. The first case examined a brick-mortar wall system (Fig. 1) with a 0.5 mm gap between the brick and mortar layer (uncoated). This wall was then coated with a 1 mm thick waterproof coating (coated) and represents the second case. In the third case, the coating had a small crack the size of the gap between mortar and brick layers (coated & crack). The moisture contents of the exterior brick in these three different cases are shown in Figure 4. The third dimension of the brick - named length - is 1 m due to two-dimensional nature of the calculations.

The average moisture contents in the exterior brick layer rise to 3/4 of the full saturation (0.66 vs. 0.84 kg) during the cool and wet periods when the exterior surface is either uncoated or the waterproof coating has a crack (Fig. 4). The ideally coated wall maintained low moisture contents throughout the two-year simulation period. It is evident from the simulation results that the presence of a small crack in the coating can destroy the purpose of waterproofing. The uncoated brick was found to have higher mass transfer exchanges of moisture with the exterior environment than the coated wall and a crack, because the entire brick surface is open to water absorption and evaporation. The waterproof coating slows down the rate of vapor transfer and does not allow liquid water penetration. In the coated wall with crack case, the rain water entered into the wall only through the small crack area.   To escape the building envelope, moisture first has to redistribute and then move in vapor phase through the brick and the coating. The waterproof coating's vapor permeance increases at higher relative humidities but it still creates an additional resistance to vapor flow and, thus, the moisture contents in the wall with a cracked coating stay at higher moisture content levels for a longer period of time.

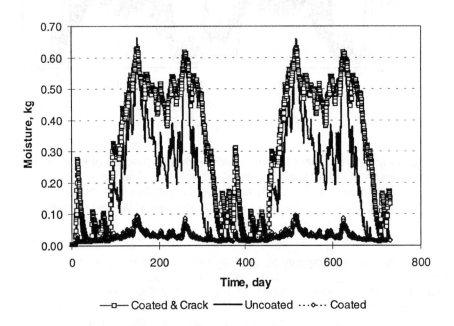

FIG 4.--Moisture content in the exterior brick as a function of time for three different cases: coated brick with a crack in the coating, brick without a coating and coated brick without a crack. The starting date is 1 July. Dimensions of the brick are: height/depth(/length)= 50mm/90mm(/1000mm).The full saturation of the brick amounts to 0.84 kg of water.

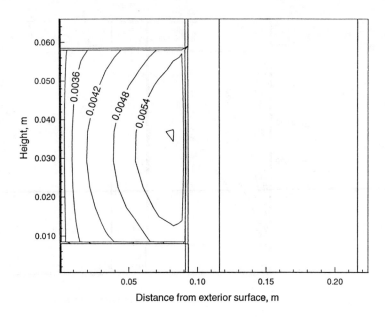

FIG 5.--Moisture content distribution in the brick layer in the middle of December at 96 days from the beginning of the simulations. Brick wall has an ideal waterproof coating without the existence of a crack.

The local moisture contents in the brick show clearly the effect of the crack on the moisture performance of the wall structure. When the waterproof coating is ideal and has no cracks, the moisture contents, shown in Figure 5 in units kg-water/kg-dry material, are well below the saturation level 0.111 kg_w/kg_d. A small crack on the exterior surface at the same location of the gap between brick and mortar changes the situation totally (Fig. 6). The moisture content distribution is skewed towards the source of moisture penetration and moisture contents close to saturation exist inside the brick

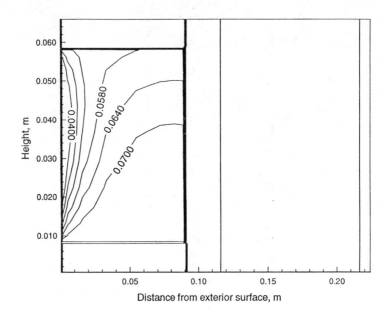

FIG 6.--Moisture content distribution in the brick layer in the middle of December at 96 days from the beginning of the simulations. Brick wall has a waterproof coating with the existence of a crack at the location in the bottom part where brick and mortar meet.

Thermal Behavior

The exterior waterproofing has a significant effect on rain water penetration into the wall structure. The layer does not allow rain water to penetrate into the wall in liquid form and the initially dry ideal walls stay relatively dry throughout the test period. Small differences in the moisture contents of the initially dry wall with a waterproofing coating were caused by differences in vapor diffusion fluxes.

The thermal conductivity of each of the material layers is a function of moisture content. Walls without waterproofing occasionally have higher moisture contents in the exterior layers, which may result in a decrease of the thermal resistance of the wall and, therefore, in an increase of heat loss.

The water that is absorbed in liquid form by the exterior brick during rainy periods can eventually be evaporated outwards causing the latent heat involved in this process to further increase the heat loss. Moisture that comes into the wall in vapor phase and is absorbed by the structure does not affect the long-term average heat flux unless yearly accumulation (or drying) occurs. However, instantaneous heat fluxes may be influenced by the phase changes of vapor or liquid. Some savings in heating energy loss can be expected in walls with dry initial conditions if the waterproof coating behaves ideally and does not allow liquid water to migrate into the wall. These savings, however, depend on the moisture properties of the exterior brick, i.e., how moisture-absorbing the surface is without any coating. The analyzed wall structure was found to have 3% lower heat losses with a coating (without cracks) than without a coating in Vancouver.

The crack in the coating destroyed these savings and the heat losses in this case were very close to the same as in the uncoated wall case. A higher increase of 9% in heat loss for a south facing brick cavity wall was found in the previous study [2], which was mainly due to different properties of the brick used in the analysis and the south orientation of the wall. The brick in the previous study had much higher moisture diffusivity and vapor permeability resulting in increased absorption and evaporation of moisture. Solar radiation also is higher on the wall facing south. The results presented here are valid only for this east facing wall that is exposed to solar radiation and should not be generalized to other directions.

The uncoated walls absorbed rain water and allowed more moisture to evaporate through the exterior surface. Thus, in these walls, the primary reason for increases in heat losses was the wind driven rain and liquid absorption - evaporation cycles.

CONCLUSIONS

In this investigation the hygrothermal performance behavior of the waterproof coating was measured and incorporated in the numerical long-term analysis of a wall system. The experiments showed conclusively that this particular waterproofing coating performed strongly as a function of the ambient relative humidity. The vapor resistance was found to be larger at low relative humidities but negligible at high relative humidities. The water vapor permeances of the waterproof coating is strongly dependent on the surface to which it is applied. The analysed coating showed significantly higher permeances on mortar surfaces than on brick surfaces. The water vapor permeance increases tremendously at higher relative humidities. This phenomenon is very beneficial and allows faster drying when moisture contents in the exterior material layer increase to critical levels. The study also showed the important influence of the waterproof coating used in cold climatic conditions.

This study also showed the influence of rain on thermal and moisture performance in walls. The waterproof coating used in cold climates proved to be an effective method to control water penetrating the structure when applied to a brick wall with a vapor retarder. The underlying assumption is that the coating was maintained without the existence of cracks. The calculated moisture contents in the walls were low throughout the years and no moisture problems were found to develop. However, if cracks in the surface coating develop, the protective properties of a waterproof coating can be lost and moisture accumulation may occur.

The wall without waterproofing displayed higher average yearly heat losses than those with the ideal coating (+3% in Vancouver). This was caused by the latent heat effects of absorbed moisture from wind driven rain and by the increase in thermal conductivities.

The results clearly show that computer models used in investigating hygrothermal behavior of building structures should have capabilities to handle rain penetration. Rain penetration can be far more important than ambient surface diffusion fluxes in estimating the moisture behavior of building structures. The moisture contents in walls with an ideal waterproof coating (no cracks) at times contained the highest moisture contents (winter season), 6-7 times lower than in open surface walls.

The results provided in this paper are only applicable to the specific materials that were chosen. Further modeling research is needed to determine the applicability of the exterior surface coating on building envelopes in cold climates for different facade and wall configurations. Since perfect capillary contact is not present in air-entrained mortar, this effect should be studied both by combining experiments and numerical simulations. An extension of this work would be to investigate the influence of randomly varying properties and surface coatings as observed in practice. These influences can allow additional insight to the overall effect of waterproofing building envelope systems. Finally, special care should be taken not to apply any coating with low vapor permeance on wet walls that do not have proper cavity ventilation or any other means to allow the drying out of initial moisture.

ACKNOWLEDGMENTS

The authors of this study would like to thank Dr. Kumar Kumaran, senior research officer at NRC, for water vapour transmission measurements and Mr. John Lackey, technical officer at NRC, for his assistance in the measurements and sample preparation. Thanks are also due to Mr. John King who also assisted in the sample preparation.

REFERENCES

[1].   Karagiozis, A. and Hadjisophocleous G. "Wind-Driven Rain on High-Rise Buildings", Thermal Performance of Exterior Envelopes of Buildings VI, Clearwater Beach, Florida, 4-8 Dec. 1995.

[2].   Karagiozis A. and Salonvaara M., "The Effect of Waterproof Coating on Hygrothermal Performance of a High-Rise Wall Structure", Thermal Performance of the Exterior Envelopes of Buildings VI. Clearwater Beach, Florida, USA, 4 - 8 Dec. 1995.

[3].   Karagiozis, A., Salonvaara, M. and Kumaran, K., "LATENITE Hygrothermal Material Property Database, IEA Annex 24 Report T1-CA-94/04, Trondheim, Norway, 1994.

[4].   Hens, H. and Janssens A., "Inquiry on HAMCAT CODES", International Energy Agency, Heat, Air and Moisture Transfer in Insulated Envelope Parts, Report Annex 24, Task 1, Modeling, 1993.

[5].   Karagiozis, A., "Overview of the 2-D Hygrothermal Heat-Moisture Transport Model LATENITE", Internal IRC/BPL Report, 1993

[6].   Salonvaara M. and Karagiozis A., "Moisture Transport in Building Envelopes using an approximate Factorization Solution Method", CFD Society of Canada, Toronto, June 1-3 1994.

[7].   ASC (1993) Theory Documentation for TASCflow, Version 2.2, Advanced Scientific Computing Ltd., Waterloo, Canada.

[8].   AESC.(Atmospheric Environment Service of Canada).

[9].   Environment Canada, Canadian Climate Normals. Vol. 3, Atmospheric Environment Service, Downsview, Ontario, 1983.

Author Index

Subject Index

A

Air barrier, 47, 57, 244
Air infiltration, 232
Air pressure, 115, 236, 267
Air seals, 33, 47, 57
Aluminum, 267
  panels, 187
American Architectural
      Manufacturers Association
  ANSI/AAMA certification
      program, 232
  hose test, 207, 236
  leakage test method, 207
American National Standards
      Institute, 33
Architectural Aluminum
      Manufacturing
      Association, 33
ASHRAE methods, 91
ASTM standards
  E 331, 3
  E 547, 33
  E 1105, 115, 236, 267

B

Bond breaker, 115
Brick veneer, 73, 142, 168
  brick-mortar interaction, 295

C

Chamber tests, 207
Cladding systems, 288
  brick, 73
  stucco, 155
  synthetic stucco, 277
  water penetration through,
      47, 57, 142
  wetting, 73
Compartment seals, 47, 57
Computational fluid dynamics, 3
Concrete, 17, 168, 267
  facades, 129
  panels, precast, 115

D

Dew point, 91
Door leaks
  ASTM E 1105, 115, 236
  sliding glass, 105, 232
Drop size modeling, rain, 17

E

Exterior insulation and finish
      sytem (EIFS), 91, 236,
      267, 277, 288

F

Facade interfaces, leakages, 142
Facades, concrete, 129
Facade waterproofing
      integration, 33
Fastener location and selection,
      33
Fasteners, doors and windows,
      232
Flashing, 129, 155, 187
  systems, secondary, 33
Forced entry requirements, 232

G

Glass doors, sliding, leaks, 105,
      232
Glazing, sloped, 187
Granite panels, 187

Condensation
  troughs, 187
  wall problems, 91
  water leakage, 129
Cracks, shrinkage, 129
Curtain walls, 142, 168, 267
  ASTM E 1105, 115, 236, 267
  leakage tests, 207
  mockup test, 218
  sloped, 187